STRUCTURAL
MECHANICS

BY

W. MORGAN

B.Sc., A.M.I. Struct.E.

Senior Lecturer in Structures at Northern Polytechnic, London

AND

D. T. WILLIAMS

A.M.I.Struct.E., M.Soc.C.E. (France)

SECOND EDITION

Pitman Paperbacks

Second edition 1963

First paperback edition 1968

Reprinted 1969

Reprinted 1971

SIR ISAAC PITMAN AND SONS LTD.
Pitman House, Parker Street, Kingsway, London, WC2B 5PB
P.O. Box 6038, Portal Street, Nairobi, Kenya

SIR ISAAC PITMAN (AUST.) PTY. LTD.
Pitman House, Bouverie Street, Carlton, Victoria 3053, Australia

PITMAN PUBLISHING CORPORATION (S.A.) PTY. LTD.
P.O. Box 11231, Johannesburg, Transvaal, S. Africa

PITMAN PUBLISHING CORPORATION
6 East 43rd Street, New York, N.Y. 10017

SIR ISAAC PITMAN (CANADA) LTD.
Pitman House, 381-383 Church Street, Toronto, 3

THE COPP CLARK PUBLISHING COMPANY
517 Wellington Street, Toronto, 2B

00427967↓

©
W. Morgan and D. T. Williams
1963

ISBN: 0 273 40116 5

MADE IN GREAT BRITAIN AT THE PITMAN PRESS, BATH
G1-(T 1311)

Preface to Second Edition

THE British Standard 449:1959, *The Use of Structural Steel in Building*, which was published in 1959, superseded the previous B.S. and also the British Standard Code of Practice C.P. 113 (1948). This Code of Practice is now incorporated in B.S. 449:1959.

In general, permissible stresses have been increased, and throughout the book text and problems have been altered to take advantage of the revised stresses. Slight alterations have been made to Chapters 9 and 12 but the principal alterations are to Chapters 16 and 17. Table 16.2 on page 320 gives the revised permissible stresses for steel columns, and the revised treatment of Cased Columns is given on page 319.

An amendment (published in 1961) to B.S. 449 : 1959 contained new permissible stresses for rivets and bolts. Text and problems have therefore been revised to make use of the new stresses.

Advantage has been taken of the necessity for a second edition to give symbols for reinforced concrete design which accord more closely to the recommended list of symbols contained in C.P. 114 (1957). *The Structural Use of Reinforced Concrete in Building*.

Extracts and tables from C.P. 114 (1957) and B.S. 449:1959 are reproduced by permission of the British Standards Institution. For further information the student is recommended to obtain complete copies of the Code and Standard from the British Standards Institution, 2, Park Street, London, W.1.

The Safe Load Tables relating to beams (pages 252 to 255), to joist stanchions (pages 338 to 341), and to rivets and bolts (pages 360 to 365), are reproduced by permission of the British Constructional Steelwork Association and the British Steel Makers.

It should be noted with regard to the Safe Load Tables for beams and stanchions that B.S. 4:1962 revises entirely the complete range of rolled sections. It is probable that within a year or two the ordinary beam sections given in this book will become obsolete. There will be a greater concentration on universal beams and columns which are more efficient than the conventional beams they will replace. The Safe Load Tables, issued jointly by the British Constructional Steelwork Association and the British Steel Makers, are being revised and it is expected that they will be published in December 1962. Copies of the Tables may be purchased from the B.C.S.A., Artillery House, Artillery Row, Westminster, London, S.W.1. These tables will include safe loads for both mild steel to B.S. 15, and high yield stress steel to B.S. 968:1962 which has improved mechanical and welding properties over the steel given in B.S. 968:1941. No doubt there will be increasing use of this new high yield point steel which has a maximum permissible bending stress of 14·5 tons per sq in.

Preface to First Edition

THIS book is intended to provide an approach to the Theory of Structures for (a) Students of Building, Architecture and Surveying preparing for their professional examinations, and (b) Students in the earlier stages of their studies for the Graduateship examination of the Institution of Structural Engineers.

The authors have felt that this elementary stage of Theory of Structures is often rendered unnecessarily difficult by a highly mathematical approach, and therefore the mathematical treatment here has been kept as simple as is consistent with accuracy. In all cases a full understanding of the basic principle has been considered more important than mere mathematical agility.

A large number of examples, together with answers has been included in every chapter, and the reader is strongly recommended to attempt as many as possible of these examples, which have been carefully chosen and graded to test the thoroughness of his understanding of the basic fundamentals concerned.

Throughout the book most of the calculations have been made with the aid of a 10-inch slide-rule, and for practical problems such accuracy is sufficient. It is, for example, of small concern to know by a laborious calculation that the deflexion of a beam is 0·4375 in. where the use of a slide-rule would have given the answer in a very short time as 0·44 in.

Extracts and tables from the British Standard Codes of Practice C.P. 114 (1957) and C.P. 113 (1948) are reproduced by permission of the British Standards Institution. For further information, the student is recommended to obtain complete copies of the Codes from the British Standards Institution, 2 Park Street, London, W.1.

Extracts and tables from the L.C.C. Constructional By-laws (1952) are reproduced by permission of the London County Council.

The Safe Load Tables relating to beams, to joist stanchions, and to rivets and bolts are reproduced by permission of the British Constructional Steelwork Association and the British Steel Makers.

Contents

CHAPTER 1

Reactions

ALL structures whether houses, cinemas, hospitals, factories or bridges have at least one thing in common: they are expected to be safe from collapse when used for the purpose for which they were intended. In order to ensure this structural safety without un-economical use of the materials of construction the designer has first to investigate the effect of *forces*.

Force is measured in *weight* units, e.g. pounds or tons or hundred-weights. Confusion sometimes exists in the minds of students about this. They would not dream, for instance, of ordering 2 lb-ft of apples or 1 ton-ft of coal yet they frequently express forces or the effects of forces in this way.

Examples of Force

A man weighing 160 lb standing on a plank is pressing down-wards on the plank with a force (or weight) of 160 lb.

An engine exerts a force of so many pounds or tons upon the carriages it is pulling.

A girder weighing 1 ton, supported by two walls is pressing down on the walls with a total force (or weight) of 1 ton.

A strong wind blowing on a structure exerts a force of so many pounds.

Water exerts a force of so many pounds or tons on the dam which retains it.

A building presses down on the soil with a force (i.e. weight) measured in tons, equal to the weight of the building.

Force of Gravity

Everything on (and above) the surface of the earth is attracted vertically downwards by the earth. This attraction is called the weight of the body or the *force of gravity*. The greater the amount of matter in a body, the greater is the attraction of the earth upon it, or, in other words, the greater is its weight. The important fact is, that the weight of a body such as a building, or a beam or column in a building, always acts vertically downwards.

Not all forces acting on structures are vertical (e.g. wind), but

1

they are still expressed in weight units, i.e. pounds, tons, hundred-weights, etc.

Measurement of Weight

One instrument for weighing small objects and for measuring forces is the spring-balance (Fig. 1.1) the action of which is due to the extension of a spring.

Reaction

Referring to Fig. 1.1 it must be noted that if the spring-balance is to remain stationary (or at rest, or in equilibrium) the upward force

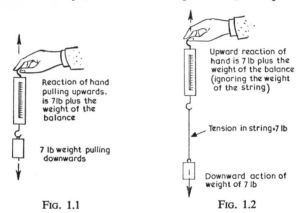

Reaction of hand pulling upwards, is 7lb plus the weight of the balance

7 lb weight pulling downwards

Upward reaction of hand is 7 lb plus the weight of the balance (ignoring the weight of the string)

Tension in string = 7 lb

Downward action of weight of 7 lb

Fig. 1.1   Fig. 1.2

(reaction) exerted by the hand must equal the downward pull (action) of the weight plus the weight of the balance. The reading of 7 lb on the balance is due as much to the upward reaction of the hand as to the downward pull (action) of the weight.

Tension

Note that the string in Fig. 1.2 is acted upon by two forces, the downward action of the weight and the upward reaction of the hand

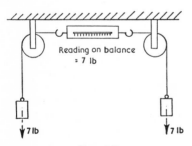

Reading on balance = 7 lb

7 lb   7 lb

Fig. 1.3

transmitted through the balance. These two forces of 7 lb each (action and reaction) are necessary to produce a tension of 7 lb in the string.

In Fig. 1.3 the smooth running pulleys alter the direction of pull of the weights from vertical to horizontal. The tension is constant in the string and is 7 lb.

Compression

The blocks of timber in Fig. 1.4 are being compressed between the downward action of the weight and the upward reaction of the hand.

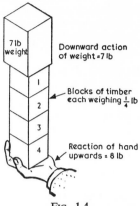

Note that block 2 is reacting upwards with a force of $7\frac{1}{4}$ lb on block 1 and pressing downwards with a force of $7\frac{1}{2}$ lb on block 3. Similarly, block 3 is reacting upwards on block 2 with a force of $7\frac{1}{2}$ lb and pressing downwards with a force of $7\frac{3}{4}$ lb on block 4.

Equilibrium

A structure has to be designed so that it is in equilibrium (i.e. at rest) under the forces acting upon it. One task of the structural designer is therefore the estimation of all the external forces and reactions (due to the weight of the

FIG. 1.4

building, wind forces, etc.), and to ensure that these forces will be in equilibrium. The designer has then to choose suitable materials of adequate dimensions to withstand the tensions, compressions, bending, etc., which are the result of the external forces and reactions. Simple examples are illustrated in Figs. 1.5 and 1.6.

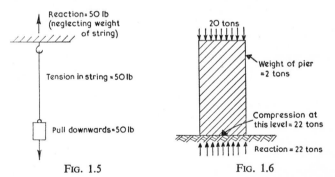

FIG. 1.5   FIG. 1.6

In Fig. 1.5, the string has to be capable of sustaining a tension of 50 lb. In Fig. 1.6, the downward pressure on the top of the pier due to a beam or column is 20 tons, and the weight of the pier is 2 tons. The upward reaction from the soil is 22 tons. (A foundation is usually necessary to spread the load over a greater area.) Note that the compression in the brickwork is due as much to the upward reaction of the soil as to the downward weight.

SUMMARY

Force (whether acting vertically, horizontally, or in any other direction) is measured in weight units, i.e. pounds, hundredweights, tons. etc.

Other words similar in meaning to force are weight, pressure, pull, push, load, thrust.

When two bodies are in contact each exerts a force on the other. These forces can be called *action* and *reaction*.

Action and reaction are always equal and opposite.

Two equal forces of x lb acting in opposite directions in the same straight line are necessary to produce a tension (or compression) of x lb.

When all the forces acting on a body which is in equilibrium are vertical, the sum of the upward forces equals the sum of the downward forces.

When a string or cable passes over a smooth (frictionless) pulley, the tension in the string or cable remains unaltered.

EXERCISE 1

1. A string attached to a hook in the ceiling is pulled vertically downwards with a force of 50 lb. What is the value and direction of the reaction of the hook on the string? What is the tension in the string?

2. Two tug of war teams are pulling in opposite directions, each team pulling with a force of 300 lb. What tension is the rope sustaining?

3. A man of weight 150 lb is sitting on a box weighing 10 lb. His feet are pressing on the ground with a total force of 20 lb. State the reaction of the ground on the box. What compressive force is the box sustaining where it is in contact with the ground?

4. The total weight of a building is 400 tons, and this weight is transmitted equally by 8 columns to the soil. Calculate the reaction under each column.

5. A column weighing 2 tons supports a load of 100 tons. The column in turn is supported by a concrete foundation block weighing 10 tons. Calculate the reaction of the concrete block on the column and the reaction of the soil on the concrete block.

6. A weight of 6 tons is supported equally by four vertical cables connected to overhead supports. What is the reaction of the support on each cable? What tension must each cable be capable of sustaining? Neglect the weight of the cables.

7. A man weighing 160 lb standing on the ground holds a weight of 28 lb in one hand and a weight of 56 lb in the other hand. What are the reactions of the hands? What is the pressure on the ground?

8. A chain consists of eleven links, each link weighing $\frac{1}{2}$ lb. The chain is supported at the top and hangs vertically with a weight of 100 lb on the bottom link. State the values and directions of the reactions of the central link on the links immediately above and below. Which link is subjected to the greatest tension and what is the value of the tension?

9. Three acrobats, A, B and C, weigh respectively 12 stone, 10 stone, 8 stone. B stands on A's shoulders and C stands on B's shoulders. State: the reaction of B's shoulders on C's feet; the reaction of A's shoulders on B's feet; the pressure of A on the ground.

10. Two men lift a box from the floor. A, weighing 10 stone, lifts vertically upwards with a force of 50 lb and B, weighing 12 stone, lifts vertically upwards with a force of 70 lb. What is the weight of the box? What is the pressure that each man exerts on the floor?

11. A spring balance is held in the hand. From the balance is suspended a weight of 4 lb. From this weight is suspended another balance and from this balance a weight of 5 lb. Each balance weighs ¼ lb and the weights of the strings may be ignored. State: the readings on the two balances and the reaction of the hand.

12. Referring to Fig. 1.7 state the reaction of the floor on the rope, the reaction of the ceiling, and the tension in the rope. Ignore the weights of the pulley and the rope.

13. A weight is kept stationary as in Fig. 1.8 by a man who weighs 150 lb. What is the reaction of the floor on the man? What is the reaction at the ceiling? What is the tension in the rope? Ignore the weights of pulley and rope.

14. Referring to Fig. 1.9 each pulley weighs 2 lb. State: the tension in the string; the reactions at A, B and C. Ignore the weight of the string.

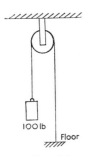

FIG. 1.7

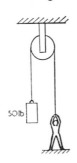

FIG. 1.8

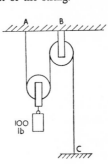

FIG. 1.9

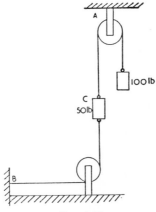

FIG. 1.10

15. The system of forces shown in Fig. 1.10 is in equilibrium. Determine the reactions at A and B; the tension in the rope between A and C and the tension in the rope between C and B. (The weight of the smooth pulleys and of the rope may be ignored.)

CHAPTER 2

Concurrent Co-planar Forces

ALL the problems in this chapter, together with most of the problems throughout the book, are concerned with forces acting in one plane (co-planar). When the forces meet at a point, they are said to be concurrent. Forces which do not meet at a point are dealt with in Chapter 3.

Experimental Demonstration of the Principle of the Triangle of Forces

AB in Fig. 2.1 represents a horizontal wooden beam containing a number of hooks. By means of string, a small ring, and two

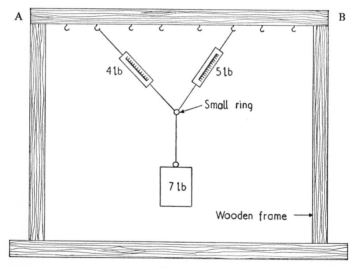

FIG. 2.1

spring balances a weight of 7 lb is suspended as shown. It is assumed in this example that the readings on the balances are 4 lb and 5 lb respectively. The ring is in equilibrium (at rest) under the action of three forces, i.e. the vertical pull downwards of the weight and the

6

pulls exerted by the two strings. The condition can be represented on drawing paper by Fig. 2.2 which is called the free-body diagram with respect to point *O*.

The three lines are called the *lines of action* of the forces and the arrows represent the *direction* in which the forces are acting on the ring. In order to plot on paper the lines of action of the forces, the angles between the strings can be measured by means of a circular

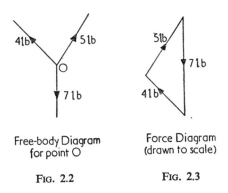

Free-body Diagram
for point O

Force Diagram
(drawn to scale)

FIG. 2.2   FIG. 2.3

protractor. An alternative and simpler method of transferring to paper the lines of action is to hold a sheet of paper or cardboard behind the strings and by means of a pin to prick two or three points along each string. Pencil lines can then be drawn to connect these points and thus to fix on paper the free-body diagram.

The magnitudes of the forces can be represented on paper by lines drawn to scale, e.g. if it is decided to let $\frac{1}{2}$ in. represent 1 lb then the force of 7 lb will be represented by a line $3\frac{1}{2}$ in. long, the force of 5 lb by a line $2\frac{1}{2}$ in. long, etc.

Now, if the free-body diagram be drawn on paper to represent the lines of action and directions of the forces and three lines are drawn, as shown in Fig. 2.3, parallel to these forces to represent to scale their magnitudes, it will be found that a triangle will be formed. In an actual experiment the result may not be quite as accurate as indicated in Fig. 2.3 because of possible lack of sensitivity of the spring balances and the difficulty of transferring accurately to paper the free-body diagram. The fact is, however, that if three forces meeting at a point are in equilibrium they may be represented in magnitude and direction by the three sides of a triangle drawn to scale.

By placing the spring balances on different hooks, e.g. as in Fig. 2.4, further illustrations of the principle of the triangle of forces can be obtained.

It was stated in Chapter 1 that action and reaction are equal and opposite, yet in Fig. 2.4 it appears that 17 lb are required to support a downward weight of 7 lb. This is because the strings are inclined in opposite directions and react on each other as well as on

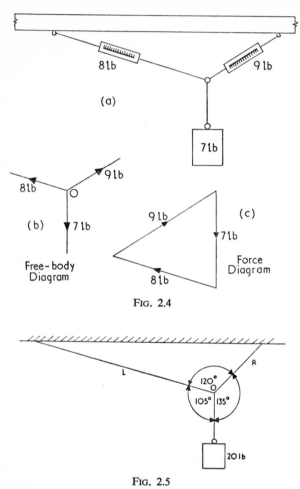

(a)

(b)

Free-body Diagram

(c)

Force Diagram

FIG. 2.4

FIG. 2.5

the weight of 7 lb. For example, the string which has a tension of 8 lb is pulling towards the left in addition to pulling up. This pull to the left is resisted by the other string pulling to the right, so that only a part of the force in each string is effective in holding up the weight. This will be demonstrated more formally on page 17.

The student is advised to carry out a few experiments similar to those of Figs. 2.1 and 2.4 in order to verify the law of the triangle of forces. The law can then be used to determine unknown forces and reactions.

EXAMPLE 1

Determine the tensions in the two strings L and R of Fig. 2.5.

Point O is in equilibrium under the action of three forces as shown in the free-body diagram of Fig. 2.6, therefore the triangle of forces law must apply.

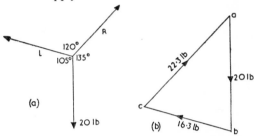

FIG. 2.6. (*a*) FREE-BODY DIAGRAM FOR POINT O;
(*b*) FORCE DIAGRAM (DRAWN TO SCALE)

Draw a line *ab* parallel to the force of 20 lb to a scale of so many pounds to the inch. From *b* draw a line parallel to string L. From *a* draw a line parallel to string R. The two lines intersect at point *c*. The length of line *bc* gives the tension in string L (i.e. 16·3 lb) and the length *ca* gives the tension in string R (i.e. 22·3 lb). (A student with a knowledge of trigonometry can obtain the magnitudes of the forces by calculation.)

Equilibrant

EXAMPLE 2

Two ropes are attached to a hook in the ceiling and a man pulls on each rope as indicated in Fig. 2.7. Determine the direction and magnitude of the reaction at the ceiling (neglect the weights of the ropes).

Since the hook is in equilibrium under the action of the forces in the ropes and the reaction at the ceiling, the triangle of forces principle applies. Draw *ab* parallel to the force of 50 lb to a suitable scale of so many pounds to the inch (Fig. 2.8). From *b* draw *bc* parallel to the other rope to represent 100 lb. The closing line *ca* of the force triangle represents to scale the reaction at the ceiling and is nearly 123 lb, acting at approximately 7° to the vertical. This force can be called the *equilibrant* of the two forces in the ropes,

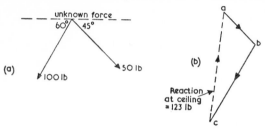

FIG. 2.8. (*a*) FREE-BODY DIAGRAM; (*b*) FORCE DIAGRAM

since the ceiling must supply a force of 123 lb in order that equilibrium may be maintained.

Resultant

In the last problem, the reaction at the ceiling due to the pulls in the two ropes equalled 123 lb acting as shown in Fig. 2.9. If we

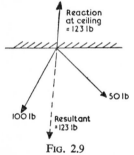

FIG. 2.9

substitute one rope for the two ropes and pull with a force of 123 lb in the direction indicated, the effect on the ceiling will be exactly as before, i.e. the result of the two forces is equivalent to one force of 123 lb. Note also that the resultant is equal in value to the equilibrant and acts in the same straight line but in the opposite direction. The resultant of a given number of forces is therefore the single force which has the same effect on the equilibrium of the body as the combined effects of the given forces.

Parallelogram of Forces

The law of the parallelogram of forces is in essentials the same as the law of the triangle of forces. Any problem which can be solved by the parallelogram of forces law can be solved by the triangle of forces law, although it may sometimes be slightly more convenient to use the former method.

EXAMPLE 3

Referring to Example 2 determine the resultant of the pulls in the two ropes by using the parallelogram of forces.

Measure a distance *oa* along line *OA* in Fig. 2.10 to represent 100 lb and measure a distance *ob* along line *OB* to represent 50 lb.

From *a* draw a line parallel to *OB* and from *b* draw a line parallel to *OA* thus forming a parallelogram. The length of line *oc*, which is the diagonal of the parallelogram (from the point where the two forces meet), gives the value of the resultant of the two forces (123 lb) and also its direction. Note that the triangle *obc* is identical with the triangle of forces in Fig. 2.8.

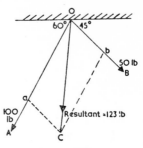

FIG. 2.10

EXAMPLE 4

Two ropes pull on an eye bolt as indicated in Fig. 2.11. Determine the resultant pull on the bolt (the solution is indicated in Fig. 2.12).

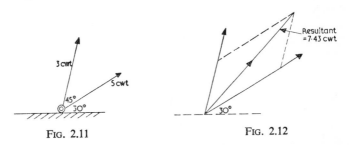

FIG. 2.11   FIG. 2.12

When using the parallelogram of forces law to determine the resultant of two forces, the two forces must be drawn so that the arrows representing their directions either both point towards the meeting point or both point away from it. In other words, a thrust and a pull must either be converted into two thrusts or into two pulls.

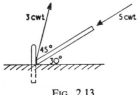

FIG. 2.13

EXAMPLE 5

Determine the resultant force on the peg due to the thrust of 5 cwt and the pull of 3 cwt (Fig. 2.13).

At first glance this problem might appear identical with that given in Fig. 2.11. Obviously, however, the resultant of these two forces must be different from the resultant of the two forces in Fig. 2.11.

The resultant is found either as shown in Fig. 2.14 or as shown in Fig. 2.15. Note that the effect on the peg is the same whether it is pushed or pulled with a force of 3·58 cwt.

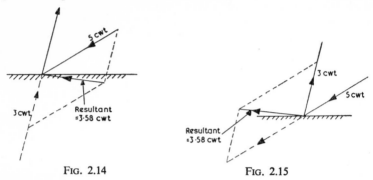

Fig. 2.14   Fig. 2.15

Hinge Joints

Problems in books on mechanics frequently refer to hinge joints. Joints which are almost pure hinges do occur sometimes in structures. In other cases (notably in roof trusses) the joints between members, although not hinged, are assumed to be so, for the purpose of

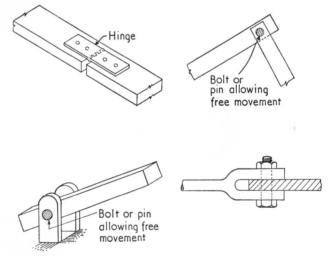

Fig. 2.16

determining the tensions or compressions acting in the members. This will be discussed later on page 119 but for the present it will be sufficient if students think of hinge joints as being similar to those shown in Fig. 2.16. These joints enable members to move freely relatively to each other. It is hoped that examples will be given of hinge joints actually used in structures, in a subsequent volume.

EXAMPLE 6

A rigid rod is hinged to a vertical support and held at 60° to the horizontal by means of a string when a weight of 50 lb is suspended as shown in Fig. 2.17. Determine the tension in the string and the compression in the rod, ignoring the weight of the rod.

Point *O* is in equilibrium under the action of three forces which meet at the point, i.e. the weight of 50 lb, the tension in the string and the compression in the rod. The solution is given in Fig. 2.18. Note that a tension member is called a *tie* and a compression member is called a *strut*.

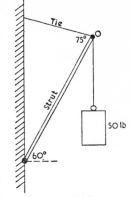

FIG. 2.17

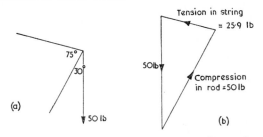

FIG. 2.18. (*a*) FREE-BODY DIAGRAM FOR POINT *O*; (*b*) FORCE DIAGRAM

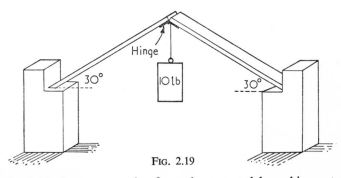

FIG. 2.19

Fig. 2.19 shows two rods of wood connected by a hinge at the top and supported by two concrete blocks. Determine the compressions in the rods ignoring their own weight.

Considering the equilibrium at the hinge, the free body and force diagrams are shown in Fig. 2.20. The compression in each rod is 10 lb. If the angle of slope of the members is made greater, e.g. in Fig. 2.21, the compressions in the members are less than in Fig. 2.20.

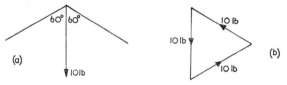

FIG. 2.20. (*a*) FREE-BODY DIAGRAM; (*b*) FORCE DIAGRAM

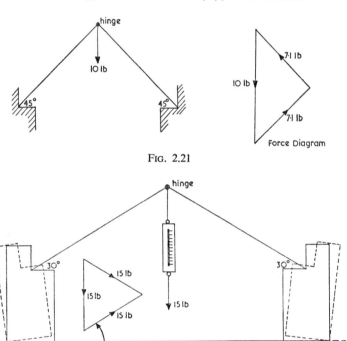

FIG. 2.21

FIG. 2.22

Rectangular Components

The apparatus of Fig. 2.19 is shown in elevation in Fig. 2.2.2 If a gradually increasing pull is applied to the spring balance the vertical force necessary to cause lifting of the blocks can be recorded. Assume this downward force is 15 lb when the angles are as given and when the blocks just begin to lift. The compression acting along each member is 15 lb as obtained by the force diagram. Now consider what happens at the bottom end of one compression member. The member is pushing on the block with a force of 15 lb (Fig. 2.23). Since this force is inclined it has a twofold effect. It is tending to cause crushing of the concrete as well as to cause over-turning. If the force were vertical (and axial) there would be crushing effect only and no overturning effect. If the force were horizontal there would be overturning effect and no crushing effect.

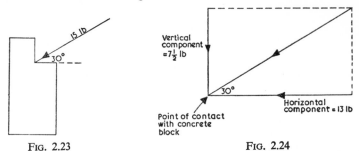

FIG. 2.23   FIG. 2.24

It is sometimes convenient to *resolve* such a force into its *horizontal component* and its *vertical component*.

It was demonstrated on page 11 that the resultant of two forces meeting at a point is given by the diagonal of a parallelogram. By a reverse process, one force can be replaced by (or resolved into) two forces. By constructing a rectangle (parallelogram) (Fig. 2.24) with the force in the rod (15 lb) as the diagonal, the horizontal and vertical components are given by the two sides respectively of the rectangle. The components can be found either by drawing to scale or by calculation.

EXAMPLE 7

Replace the tie rope shown in Fig. 2.25 by two ropes, one vertical and one horizontal which together will have the same effect on the eye bolt.

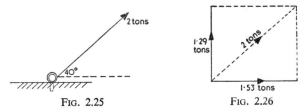

FIG. 2.25   FIG. 2.26

By constructing a rectangle with the force of 2 tons, drawn to scale, as the diagonal (Fig. 2.26) the vertical component (and there-fore the force in the vertical rope) is found to be 1·29 tons. The horizontal component is 1·53 tons.

In the above problem, the components are called *rectangular components* because the angle between them is 90°. When a force has to be split into two components it is usually the rectangular components which are required. It is possible, however, to resolve a force into two components with any given angle between them.

EXAMPLE 8

Replace the rope X which is pulled with a force of 100 lb by two ropes L and R as indicated in Fig. 2.27.

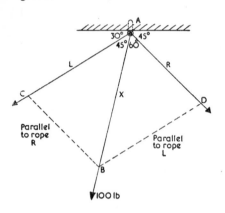

FIG. 2.27

Measure a length along line AB to represent 100 lb and assume this line to be the diagonal of a parallelogram by drawing lines from B parallel to ropes L and R respectively. The forces in the two ropes which together have the same effect on the bolt as the single rope can now be scaled off, i.e.

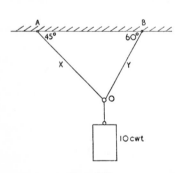

FIG. 2.28

Force in rope $L = 90$ lb (length AC)

Force in rope $R = 73$ lb (length AD)

These two forces can be said to be components of the original force of 100 lb.

EXAMPLE 9

Determine the tensions in the two chains X and Y of Fig. 2.28 then determine the horizontal and vertical components of these tensions. In addition, determine the horizontal and vertical components of the reactions at A and B. Neglect the weight of the chains.

The free-body and force diagrams for the point are given in Fig. 2.29. The tensions in the chains are respectively 5·18 cwt and

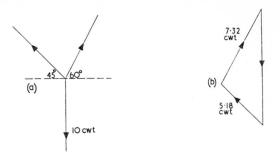

FIG. 2.29. (*a*) FREE-BODY DIAGRAM; (*b*) FORCE DIAGRAM

7·32 cwt. The horizontal and vertical components of the tensions in the chains are given in Fig. 2.30.

Note that the sum of the two vertical components is equal to the value of the suspended load of 10 cwt (action and reaction are equal and opposite). Note also that the horizontal component of

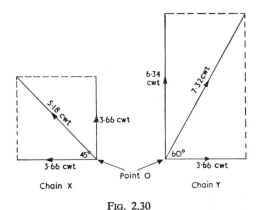

FIG. 2.30

the force in chain *X* is equal to the horizontal component of the force in chain *Y* and acts in the opposite direction (action and reaction are equal and opposite).

Now consider the reactions at points *A* and *B* which equal the tensions in the chains (Fig. 2.31). Again, it is demonstrated that, neglecting the weights of the chains, the sum of the vertical components of the reactions is equal to 10 cwt and that the horizontal components are equal and opposite.

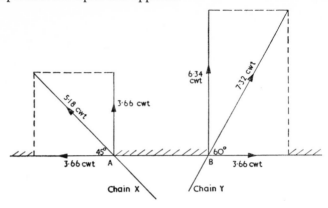

FIG. 2.31

Effect of Tie Member in Simple Roof Truss

Referring back to Fig. 2.22 on page 14, it was stated that the concrete blocks were on the point of overturning when the compression acting along each member was 15 lb. The horizontal component of this force is 13 lb, and this component can be prevented from having an overturning effect by connecting the two inclined members by a horizontal tie member (Fig. 2.32). It will now be impossible to

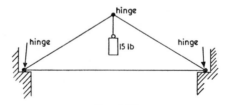

FIG. 2.32

cause overturning of the concrete blocks by pulling downwards at the apex. The tension in the tie member will be equal to the horizontal component (13 lb) of the thrust in the inclined member.

Another way of finding the tension in the tie is by applying the triangle of forces law to the joint between the inclined and horizontal members (Fig. 2.33). Neglecting the weights of the members, the vertical downward force of 15 lb is balanced by the reactions of the blocks ($7\frac{1}{2}$ lb each block). Consider the equilibrium of point O (Fig. 2.34).

Note that when three forces meeting at a point are in equilibrium, the arrows in the force diagram follow one another around in the

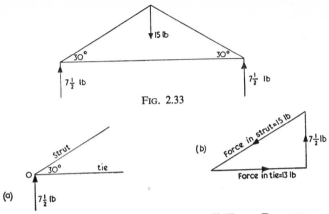

FIG. 2.33

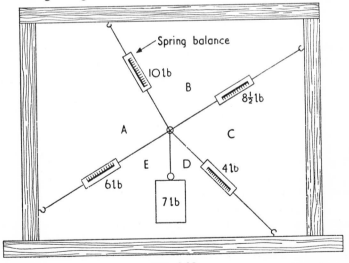

FIG. 2.34. (*a*) FREE-BODY DIAGRAM; (*b*) FORCE DIAGRAM

same direction. Thus it will be seen that the strut is pushing towards point *O* and that the tie is pulling away from the same point.

Polygon of Forces

The same apparatus that was used in Fig. 2.1 can be employed to demonstrate the principle of the polygon of forces.

Referring to Fig. 2.35, the small ring is at rest (i.e. in equilibrium)

FIG. 2.35

as the result of the downward pull of the 7 lb weight and the pulls in the four strings. The forces in the strings are given by the readings on the spring balances and these forces are given in Fig. 2.35 for one particular arrangement of the strings.

The lines of action of the forces can be transferred to a piece of paper or cardboard (in the manner described on page 7) to give the free-body diagram (Fig. 2.36).

It will be noted that the *spaces* between the forces in the free-body diagram have been lettered *A*, *B*, *C*, etc., and each force is therefore

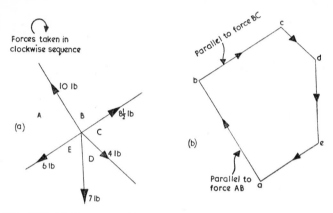

Fig. 2.36. (*a*) Free-body Diagram for Meeting Point of Forces; (*b*) Force Polygon

denoted by two letters, e.g. force *AB* (which separates space *A* from space *B*), force *BC*, force *CD*, etc. (If the forces are taken in anti-clockwise sequence they will be called force *DC*, force *CB*, force *BA*, etc., but it is more usual to take the forces in clockwise sequence.) This method of notation was devised by an engineer (R. H. Bow) about 1870 and is known as *Bow's Notation*. It is not essential to use a notation for simple problems but some form of notation is indispensable when a large number of forces are involved such as in roof trusses (see Chapter 7).

Having plotted the lines of action of the forces in the free-body diagram, the next step is to choose a scale of so many pounds to the inch in order to plot the force diagram. Starting with the force *AB*, a line *ab* is drawn parallel to it, the length *ab* representing to scale the magnitude of the force (10 lb). From *b* a line *bc* is drawn in the direction indicated by the arrow on force *BC* (8½ lb).

The other forces are drawn in the same manner and if the experiment has been performed accurately it will be found that the last line drawn parallel to force *EA* (6 lb) will finish at *a*, where line *ea* represents to scale the force *EA*.

It is not necessary to start the force diagram with force *AB*. Any one of the forces can be chosen as the starting force.

Further experiments can be performed by connecting the strings to the other hooks in the framework, and it will be found in every case (apart from small experimental errors) that when a number of forces are in equilibrium the force diagram will form a polygon, the sides of which represent to scale the magnitudes and directions of the forces.

Study carefully the force diagram or polygon in Fig. 2.36 and note that the arrows "chase each other" in the same sense around the diagram, i.e. the tip of each arrow is pointing to the tail of the arrow in front of it. This will always be true for force diagrams when the forces are in equilibrium, and we can make use of this fact to discover the direction of unknown forces, as in the following example.

EXAMPLE 10

A rod (the weight of which is negligible) is hinged to a support at *S* and is supported by a tie (Fig. 2.37). From the point *O* three ropes are pulling with the forces indicated. Determine the forces in the rod and tie.

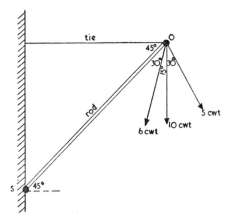

FIG. 2.37

The point *O* is in equilibrium as the result of the action of five forces, i.e. the three given forces and the forces in the rod and tie.

The free-body diagram for point *O* is given in Fig. 2.38.

It is an advantage to start Bow's Notation in such a manner that the two unknown forces are last. First, draw a line *ab* parallel to force *AB* to represent to scale 5 cwt, then draw lines *bc* and *cd* to represent the other known forces. From *d* draw a line parallel to force *DE*. Since point *O* is in equilibrium the force diagram must form a closed polygon, therefore from *a* draw a line parallel to force *EA* to intersect the line drawn parallel to force *DE*. The intersection

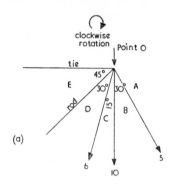

(a)

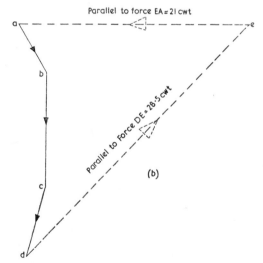

(b)

Fig. 2.38. (*a*) Free-body Diagram; (*b*) Force Polygon

point of these two lines is point *e*. The force in the rod is given by the length of line *de* and is 28·5 cwt approximately. Similarly, the force in the tie is given by the length of line *ea* and is 21 cwt approximately. The arrows on lines *de* and *ea* must follow the general direction, therefore the tie is pulling away from point *O* and the rod (which is a strut) is pushing towards point *O*.

EXAMPLE 11

Two rigid rods *XO* and *YO* of negligible weight are hinged at *X*, *Y*, and *O* (Fig. 2.39). Weights are attached by strings as shown. Determine the forces in the two rods and state whether the rods are struts or ties.

Note that if we letter the forces as they are depicted in Fig. 2.39 the force of 20 lb comes between the two unknown forces. It is more

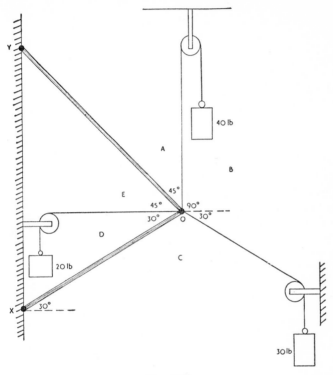

FIG. 2.39

convenient to deal with the known forces in consecutive order and the horizontal force of 20 lb can therefore be shown as pushing towards the point *O* (see free-body diagram Fig. 2.40) instead of pulling away from it.

The known forces *AB*, *BC* and *CD* are plotted on the force polygon as explained in Example 10, taking care to draw the forces in the directions indicated by the arrows on the free-body diagram. From *d*, a line is drawn parallel to the rod *DE* and a line from *a* parallel to rod *EA*. Where these lines intersect is the point *e*. Rod *DE* is a tie since it is pulling away from point *O* and the force in it is 23 lb approximately. Rod *EA* is a strut since it is pushing towards point *O* and the force in it is 19·5 lb approximately. The fact that the lines in the force diagram cross one another is of no importance. The figure is still considered to be a polygon.

Note that the forces in the tie and strut have been stated to be 23 lb, and 19·5 lb *approximately*. The forces can be obtained by

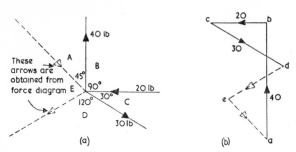

(a)   (b)

FIG. 2.40. (*a*) FREE-BODY DIAGRAM FOR POINT *O*; (*b*) FORCE POLYGON

calculation and may be slightly different from the values given, since calculation is more accurate than drawing. Graphical methods are, however, sufficiently accurate for most structural work and should be used when, as in the above problem, they are quicker and more easily applied than calculation methods.

Resultant of Concurrent Forces

The resultant of two forces meeting at a point can be found by the triangle or parallelogram of forces as described earlier. The resultant of any number of forces can be determined by the polygon of forces.

EXAMPLE 12

Three ropes pull on a bolt as indicated in Fig. 2.41. Determine the resultant pull.

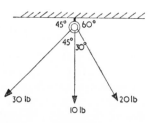

FIG. 2.41

The force polygon is constructed from *a* to *d* by drawing lines to scale parallel to the three given forces (Fig. 2.42). The closing line *da* of the polygon gives the magnitude and direction of the reaction

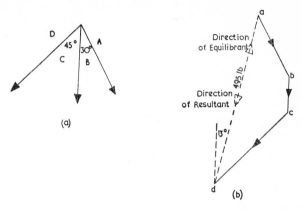

FIG. 2.42. (*a*) FREE-BODY DIAGRAM; (*b*) FORCE POLYGON

(equilibrant) supplied by the support. The resultant of the pulls in the three ropes is, of course, equal to the equilibrant and is 49·5 lb pulling downwards at an angle of 13° approximately to the vertical.

SUMMARY

Triangle of Forces. If three forces, the lines of action of which meet at one point, are in equilibrium they can be represented in magnitude and direction by the sides of a triangle if these sides are drawn parallel to the forces.

Equilibrant. The equilibrant of a given number of forces which are acting on a body is the single force which keeps the other forces in equilibrium. Any one of the forces can be considered as being the equilibrant of the remainder of the forces.

Resultant. The resultant of a given number of forces is the single force which, when substituted for the given forces, has the same effect on the state of equilibrium of the body.

Parallelogram of Forces. If two forces meeting at a point are represented in magnitude and direction by the two sides of a parallelogram their resultant is represented in magnitude and direction by the diagonal of the parallelogram which passes through the point where the two forces meet.

Components of Forces. A given force can be replaced by any two forces (components) which meet at the point of application of the given force. When the angle between the two forces is a right angle the components are called rectangular components.

Polygon of Forces. If any number of forces acting at a point are in equilibrium they can be represented in magnitude and direction by the sides of a closed polygon taken in order.

EXERCISE 2

1. Determine the tensions in the two chains L and R in the case of Fig. 2.43 (*a*), (*b*) and (*c*).

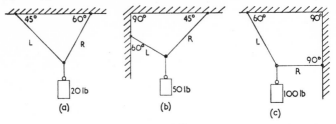

FIG. 2.43

2. The angles marked A in Fig. 2.44 are equal. Determine the minimum value of this angle if the tension in each rope must not exceed 200 lb.

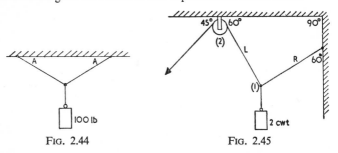

FIG. 2.44   FIG. 2.45

3. The string marked L in Fig. 2.45 passes over a smooth pulley. Determine the tensions in the two strings L and R by considering the equilibrium of point (1) then determine the reaction at the pulley by considering the equilibrium of point (2).

4. The string marked L in Fig. 2.46 passes over a smooth pulley and the system is in equilibrium. Determine the tensions in the strings L and R, then determine the magnitude of the weight W and the tension in the string M (Consider first the equilibrium of point (1).)

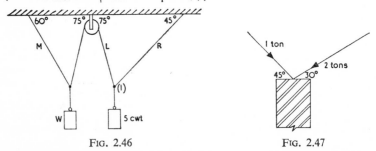

FIG. 2.46   FIG. 2.47

5. Two struts thrust on a wall as indicated in Fig. 2.47. Determine the magnitude and direction of the resultant thrust.

6. The top of a pole resists the pulls from two wires as indicated in Fig. 2.48. Determine the magnitude and direction of the resultant pull.

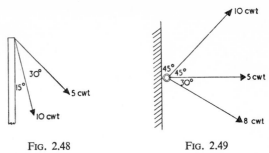

FIG. 2.48   FIG. 2.49

7. A bolt resists the pull from three wires as indicated in Fig. 2.49. Determine the resultant of the two pulls of 10 cwt and 5 cwt then combine this resultant with the remaining pull of 8 cwt to determine the resultant pull on the bolt.

8. Referring to Fig. 2.50, determine the value of the angle A so that the resultant force on the wall is vertical. What is the value of the resultant?

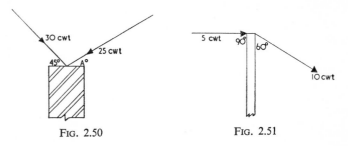

FIG. 2.50   FIG. 2.51

9. The top of a pole sustains a pull and a thrust as shown in Fig. 2.51. Determine the resultant force.

10. Two men pull on ropes attached to a peg as shown in Fig. 2.52. Determine the resultant pull on the peg.

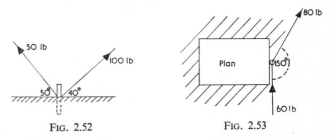

FIG. 2.52   FIG. 2.53

11. In trying to move a block of stone resting on the ground, one man pushes and another man pulls as shown in plan in Fig. 2.53. Determine the resultant of the two forces.

12. Determine the resultant pull on the bolt in Fig. 2.54 and the reactions at the pulleys.

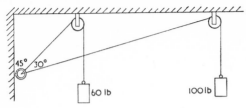

Fig. 2.54

13. Determine the forces in the tie and strut in the case of Fig. 2.55 (*a*), (*b*) and (*c*) neglecting the weights of the members. All joints are hinged.

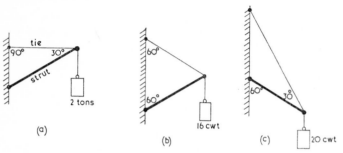

Fig. 2.55

14. Referring to Fig. 2.56 a weight of 10 cwt is suspended from *A* by a flexible cable. The rope *C* is parallel to the member *AB*. Determine the force in the cable, the angle *x* and the forces in the strut and tie. Ignore the weights of the members.

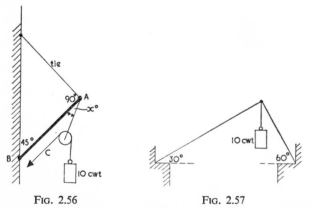

Fig. 2.56   Fig. 2.57

15. Determine the forces in the two struts of Fig. 2.57 then determine the vertical and horizontal thrusts at each support.

16. Fig. 2.58 shows a simple roof truss consisting of two struts and a tie. Consider the equilibrium of joint *C* to determine the forces in the two struts, then, using these values, apply the triangle of forces law to joints *A* and *B* respectively to determine the tension in the tie and the vertical reactions at the supports.

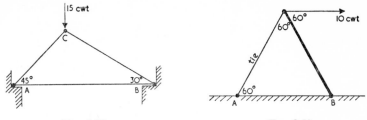

FIG. 2.58   FIG. 2.59

17. Determine the forces in the tie and strut of Fig. 2.59, then determine the vertical and horizontal components of the reactions at *A* and *B*.

18. A continuous string *ABCDE* has weights suspended from it as shown in Fig. 2.60. Determine the tensions in the portions *AB* and *BC*. In addition, determine the horizontal and vertical components of the reactions at *A* and *E*.

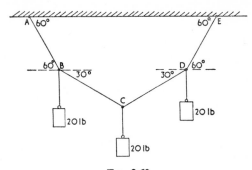

FIG. 2.60

19. In Fig. 2.61 the masts are vertical and hinged at their bases. Determine the tension in the rope supporting the weight, the tension in the stays and the compression in the masts.

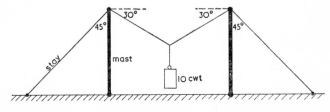

FIG. 2.61

20. In Fig. 2.62 the rope supporting the weight passes over smooth pulleys at the tops of the masts. Determine the angle *A* that the masts make with the horizontal and determine the compression in the masts.

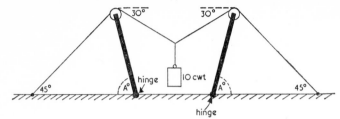

FIG. 2.62

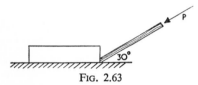

FIG. 2.63

21. The block of stone of Fig. 2.63 will begin to slide when the horizontal force is 5 cwt. What is the maximum value of the thrust *P* without sliding occurring.

22. Determine the force in the ropes *A* and *B* which will replace the rope *C* of Fig. 2.64.

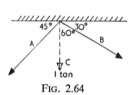

FIG. 2.64

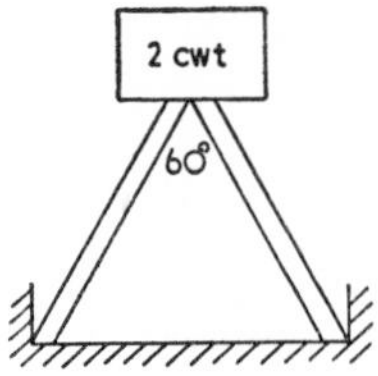

FIG. 2.65

23. Two posts support a weight of 2 cwt as shown in Fig. 2.65. What horizontal force is each post exerting on the other?

24. A triangular framework of hinged rods is supported by two cables (Fig. 2.66). Determine the forces in the framework and in the cables, and determine the vertical components of the reactions at *A* and *B*. Neglect the weights of the members.

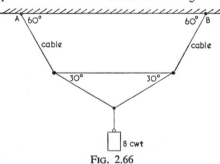

FIG. 2.66

25. A framework consisting of five rods hinged at their joints is supported as shown in Fig. 2.67. Neglecting the weights of the members, determine the forces in the members of the framework and the reaction at *A*.

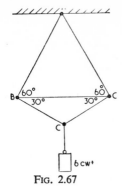

FIG. 2.67

26. Fig. 2.68 (*a*) to (*f*) shows the free-body diagrams for systems of concurrent forces which are in equilibrium. Determine the magnitude and direction of the unknown force (or forces) marked *X* and *Y*.

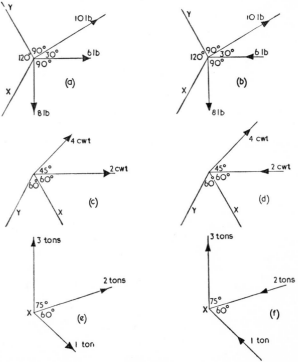

FIG. 2.68

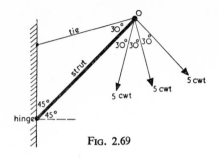

Fig. 2.69

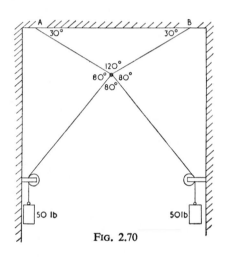

Fig. 2.70

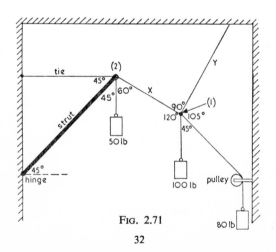

Fig. 2.71

32

27. Three ropes are attached to point *O* and are pulled with forces as indicated in Fig. 2.69. Determine the forces in the strut and tie.

28. Referring to Fig. 2.70, determine the tension in the string which is supported at *A* and *B* and the vertical components of the reactions at *A* and *B*.

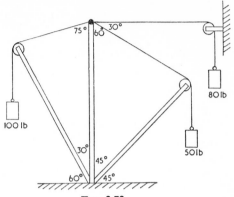

FIG. 2.72

29. By considering the equilibrium of point (1) in Fig. 2.71, determine the tensions in the two strings *X* and *Y*, then by considering the equilibrium of point (2) determine the forces in the strut and tie.

30. Three posts are fixed at their bases as shown in Fig. 2.72. The pulleys are smooth. Determine the magnitude and direction of the resultant force at the top of each post.

CHAPTER 3

Triangle of Forces—Further Problems—Non-concurrent Forces The Link Polygon

Further Problems

FOR the solution of the problems in this chapter it is necessary to know the following facts—

1. The whole weight of a body can be assumed to act at one point for the purpose of determining supporting reactions, etc., in a system of forces which are in equilibrium. This point is called the *centre of gravity* of the body. This subject will be discussed further on page

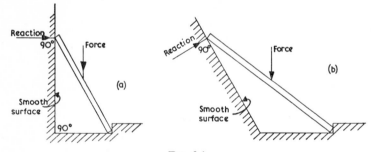

FIG. 3.1

62 and in Chapter 6. For the present, it will be sufficient to remember that the centre of gravity (c.g.) of a rod or beam which is uniform in cross-section is at the centre of its length, the c.g. of a thin rectangular plate is at the intersection of the diagonals of the rectangle, the c.g. of a thin circular disc is at the centre of the circle and the c.g. of a cube or rectangular solid is at the intersection of its diagonals.

2. If a body is supported by a perfectly smooth surface the reaction of the surface upon the body acts at right angles to the surface (Fig. 3.1).

If the reaction were not at right angles to the surface it would mean that there would be a component of the reaction acting along the wall surface as shown in Fig. 3.2. This shows there is frictional resistance of the wall opposing the downward trend of the ladder, and if the wall is smooth it can offer no frictional resistance.

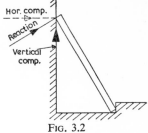

FIG. 3.2

3. If two forces (which are not parallel) do not meet at their points of contact with the body, their lines of action can be produced until they do meet.

4. If a body is in equilibrium under the action of three forces and two of these forces are known to meet at a point, the line of action of the remaining force must pass through the same point.

EXAMPLE 1

A thin rectangular plate weighing 20 lb is supported by two strings as indicated in Fig. 3.3. Determine the tensions in the strings.

The whole weight of the plate can be assumed to act at its centre of gravity. The lines of action of the forces in the strings, when produced, meet the line of action of the weight of the plate at O. Consider the equilibrium of this point (Fig. 3.4).

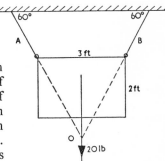

FIG. 3.3

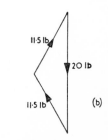

FIG. 3.4. (*a*) FREE-BODY DIAGRAM FOR POINT O OF FIG. 3.3; (*b*) FORCE DIAGRAM

The tension in string A (and B) is 11.5 lb. The student could demonstrate the principle involved in the solution of the above problem on the apparatus illustrated in Fig. 2.1.

EXAMPLE 2

A ladder rests against a smooth wall and a man weighing 150 lb stands on it as indicated in Fig. 3.5. Neglecting the weight of the ladder determine the reactions at the wall and at the ground.

The ladder is in equilibrium as the result of the action of three forces; the weight of the man, the reaction at the top of the ladder, and the reaction at the foot. Since the wall is smooth the reaction

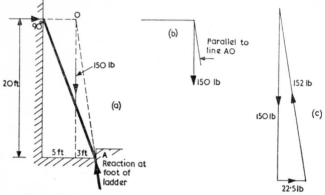

FIG. 3.5. (*a*) LADDER RESTING AGAINST A SMOOTH WALL;
(*b*) FREE-BODY DIAGRAM FOR POINT *O*; (*c*) FORCE DIAGRAM

at the top of the ladder is at right angles to the wall. Draw Fig. 3.5(*a*) to scale. The vertical line representing the weight of the man and the horizontal line representing the reaction at the top of the ladder

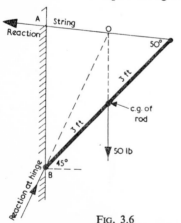

FIG. 3.6

meet at point *O*. The line of action of the reaction at the foot of the ladder must therefore pass through the same point. We now have three forces meeting at a point and the solution is shown in Figs. 3.5(*b*) and (*c*) which give the reaction at the top of the ladder as 22·5 lb, and the reaction at the foot as 152 lb.

EXAMPLE 3

The uniform rod 6 ft long shown in Fig. 3.6 weighs 50 lb. Determine the reactions at *A* and *B*.

The reaction at *A* is in line with the string. The weight of the rod can be assumed to act at its centre of gravity and to act vertically downwards. Draw the diagram to scale. Produce the line of action of the force of 50 lb to meet at O the line of action of the reaction at A. The line of action of the reaction at B is given by joining B

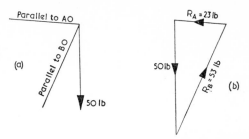

FIG. 3.7. (*a*) FREE-BODY DIAGRAM FOR POINT O; (*b*) FORCE DIAGRAM

to O. Consider the equilibrium of point O as shown in Fig. 3.7. The reactions are 23 lb at A and 53 lb at B.

Non-concurrent Forces—The Link Polygon

Non-concurrent forces are forces the lines of action of which do not all meet at one point. (A system in which the forces are all parallel

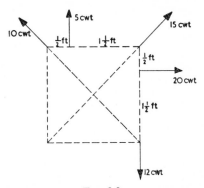

FIG. 3.8

to one another is a special example of non-concurrent forces.) This chapter will deal only with forces which are in one plane (co-planar).

Fig. 3.8 shows a system of non-concurrent forces; it can be assumed (if the reader desires a concrete example) that the forces are acting on a block of stone, the plan view of which is a square of 2 ft side, the forces being co-planar. If the resultant force on the stone is required, one method of solution based on work in previous chapters is first to produce any two of the forces until they meet, and then to find the resultant of these two forces by the parallelogram of forces. This resultant can now be combined with

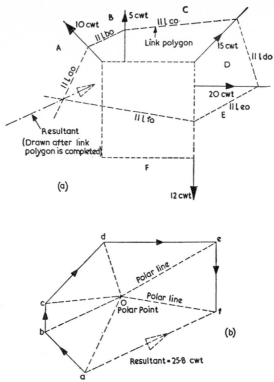

FIG. 3.9. (*a*) FREE-BODY DIAGRAM; (*b*) FORCE POLYGON

one of the remaining forces and a new resultant found, and so on until the forces have been reduced to one resultant. This method, however, is cumbersome when the number of forces is large and a much neater solution is shown in Fig. 3.9.

The free-body diagram giving the lines of action of the forces is drawn accurately and the forces lettered with Bow's Notation. These forces are treated as if they all meet at one point and a force polygon is drawn, the sides of which are parallel to the given forces

The closing line *fa* (direction from *f* to *a*) of the force polygon will give the magnitude and direction of the equilibrant of the five forces and the same line in the direction *a* to *f* will give the resultant. If the five forces met at one point the answer to the problem would be complete since the resultant must pass through the same point. In this case, there is no common meeting point of the forces and the position (of the resultant) on the body must be determined. This is done by placing a point *O* (the polar point) *anywhere* inside or outside the force polygon and connecting it to the letters *a, b, c,* etc., by polar lines. A line parallel to the polar line *ao* is now drawn on the free-body diagram *anywhere across space A* to cut force *AB*, then a line parallel to *bo* is drawn *across space B* to cut force *BC* and so on. Where the last line (parallel to the polar line *fo*) intersects the first line (parallel to polar line *ao*) is one point on the line of action of the resultant (or equilibrant). The resultant can now be shown in its position on the free-body diagram by drawing a line parallel to the closing line *af* of the force polygon. It will be noted that in this construction the link lines form a polygon on the forces of the free-body diagram and it is known as a *link polygon*.

The graphical conditions of equilibrium for a system of non-concurrent forces are—

> (*a*) the force polygon must be a closed one;
> (*b*) the link polygon must be a closed one.

Proof that the Construction is Valid

Consider the two forces *AB* and *BC* of 10 lb and 5 lb respectively, which are shown to a larger scale in Fig. 3.10 than in Fig. 3.9.

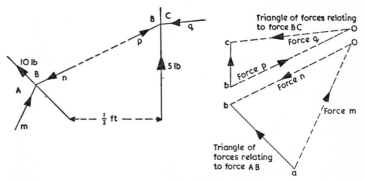

Fig. 3.10

Any two forces *m* and *n* can be substituted for the one force *AB* without altering the state of equilibrium of the body. The value of these two components *m* and *n* which replace force *AB* can be obtained from a triangle of forces (Fig. 3.10) the force of 10 lb represented by the line *ab* being the resultant of the two forces. In a similar manner, force *BC* can be replaced by two forces *p* and *q*; the values of these two forces also being given by a triangle of forces. If it is arranged that component *n* of force *AB* is equal to component *p* of force *BC* the net result on the body of these two components is nil, since they act in the same straight line but in the opposite direction (see Fig. 3.10). Similarly, by having a common polar point in the force diagram (given again in Fig. 3.11) component

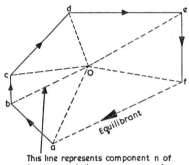

This line represents component n of force AB and also component p of force BC

FIG. 3.11

q of force *BC* will balance with an equal component of force *CD* and so on. It follows that, assuming the equilibrant acts through the point where the two link lines parallel to polar lines *ao* and *fo* meet, the net result on the body of all the forces, including the equilibrant, is nil, therefore the construction is valid.

Note: the arrow representing the direction of the equilibrant will be in the opposite direction to that given for the resultant in Fig. 3.9.

In brief, this method of dealing with non-concurrent forces consists in replacing each of the given forces by two forces or components and arranging that one component of each force is equal in value to a component of the succeeding force. This can be done by having a common polar point in the force diagram. If the polar point is at any other position different to that shown in Figs. 3.9 and 3.11 the construction is still valid, since a force can be replaced by two components in a multitude of ways. Although the polar point can theoretically be placed anywhere, a neater solution can be obtained by choosing its position so that the link polygon will fit nicely on the free body diagram. A multitude of link polygons can be drawn for any one problem, by using different positions of the

polar point, but the closing lines (such as lines drawn parallel to
ao and *fo* in Fig. 3.9) will all intersect on points along the line of
action of the equilibrant (or resultant).

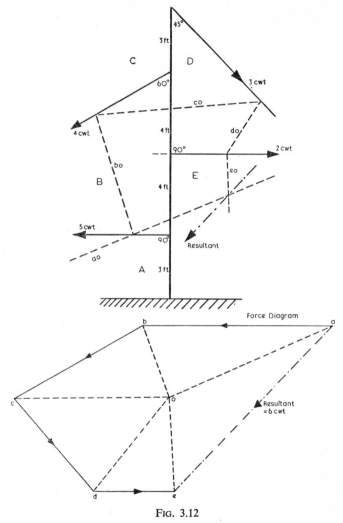

Fig. 3.12

EXAMPLE 4

A vertical post is subjected to pulls from four cables as shown in Fi g. 3.12.
The magnitude, direction and position of the resultant pull is obtained as shown.

Resultant of Parallel Forces by Application
of the Link Polygon

It is usually quicker and easier to obtain the resultant of parallel forces by calculation (see Chapter 6).

EXAMPLE 5

A vertical post it subjected to horizontal pulls from four cables as shown in Fig. 3.13. Determine the position of the resultant pull.

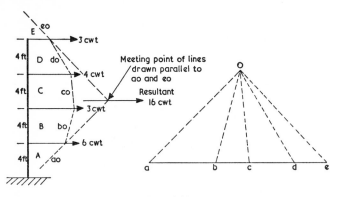

FIG. 3.13

The resultant pull is 16 cwt acting at a point 9 ft from the foot of the post as shown in Fig. 3.13.

To Determine two Unknown Reactions by the Link Polygon

The values of two unknown forces in a system of non-concurrent forces which are in equilibrium can only be determined when the following conditions are satisfied—

1. All the forces (apart from the two unknowns) must be known completely, that is, in magnitude, line of action and direction.

2. The line of action of one of the unknown reactions (not necessarily its direction) must be known.

3. At least one point on the line of action of the remaining reaction must be known.

EXAMPLE 6

A horizontal beam is hinged at one end and supported on a smooth wall at the other end. It is loaded as indicated in Fig. 3.14 (the central load including the weight of the beam). Determine the reactions at the supports.

Since the wall is smooth the reaction at the wall is at right angles to the surface and is therefore vertical. The line of action of one of the reactions is thus known and one point (the hinge) on the line of action of the remaining reaction is known. It is not necessary for

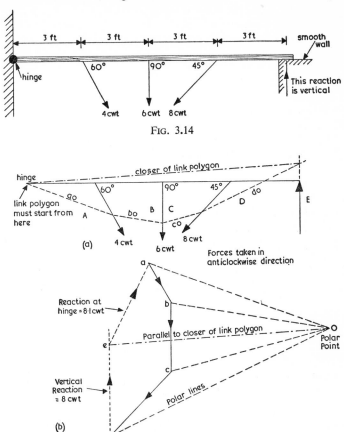

FIG. 3.14

FIG. 3.15. (*a*) FREE-BODY DIAGRAM; (*b*) FORCE DIAGRAM

the solution, to know beforehand the direction of the arrow on the vertical reaction, but it should be obvious that in this example the reaction is acting in an upward direction. The solution is shown in Fig. 3.15 and it is followed by a description of the procedure.

The free-body diagram is drawn to scale and the three known forces are plotted on the force diagram, i.e. *a* to *b*, *b* to *c*, and *c* to *d*. From *d* a vertical line is drawn parallel to the force *DE* (the unknown vertical reaction). The letter *e* will be somewhere on this line, and its position cannot be fixed until the link polygon is drawn. (When point *e* is found, the force polygon can be closed by the line *ea* and this line will give the magnitude and direction of the reaction at the hinge.) Choose a polar point *O* and draw the polar lines. *From the hinge* draw a line across the *A* space parallel to polar line *ao*. Where this line cuts the force *AB*, draw a line across the *B* space parallel to polar line *bo* and so on, the last line being drawn parallel to the polar line *do* to cut the vertical reaction (force *DE*). From this point on the force *DE* draw a line to the hinge. This line closes the link polygon and is known as the *closer*. Draw a line on the force diagram from the polar point *O* and parallel to the closer. Where this line cuts the vertical line from *d* is the position of *e*. Join *e* to *a*. The length of line *de* gives the magnitude of the vertical reaction at the right hand support (8 cwt) and the length of line *ea* gives the magnitude and direction of the reaction at the hinge (8·1 cwt).

It is absolutely essential that the link polygon be started by drawing a line from the *only known point* on the reaction at the hinge. Referring to Fig. 3.10 and the accompanying description and proof of the procedure necessary to obtain the equilibrant of a system of non-concurrent forces, it was shown that lines drawn parallel to the first and last polar lines intersect on one point of the line of action of the equilibrant. In the procedure just described for obtaining two unknown forces, advantage has been taken of the fact that one point on the unknown reaction is known and therefore it can be arranged that lines drawn parallel to the first and last polar lines meet at this point (the last polar line being the closer).

EXAMPLE 7

A beam as shown in Fig. 3.16 is supported by two walls and loaded as shown, the central load including an allowance for the weight of the beam. Determine the value of the reactions.

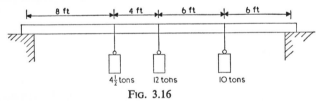

FIG. 3.16

The student should be reminded again that solving a problem of this type (where all the forces are vertical) by means of the link polygon is equivalent to using a sledge hammer to drive in a tin-tack. Solution by calculation is much quicker and easier (Chapter 5). The graphical solution is shown in Fig. 3.17. The reaction at the right support is 15 tons (given by *de* on the force diagram) and the reaction at the left support is 11½ tons (given by *ea*).

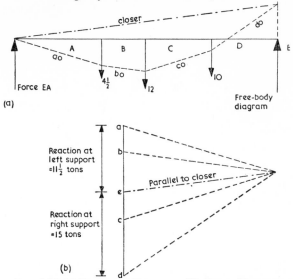

(a)

Force EA

Free-body diagram

(b)

Reaction at left support = $11\frac{1}{2}$ tons

Reaction at right support = 15 tons

FIG. 3.17. (*a*) FREE-BODY DIAGRAM; (*b*) FORCE DIAGRAM

EXAMPLE 8

Fig. 3.18 represents a roof truss one end of which is supported by a roller bearing. The reaction at this end is therefore vertical because the rollers, as indicated, cannot resist horizontal forces. Any horizontal components of the applied forces must, therefore, be resisted entirely by the left hand reaction. The vertical loads are due to the weight of the roof covering, etc., and the inclined forces (which are at right angles to the slope of the roof) are due to wind pressures.

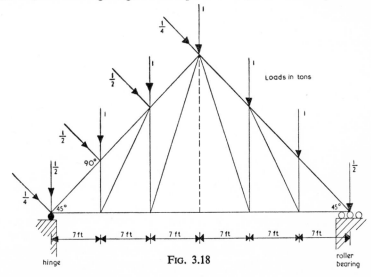

Loads in tons

hinge

roller bearing

FIG. 3.18

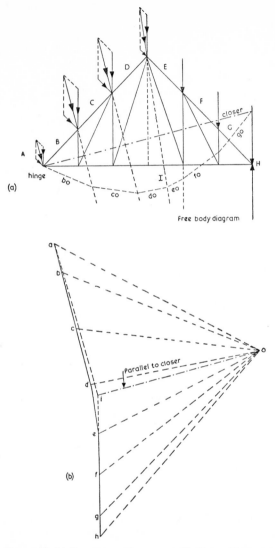

(a)

Free body diagram

(b)

FIG. 3.19. (*a*) FREE-BODY DIAGRAM; (*b*) FORCE DIAGRAM

The manner in which the reactions are determined is shown in Fig. 3.19. Although the reactions can be determined without combining the pairs of forces by the parallelogram law, the solution given here is probably the most straightforward.

Procedure. The free-body diagram is drawn and the parallelogram of forces law used to combine the vertical and inclined forces. The known loads *AB*, *BC*, etc., are plotted in the force diagram, the last load to be plotted being force *GH* (represented by *gh* on the force diagram). Since the reaction at the right support (force *HI*) is vertical, the point *i* will be somewhere on the vertical line drawn from *h* and the link polygon will be the means of fixing this point *i*. It will be observed that two polar lines (*ao* and *ho*) appear not to be used for constructing the link polygon, and this fact needs explanation. The link polygon must start from the hinge which is the only known point on the line of action of the reaction *IA*. Going clockwise, the next force to the reaction is the force *AB*, therefore from the hinge a line must be drawn parallel to *ao* across the *A* space to cut force *AB*. But force *AB* passes through the hinge, therefore a line parallel to *ao* must be drawn *from* the hinge *to* the hinge. A line drawn parallel to polar line *ao* may therefore be considered as contained in the hinge. The next force in order is *BC*, so a line is drawn from the hinge (which is a point on force *AB* as well as a point on the reaction) parallel to polar line *bo* to cut force *BC* and so on, finishing with a line drawn parallel to polar line *go* to cut force *GH*. The next force to *GH* is the vertical reaction *HI* so a line parallel to polar line *ho* must be drawn from force *GH* to cut force *HI*. But these two forces are in the same straight line, so, in effect, the line drawn parallel to polar line *ho* from force *HG* to force *HI* is of zero length. When the point *i* is fixed by drawing a line parallel to the closer of the link polygon, the line *hi* gives the reaction at the right support (3·4 tons approximately) and the line *ia* gives the direction and magnitude (3·75 tons approximately) of the reaction at the left support.

Many roof trusses, particularly those of small spans, are equally supported or hinged at both ends so that neither of the reactions is actually vertical. Even so, for the purposes of determining the reactions and the forces in the members of the truss, it is frequently assumed that one reaction is vertical. An alternative assumption with respect to the reactions is, that if the ends of the truss are similarly supported, the horizontal components of the two reactions are equal. This implies that each support resists equally the tendency to horizontal movement due to any inclined loads on the truss.

EXAMPLE 9

A truss as shown in Fig. 3.20 is subjected to wind forces and dead loads. Determine the magnitudes and directions of the reactions at the supports assuming that the total horizontal component of the applied loads is shared equally by the two supports.

Procedure. After combining by the parallelogram of forces, the loads are plotted, finishing with *de* on the force diagram. The perpendicular line *ax* gives the sum of the vertical components of all the loads on the truss, and the horizontal line *xe* gives the

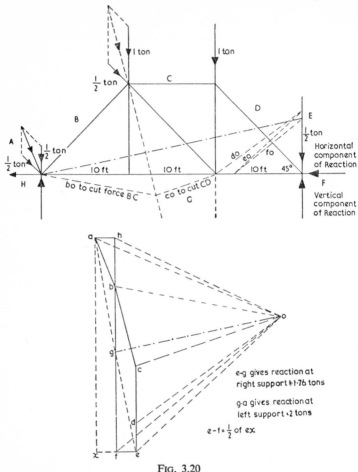

Fɪɢ. 3.20

sum of the horizontal components of the loads. The total horizontal load on the truss is therefore given by *xe* and, since this is resisted equally by the two supports, the horizontal component of each reaction is given by half the length of line *xe*. Point *f* can now be fixed, *ef* representing the horizontal component *EF* of the reaction at the right support. The next force in order is the vertical component *FG*, so from *f* a vertical line is drawn. The position of *g* on this line is not known but it is known that the vertical component *FG* plus the vertical component *GH* must equal the total vertical component of the applied loads. Point *h* must therefore be in a horizontal line from *a* and the force polygon is completed by the line *ha* which represents the horizontal component *HA* of the reaction at the left support. The problem is now reduced to determining the vertical components of the two reactions—in other words, to fixing the position of point *g* on the vertical line *fh*.

Starting the link polygon at the left hinge, the first effective link line is the one drawn parallel to polar line *bo* across the *B* space to cut force *BC*. (The first imaginary link line is *from* the hinge on the unknown vertical component *GH* to cut the horizontal component *HA at* the hinge, and the second link line is *from* the hinge on force *HA* to cut the Force *AB at* the hinge.) Link lines parallel to *co* and *do* are now drawn. The next force in order is *EF* which is horizontal therefore the link line parallel to *eo* is drawn across the *E* space to cut the horizontal force *EF*. The last link line is drawn parallel to *fo* across the *F* space to cut the unknown vertical component *FG*. Finally, the closer connecting the two unknown vertical components of the reactions is drawn, and a line parallel to the closer is drawn on the force diagram from *O*. Where this line cuts the vertical line *fh* is the position of *g*, then *fg* gives to scale the vertical component of the reaction at the right support and *gh* gives the vertical component of the reaction at the left support. The actual magnitudes and directions of the reactions are given by lines *eg* and *ga* respectively.

EXERCISE 3

1. Neglecting the weight of the pole, determine the reactions at *A* and *B*. Fig. 3.21.

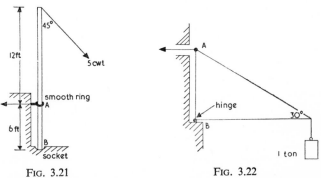

FIG. 3.21   FIG. 3.22

2. Neglecting the weights of the members, determine the reactions at *A* and *B* of Fig. 3.22. (Point *A* is supported by a horizontal cable.) In addition, determine

the forces in the three members of the framework, and the horizontal and vertical components of the reaction at *B*.

3. A gate weighing 1 cwt is supported by two hinges so that the lower hinge takes the whole weight of the gate (Fig. 3.23). Find the reactions at the hinges, and the vertical and horizontal components of the reaction at the bottom hinge.

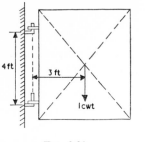
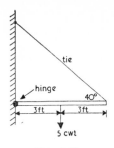

FIG. 3.23   FIG. 3.24

4. Determine the tension in the tie cable and the reaction at the hinge (Fig. 3.24).

5. Determine the tension in the cable and the reaction at the hinge (Fig. 3.25).

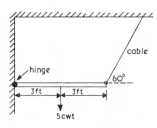

FIG. 3.25

6 A ladder rests against a smooth sloping wall, as shown in Fig. 3.26. The vertical load includes the weight of the ladder. Determine the reactions at *A* and *B*.

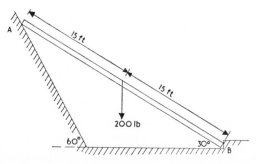

FIG. 3.26

7. The structure shown in Fig. 3.27 is supported by a smooth ring bolt at *A* and by a socket at *B*. Determine the reactions at *A* and *B*. Determine also the horizontal and vertical components of the reaction at *B*.

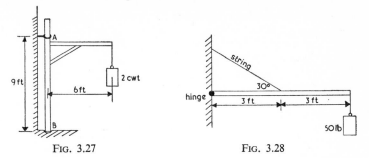

Fig. 3.27   Fig. 3.28

8. Determine the tension in the string and the reaction at the hinge (Fig. 3.28). Neglect the weight of the members.

9. Determine the tension in the tie rope and the reaction at the hinge (Fig. 3.29).

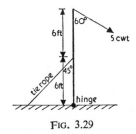

Fig. 3.29

10. A uniform beam weighing 100 lb is supported horizontally as shown in Fig. 3.30. Determine the reactions at the smooth wall and hinge.

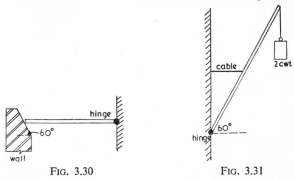

Fig. 3.30   Fig. 3.31

11. The horizontal cable of Fig. 3.31 is half-way up the rod, the weight of which may be neglected. Determine the tension in the cable and the reaction at the hinge.

12. A uniform rod is hinged half-way along its length as shown in Fig. 3.32. Determine the tension in the tie rope and the reaction at the hinge, neglecting the weight of the rod.

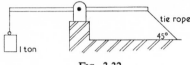

FIG. 3.32

13. A uniform rod is hinged half-way along its length as shown in Fig. 3.33. Determine the tension in the rope and the reaction at the hinge, neglecting the weight of the rod.

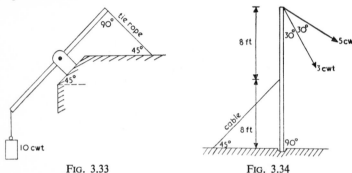

FIG. 3.33   FIG. 3.34

14. Determine the resultant of the two forces of 5 cwt and 3 cwt (Fig. 3.34), then determine the tension in the cable and the reaction at the bottom of the pole. Neglect the weight of the pole.

15. A framework consisting of three rods hinged at the joints is supported by a smooth wall at *B* and is hinged to a wall at *A* (Fig. 3.35). Determine the reactions at *A* and *B* and the forces in the three members, neglecting their weight.

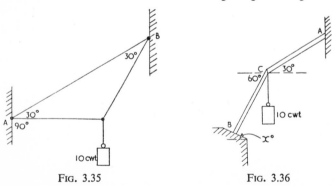

FIG. 3.35   FIG. 3.36

16. A bent rigid rod has two equal arms *AC* and *BC* as shown in Fig. 3.36. The wall at *A* is smooth. Determine the angle *x* so that the reaction at *B* is at right angles to the surface of the wall.

17. Determine the tensions in the strings and the reaction at the hook (Fig. 3.37).

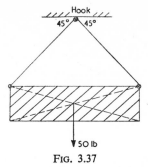

FIG. 3.37

18. A horizontal beam, the weight of which may be neglected, is loaded half-way along its length as shown in Fig. 3.38. Determine the reactions at *A* and *B*.

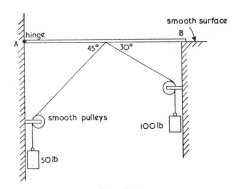

FIG. 3.38

19. Neglecting the weight of the beam, determine the reactions at *A* and *B* of Fig. 3.39.

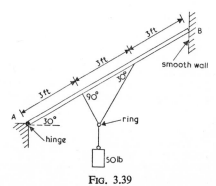

FIG. 3.39

20. Neglecting the weight of the rod, determine the reactions at A and B of Fig. 3.40.

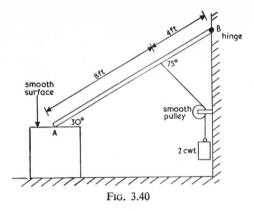

Fig. 3.40

21. A horizontal rod the weight of which may be neglected is hinged at X as shown in Fig. 3.41. Determine by the parallelogram of forces the resultant pull on the smooth pulley, then use the triangle of forces to determine the tension in the tie rope and the reaction at the hinge.

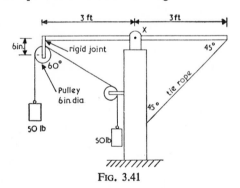

Fig. 3.41

22. A rod, the weight of which may be neglected, is hinged at A and supported by a tie rope connected to B as in Fig. 3.42. Determine the resultant pull due to the two weights of 5 cwt and 8 cwt, then determine the forces in the tie and rod.

23. Determine the reactions at A and B to the rod shown in Fig. 3.43.

24. Determine the position of the resultant for the systems of forces given in Fig. 3.44 (*a*), (*b*) and (*c*).

25. A mast, fixed at its base. is loaded as shown in Fig. 3.45. Determine the magnitude and line of action of the resultant of the given loads.

26. Determine the magnitude and line of action of the resultant of the four parallel forces acting on the mast of Fig. 3.46.

27. Determine the magnitude and line of action of the resultant of the four parallel forces given in Fig. 3.47.

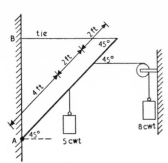

FIG. 3.42

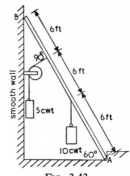

FIG. 3.43

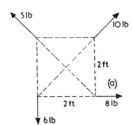

FIG. 3.44

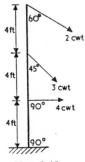

FIG. 3.45

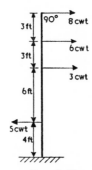

FIG. 3.46

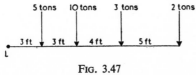

FIG. 3.47

55

28. Determine the magnitude of the vertical reaction at R and the magnitude and line of action of the reaction at L of the system of forces given in Fig. 3.48.

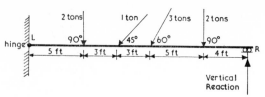

FIG. 3.48

29. A beam (Fig. 3.49) is hinged at L and supported by means of a cable at R. Determine the reactions at L and R.

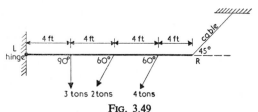

FIG. 3.49

30. A vertical mast is supported by means of a smooth ring bolt at X (which means that the reaction at X is horizontal) and by a socket at Y (Fig. 3.50). Determine the reactions at X and Y.

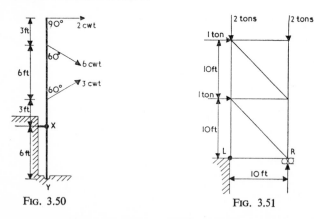

FIG. 3.50   FIG. 3.51

31. A tower (Fig. 3.51) is supported by roller bearings at R and is hinged at L. Determine the reactions at L and R.

32. Determine the reactions at L and R due to the three vertical loads of Fig. 3.52.

33. Assuming the reaction at R of Fig. 3.53 to be vertical, determine its magnitude. Also determine the magnitude and direction of the reaction at L.

34. Repeat Question 33 assuming that the total horizontal component of the applied loads is shared equally by the two supports.

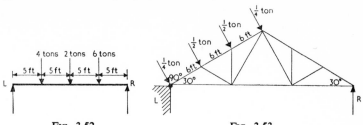

Fig. 3.52   Fig. 3.53

35. The reaction at *R* to the truss shown in Fig. 3.54 is assumed to be vertical. Determine its value due to the wind loading given and also determine the value and line of action of the reaction at *L*.

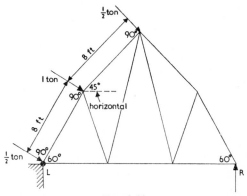

Fig. 3.54

36. Repeat Question 35 assuming that the total horizontal component of the applied loads is shared equally by the two supports.

37. Determine the reactions at *L* and *R* of Fig. 3.55 assuming the reaction at *R* to be vertical.

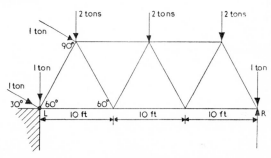

Fig. 3.55

38. Repeat Question 37 assuming that the total horizontal component of the applied loads is shared equally by the two supports.

39. The lengths of rafters represented by x and y of Fig. 3.56 are equal and the wind loads are at right angles to the slope of the roof. Determine the reactions at L and R assuming the reaction at L to be vertical.

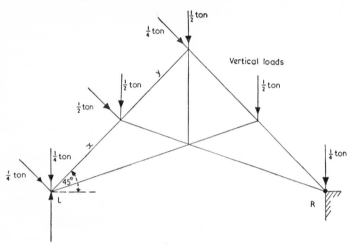

FIG. 3.56

40. Fig. 3.57 shows a truss which is supported at L and R. Determine the reactions, assuming that the total horizontal component of the applied loads is shared equally by the two supports.

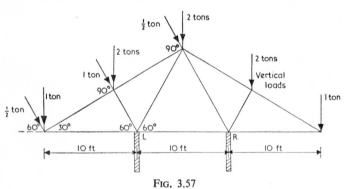

FIG. 3.57

CHAPTER 4

Moments of Forces I

IT is common knowledge that a small force can have a big turning effect or leverage. In mechanics, the word *moment* is commonly used instead of *turning effect* or *rotational effect*. Students are sometimes confused at the beginning of this subject because previously they have thought of the word moment as having some connexion with time. Moment, however, derives from a Latin word meaning movement and moments of time refer, of course, to movement of time. Similarly, the *moment of a force* can be thought of as movement of a force, although a more exact definition is "turning effect of a force." In many types of problems, there is

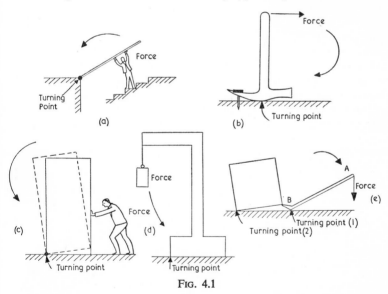

Fig. 4.1

an obvious *turning point* (or hinge or pivot or fulcrum) about which the body turns or tends to turn as a result of the effect of the force. See Fig. 4.1 (*a*) to (*e*). In other cases, where the principle of moments may be used to obtain solutions to problems, there may not be any obvious turning points.

Clockwise and Anticlockwise Moments

To solve problems by the use of the principle of moments, the effect of the forces must be considered in relation to the direction in which the body turns or tends to turn around the given point. In Fig. 4.1(*a*) the turning effect or moment of the force is anti-clockwise; in (*b*) the moment is clockwise; and in (*c*) and (*d*) the moments are anticlockwise. There are two turning points in Fig. 4.1(*e*). Considering the point where the crowbar touches the ground (point (1)) the moment of force at *A* is clockwise. At *B*, the bar

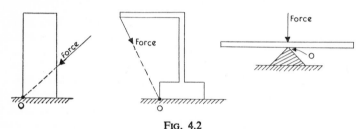

FIG. 4.2

applies a force to the stone and causes it to turn about point (2). The moment of force applied to the stone at *B* is therefore anti-clockwise.

If the line of action of a force passes through a point it can have no turning effect (moment) about that point. For example, a door cannot be opened by pushing at the hinge. Further examples are given in Fig. 4.2. The given forces have no moments about points *O*.

Equilibrium of Structures

Structures and parts of structures must be in equilibrium. If, therefore, there are clockwise turning effects due to forces, there must be equal and counterbalancing anticlockwise turning effects. In other words, *clockwise moments must equal anticlockwise moments.*

Measurement of Moments

Fig. 4.3 represents a uniform rod which balances on a fulcrum placed half-way along the length of the rod. If a weight of 5 lb is suspended at 9 in. from the fulcrum it will be found that a weight of 3 lb is required at 15 in. from the fulcrum on the other side in order to maintain equilibrium. Instead of 3 lb at 15 in. from the fulcrum we could place 4½ lb at 10 in. or 9 lb at 5 in. The results of the experiments would show that the weight causing a clockwise moment multiplied by its distance from the turning point equals the weight causing an anticlockwise moment multiplied by its distance from the turning point. For example, referring to Fig. 4.3 the clockwise moment of the 3 lb weight is 3 lb × 15 in. or 45 lb-in. Moments are always expressed in weight-length units such as tons-ft, lb-ft, lb-in., etc. A little consideration should show that this must be so, because the turning effect of a force depends on distance as well as on the magnitude of the force.

The distance from the force to the turning point is often called the *lever arm* of the force. In Fig. 4.3 the lever arm of the 3 lb weight

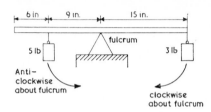

FIG. 4.3

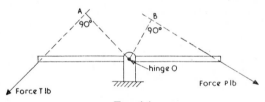

FIG. 4.4

is 15 in. and the lever arm of the 5 lb weight is 9 in. It should be noted that the lever arm should be measured from the turning point to the point where it intersects the line of action of the force at right angles. In Fig. 4.3 the lines of action of the weights are vertical and the lever arms are horizontal. In Fig. 4.4 the lever arms of the forces are AO and BO respectively and for equilibrium $T \times AO$ must equal $P \times BO$. The reason for measuring the lever arms in this way will be made clear in Example 3 on page **65**.

Further demonstrations of the principle of moments can be arranged quite easily with the aid of a fulcrum, a rod and a few weights. In Fig. 4.5 the rod itself, since it is supported at its centre of gravity, has no resultant turning effect, clockwise or anticlockwise.

$$\text{Anticlockwise moments} = \text{Clockwise moments}$$
$$(2 \times 12\tfrac{1}{2}) + (5 \times 9) = (5 \times 5) + (3 \times 15)$$
$$70 \text{ lb-in.} = 70 \text{ lb-in.}$$

Note that since the whole weight downwards is supported at the fulcrum, the upward reaction of the fulcrum is 15 lb plus the weight of the rod.

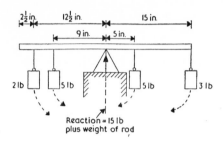

Fig. 4.5

Self Weight of Rod Taken into Account

Example 1

A plank of uniform cross-section 12 ft long and weighing 60 lb has a support placed under it at 4 ft from one end as shown in Fig. 4.6. Calculate the magnitude of the weight W required to cause the plank to balance.

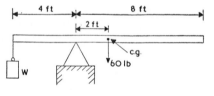

Fig. 4.6

It was stated on page 34 that when considering the equilibrium of forces, the whole weight of a body can be *assumed* to act at its centre of gravity which, in the case of a uniform rod or beam, is half-way along the rod. Taking moments about the fulcrum or turning point,

$$4W \text{ lb-ft} = 60 \times 2 \text{ lb-ft}$$

$$W = \frac{120 \text{ lb-ft}}{4 \text{ ft}} = 30 \text{ lb}$$

The whole weight of the plank is not, of course, concentrated at its centre of gravity. Each little particle of the plank is being attracted downwards by the earth and the 4 ft length of the plank to the left of the fulcrum is exerting an anticlockwise moment, whilst the 8 ft length of the plank to the right of the rod is exerting a clockwise moment. The total net effect is, however, the same as if the whole of the weight were acting at 2 ft to the right of the fulcrum.

For example, assume the plank is divided into 2 ft lengths each length weighing 10 lb, and assume that each 10 lb weight acts half-way along its 2 ft length (Fig. 4.7).

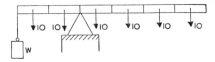

Fig. 4.7

Taking moments about the fulcrum,

$$(10 \times 1) + (10 \times 3) + 4W = (10 \times 1) + (10 \times 3) + (10 \times 5)$$
$$+ (10 \times 7)$$
$$40 + 4W = 160$$
$$4W = 120$$
$$W = 30 \text{ lb}$$

If the rod be divided into a thousand lengths each length weighing 60/1000 lb and moments be taken about the fulcrum, the answer will be the same, so the student need have no hesitation when taking moments in assuming the whole weight of a body to act at its centre of gravity.

EXAMPLE 2

A uniform rod weighing 10 lb and carrying weights as shown (Fig. 4.8) is

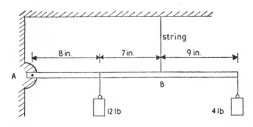

Fig. 4.8

hinged at *A*. The rod is supported in a horizontal position by a vertical string at *B*. Calculate the tension in the string and the reaction at the hinge.

The free-body diagram is given in Fig. 4.9.

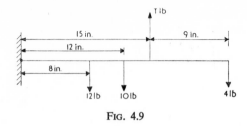

FIG. 4.9

If the string were to be cut all the weights would pull the rod downwards in a clockwise direction about the hinge. The string exerts a counterbalancing anticlockwise moment.

Taking moments about the hinge, assuming T lb to be the tension in the string,

$$15T = (12 \times 8) + (10 \times 12) + (4 \times 24)$$
$$15T = 312$$
$$T = \frac{312}{15} = 20 \cdot 8 \text{ lb}$$

The total weight downwards is $12 + 10 + 4$, i.e. 26 lb. Since the wire is only holding up with a vertical force of 20·8 lb, the reaction at the hinge must be $26 - 20 \cdot 8$, i.e. 5·2 lb acting upwards.

Questions 1 to 11 inclusive of Exercise 4 may now be attempted.

EXAMPLE 3

A horizontal rod has a weight of 20 lb suspended from it as shown in Fig. 4.10.

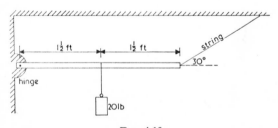

FIG. 4.10

Calculate the tension in the string and the reaction at the hinge, ignoring the weight of the rod.

Solution 1. Let the tension in the string be represented by T lb and resolve this force into its vertical and horizontal components. This may be done by calculation or by drawing a line 10 units long (i.e. 10 cm or 10 quarter-inches) to represent T (Fig. 4.11).

It is found that the vertical component V is 5 units long, i.e. $0.5T$, and that the horizontal component H is 8·66 units long, i.e.

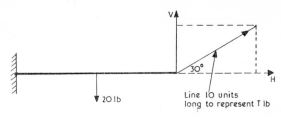

FIG. 4.11

0·866 T. The line of action of the horizontal component of the tension in the string passes through the hinge and therefore has no moment about this point. Taking moments about the hinge—

Anticlockwise moment = Clockwise moment

$$0.5T \times 3 \text{ ft} = 20 \times 1\tfrac{1}{2} \text{ ft}$$

$$1.5T = 30$$

$$T = \frac{30}{1.5} = 20 \text{ lb} = \text{tension in string}$$

Reaction at hinge: the total downward weight is 20 lb. The vertical component of the tension in the string is $0.5T$, i.e. 10 lb. (The horizontal component of the tension in the string is ineffective in holding up the suspended weight.) Since there is 20 lb pulling down, there must be 20 lb pushing up, therefore the hinge must supply a vertical reaction in the upward direction of 10 lb. But the string has also a horizontal component of $0.866T$, i.e. 17·32 lb, tending to pull the rod away horizontally from the hinge. The hinge must resist this pull therefore there must be a horizontal force acting at the hinge in addition to a vertical force.

The total reaction at the hinge is given in Fig. 4.12 and may be found from a scale drawing, or, if $R = $ reaction at hinge,

$$R^2 = 10^2 + 17.32^2$$

$$= 400$$

$$R = \sqrt{400} = 20 \text{ lb}$$

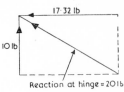

Reaction at hinge = 20 lb

FIG. 4.12

Solution 2. In Fig. 4.13 which may be drawn to scale, produce the

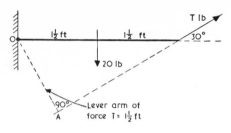

Fig. 4.13

line of action of the string and draw a line *AO* at right angles, then taking moments about *O*,

$$T \times OA = 20 \times 1\tfrac{1}{2}$$
$$T \times 1\tfrac{1}{2} = 30$$

therefore $\qquad\qquad T = 20 \text{ lb}$

This method is not so convenient as Solution 1 for determining the reaction at the hinge.

Solution 3. Since there are only three forces in this problem the triangle of forces law can be applied (see page 35), and this method may be quicker for problems in which the forces are inclined.

EXAMPLE 4

A ladder rests against a smooth vertical wall and a man weighing 150 lb stands on it as indicated in Fig. 4.14. Neglecting the weight of the ladder, determine the reactions at the wall and at the ground.

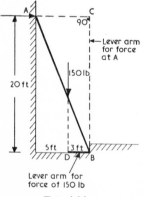

Fig. 4.14

This problem is identical with that on page 36 but we are now solving it by using the principle of moments. Since the wall is smooth, the reaction at *A* is horizontal. There may not appear to be any obvious turning point but we can consider *B* to be a turning point. (If the wall were to collapse the ladder would swing round *B* in an anticlockwise direction due to the force of 150 lb. If we could imagine the force at *A* to be increased above that necessary to maintain equilibrium, it would turn the ladder round *B* in a clockwise direction.) By taking moments about *B*, the reaction at B can be ignored since it passes through this point and therefore has no moment about it.

Reaction at $A \times$ distance $CB = 150 \text{ lb} \times$ distance DB

therefore
$$R_A \times 20 = 150 \times 3$$
$$R_A = \frac{450}{20} = 22\tfrac{1}{2} \text{ lb}$$

Reaction at B (R_B): Since the wall is smooth, it cannot help at all in holding *up* the ladder, therefore the whole weight of 150 lb is taken at B. There is therefore an upward reaction at B of 150 lb. There must also be a horizontal reaction to prevent the foot of the ladder from moving outwards. This horizontal reaction equals the force at A, i.e. $22\tfrac{1}{2}$ lb, therefore the total reaction at B which can be obtained graphically or by calculation is 152 lb (Fig. 4.15).

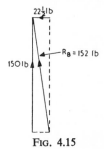

FIG. 4.15

Conditions of Equilibrium

The foregoing problem is an illustration of the application of the three laws of equilibrium which apply to a system of forces acting in one plane. These laws are—

1. The algebraic sum of the vertical forces must equal zero, i.e. if upward forces are called positive and downward forces are called negative, then a force of $+150$ lb must be balanced by a force of -150 lb and the algebraic sum of the two forces is equal to zero This can also be expressed by

$$\Sigma V = 0$$

where Σ is the Greek letter "sigma" (letter S) and in this connexion means "the sum of," whilst V represents "the vertical forces," upward forces being plus and downward forces being minus.

2. The algebraic sum of the horizontal forces must equal zero, i.e. the sum of the horizontal forces (plus forces) acting towards the left must equal the sum of the horizontal forces (minus forces) acting towards the right or $\Sigma H = 0$.

3. The algebraic sum of the moments of the forces must equal zero, i.e. if clockwise moments are called plus and anticlockwise moments are called minus then $\Sigma M = 0$.

EXAMPLE 5

A vertical pole (Fig. 4.16) is supported by being hinged in a socket at B and by a smooth ring which can give no vertical reaction, at A. Calculate the reactions at A and B neglecting the weight of the pole.

First, resolve the pull of 10 cwt into its vertical and horizontal components as shown in Fig. 4.17 and take moments about B.

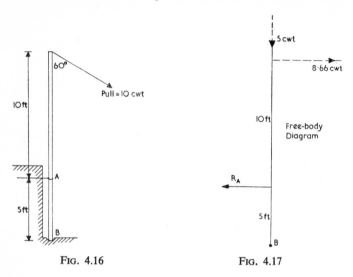

FIG. 4.16   FIG. 4.17

$\Sigma M = 0$ or clockwise moments equal anticlockwise moments.

$$8 \cdot 66 \times 15 = R_A \times 5$$

therefore $R_A = 25 \cdot 98$ cwt

(Note that the vertical component of 5 cwt has no moment about B since its line of action passes through B.)

$$\Sigma V = 0$$

The vertical component of the reaction at B must equal the vertical component of the pull at the top of the pole since the support of A can only *hold back* and cannot *hold up*. The vertical component of the reaction at B therefore equals 5 cwt and acts upwards.

$$\Sigma H = 0$$

The horizontal force at the top of the mast is $8 \cdot 66$ cwt acting $\rightarrow$ and the reaction at A is $25 \cdot 98$ cwt acting $\leftarrow$. There must be, therefore, a horizontal force at B acting $\rightarrow$ equal to $25 \cdot 98 - 8 \cdot 66$, i.e. $17 \cdot 32$ lb. The complete reaction at B is given by Fig. 4.18. Note that if the pole itself weighs, say, 1 cwt that this weight would be taken entirely at B (since the pole is vertical) and the vertical component of the reaction at B would be 6 cwt instead of 5 cwt as shown in Fig. 4.18. The complete reaction at B (R_B) would then be $\sqrt{\{(17 \cdot 32)^2 + (6)^2\}}$, i.e. 18·3 cwt.

Another method of finding the reaction at A (neglecting the weight of the pole) is shown in Fig. 4.19.

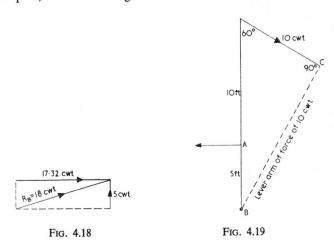

FIG. 4.18 FIG. 4.19

$$10 \text{ cwt} \times \text{distance } BC = R_A \times 5 \text{ ft}$$

Note also that the triangle of forces principle could be applied to determine both reactions.

EXAMPLE 6

A cantilever truss (Fig. 4.20) is supported at A and B in such a manner that the reaction at A is horizontal. Neglecting the weight of the truss, calculate the reactions at A and B.

Take moments about B to determine the reaction at A.

$$\Sigma M = 0$$

therefore $\qquad 4\frac{1}{2} R_A = (1 \times 4\frac{1}{2}) + (\frac{1}{2} \times 9)$

$$R_A = 2 \text{ tons acting towards the right.}$$

$\Sigma H = 0$ therefore horizontal component of reaction at $B = 2$ tons acting towards the left.

$\Sigma V = 0$, therefore vertical component of reaction at B is $1\frac{1}{2}$ tons acting upwards.

Referring to Fig. 4.21

$$R_B = \sqrt{(2^2 + 1\tfrac{1}{2}^2)}$$
$$= \sqrt{(6\cdot 25)}$$
$$= 2\cdot 5 \text{ tons}$$

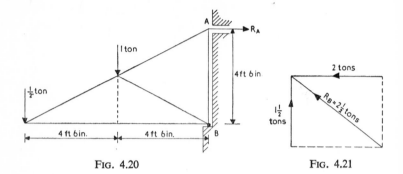

FIG. 4.20   FIG. 4.21

SUMMARY

The moment of a force means the turning effect of a force.

Moments are considered in relation to a turning point, real or imaginary.

A moment is always obtained by multiplying a force by a distance and this distance must be measured from the turning point to where it cuts the line of action of the force at right angles.

Moments are always expressed in weight-length units such as pounds-inches (lb-in.), tons-feet (tons-ft), etc.

If the line of action of a force passes through a given point, it can have no moment about that point.

The conditions of equilibrium for a system of forces acting in one plane are—

$$\Sigma V = 0; \qquad \Sigma H = 0; \qquad \Sigma M = 0.$$

EXERCISE 4

Students who have no knowledge of trigonometry may obtain any distances, etc., which may be necessary for the solution of problems, by measurements taken from scale drawings.

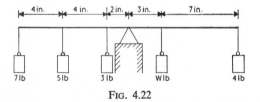

FIG. 4.22

1. A uniform rod is in equilibrium under the action of weights as shown in Fig. 4.22. Calculate the value of W and the reaction at the fulcrum, ignoring the weight of the rod.

2. Calculate the value of x ft so that the uniform rod of Fig. 4.23 will balance.

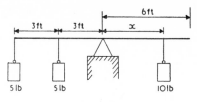

FIG. 4.23

3. A uniform rod weighing 20 lb and supporting 100 lb is hinged to a wall and kept horizontal by a vertical rope (Fig. 4.24). Calculate the tension in the rope and the reaction at the hinge.

4. A uniform rod weighing 8 lb is maintained in equilibrium as shown in Fig. 4.25. Calculate the distance x and the reaction at the fulcrum.

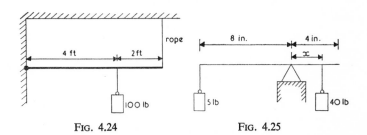

FIG. 4.24   FIG. 4.25

5. A uniform rod 16 in. long weighing 2 lb supports loads as shown in Fig. 4.26. Calculate the distance x if the rod is in equilibrium.

6. A uniform horizontal beam 4 ft long and weighing 40 lb is hinged to a wall and supported by a vertical prop as shown in Fig. 4.27. Calculate the reactions of the prop and hinge.

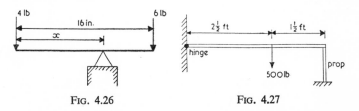

FIG. 4.26   FIG. 4.27

7. Calculate the reaction at the prop and hinge in Fig. 4.28. The uniform beam weighs 40 lb.

8. A compound lever is shown in Fig. 4.29. Each of the horizontal rods weighs 10 lb and the vertical rod weighs 8 lb. Calculate the value of the weight W which is required for equilibrium, and calculate the reactions at the fulcrums. (First take moments about A to find the force in the vertical rod, then take moments about B.)

9. Two steel pegs *A* and *B* driven into a wall support a uniform rod weighing 20 lb and a weight of 100 lb (Fig. 4.30). Calculate the reactions at *A* and *B*.

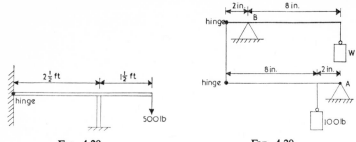

FIG. 4.28   FIG. 4.29

10. A uniform girder 24 ft long weighing 1,000 lb rests on the ground. Calculate the value of the vertical force required to just lift one end off the ground.

11. A uniform plank, 18 ft long weighs 100 lb and is supported by two trestles as indicated in Fig. 4.31. Calculate (*a*) the weight of the heaviest man who can

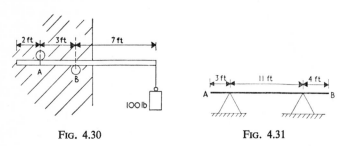

FIG. 4.30   FIG. 4.31

stand at *A* without upsetting equilibrium, (*b*) the weight of the heaviest man who can stand at *B*.

12. A uniform beam 12 ft long is hinged at its mid-point (Fig. 4.32). Determine the value of *P* for the rod to be in equilibrium.

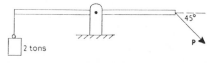

FIG. 4.32

13. Solve Questions 1 to 13 inclusive of Exercise 3, Chapter 3, with the aid of the principle of moments.

14. Determine the tension in the chain and the reaction at the hinge (Fig. 4.33). The uniform rod weighs 1 cwt.

15. The horizontal cable in Fig. 4.34 is attached to the rod half-way along its length. The uniform rod weighs ½ cwt. Calculate the tension in the cable and the reaction at the hinge.

16. Calculate the tension in the guy rope of Fig. 4.35 then use the triangle of forces law to determine the forces in the mast, tie and jib. Neglect the weight of the members.

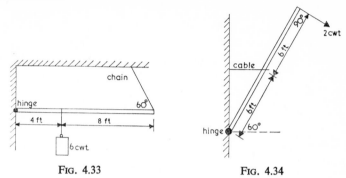

Fig. 4.33   Fig. 4.34

17. A uniform rod weighing 50 lb is loaded as shown in Fig. 4.36. Calculate the tension in the cable and the reaction at the hinge.

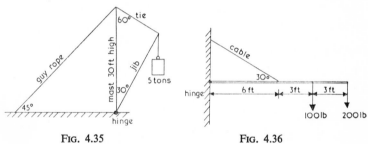

Fig. 4.35   Fig. 4.36

18. Two uniform rods each 6 ft long and weighing 50 lb are connected by a link bar (Fig. 4.37). Calculate the tensions in the link bar and chain neglecting their weights.

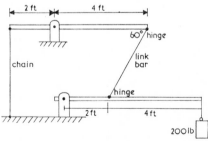

Fig. 4.37

19. A uniform vertical pole weighing 100 lb is subjected to two pulls (Fig. 4.38). The reaction at *A* is horizontal. Calculate the pull on the bolt at *A* and the reaction at the hinge socket *B*.

20. A uniform ladder 30 ft long and weighing 30 lb is supported by a smooth wall and a smooth floor. A horizontal rope keeps the ladder in equilibrium (Fig. 4.39). When a man weighing 170 lb stands half-way up the ladder, calculate the tension in the rope and the reactions at the ground and wall.

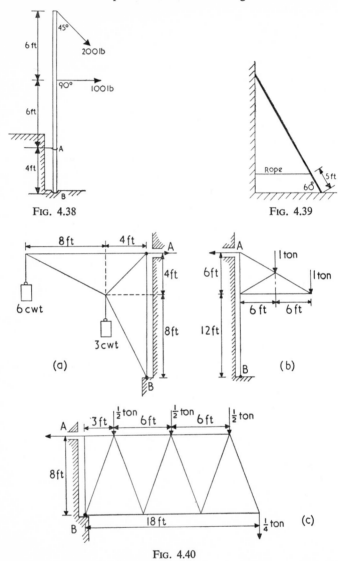

FIG. 4.38   FIG. 4.39

FIG. 4.40

21. In Fig. 4.40(*a*), (*b*) and (*c*) the reaction at *A* is horizontal and *B* is a hinge. Neglecting the weights of the members, calculate the reactions at *A* and *B*.

CHAPTER 5

Moments of Forces II

Beam Reactions and Overbalancing Problems

BEAM-REACTION problems are similar to some of the problems dealt
with in the last chapter.

Experimental Verification

A beam of wood, a little longer than 3 ft and weighing 3 lb, has
weights suspended from it as shown in Fig. 5.1. It is required to
determine the reactions at the two supports A and B.

If a spring balance is attached to the beam at B, the beam can be
lifted just clear of the support and it will be observed that the reading

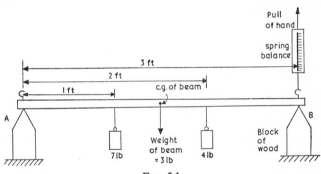

FIG. 5.1

on the balance is $6\frac{1}{2}$ lb. When the balance is released so that the
beam rests again on block B, it follows that the beam must be
pushing down on the support with a force of $6\frac{1}{2}$ lb. Similarly, the
upward reaction of the support on the beam is $6\frac{1}{2}$ lb.

If the hand holding the balance is moved up and down, the beam
will turn round the point where it is supported at A. Taking moments
about this point, representing the reaction at B by R_B,

$$R_B \times 3 \text{ ft (anticlockwise about } A) = (7 \text{ lb} \times 1 \text{ ft}) + (3 \text{ lb} \times 1\frac{1}{2} \text{ ft})$$
$$+ (4 \text{ lb} \times 2 \text{ ft})$$

therefore $\qquad 3R_B = 19\frac{1}{2}; \qquad R_B = \dfrac{19\frac{1}{2}}{3} = 6\frac{1}{2} \text{ lb}$

75

If the balance is transferred to A and the beam lifted off its support, the balance will read $7\frac{1}{2}$ lb (Fig. 5.2).

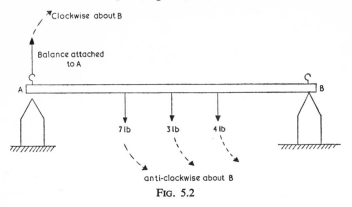

FIG. 5.2

By calculation, taking B as the turning point,

$$R_A \times 3 = (4 \times 1) + (3 \times 1\tfrac{1}{2}) + (7 \times 2)$$

clockwise   anticlockwise

$$R_A = \frac{22\frac{1}{2}}{3} = 7\tfrac{1}{2} \text{ lb}$$

Note that the sum of the reactions is 14 lb and that this is also the sum of the downward forces ($\Sigma V = 0$).

Note also that to determine the reaction at A, moments are taken about B, i.e. B is considered as the turning point and the moment of each force or load is the force multiplied by its distance from B.

Similarly, to determine the reaction at B, moments are taken about A, i.e. A is considered as the turning point.

Uniformly Distributed Loads

The two weights of 7 lb and 4 lb in the discussion above are *point loads* or *concentrated loads*, since they act at definite points on the beam. The beam itself is a *uniformly distributed load* (U.D.L.), since its weight is spread uniformly over its whole length. Fig. 5.3 represents the test beam supporting a block of lead 1 ft long of uniform cross-section and weighing 5 lb. For calculating the reactions at the supports, the whole of this uniformly distributed weight can be assumed to act at its centre of gravity.

Taking moments about A

$$3R_B = (5 \times 1) + (3 \times 1\tfrac{1}{2})$$

$$R_B = \frac{9\frac{1}{2}}{3} = 3\tfrac{1}{6} \text{ lb}$$

Similarly, taking moments about B

$$3R_A = (3 \times 1\tfrac{1}{2}) + (5 \times 2)$$

$$R_A = \frac{14\tfrac{1}{2}}{3} = 4\tfrac{5}{6} \text{ lb}$$

$$R_A + R_B = 3\tfrac{1}{6} + 4\tfrac{5}{6} = 8 \text{ lb} = \text{total load}$$

These calculated values of the reactions can be verified by means of the spring balances.

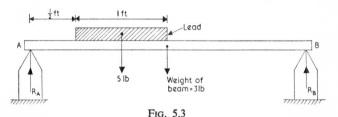

Fig. 5.3

Free-body Diagrams

Instead of drawing the beam every time, a free-body diagram can be drawn as in Fig. 5.4 or Fig. 5.5 where two methods of indicating uniformly distributed loads are shown.

Further experiments can be performed with the simple apparatus shown above by placing the supports at different points. Fig. 5.6

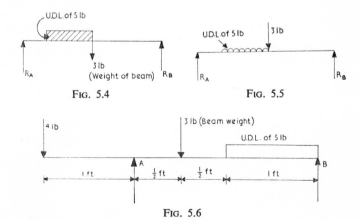

Fig. 5.6

shows the supports placed 2 ft apart. In this case, to determine experimentally the reaction at A, the spring balance must be connected to a point on the beam directly above A.

Taking moments about B, the reaction at A is clockwise and all the loads or weights are anticlockwise.

$$2R_A = (5 \times \tfrac{1}{2}) + (3 \times 1\tfrac{1}{2}) + (4 \times 3)$$
$$R_A = \frac{19}{2} = 9{\cdot}5 \text{ lb}$$

Taking moments about A, both the reaction at B and the weight of 4 lb are anticlockwise.

$$2R_B + (4 \times 1) = (3 \times \tfrac{1}{2}) + (5 \times 1\tfrac{1}{2})$$
$$2R_B = 9 - 4$$
$$R_B = \tfrac{5}{2} = 2{\cdot}5 \text{ lb}$$
$$R_A + R_B = 9{\cdot}5 + 2{\cdot}5 = 12 \text{ lb}$$
$$= \text{ sum of the vertical loads}$$

Practical Cases

In buildings, point loads on beams are usually due to loads from other beams or from columns, and uniformly distributed loads are due to floors, walls and partitions and the weights of the beams themselves.

In Fig. 5.7, assume that the beam AB weighs 1 ton and that it

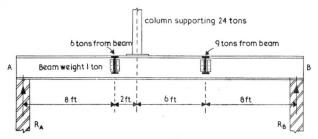

Fig. 5.7

supports two beams which transmit loads of 6 tons and 9 tons respectively to beam AB. In addition, a column transmits a load of 24 tons. The reactions are usually taken as acting at the middle of the bearing area supplied by the supporting brickwork or column. Fig. 5.8 shows the free-body diagram.

Taking moments about B

$$24R_A = (9 \times 8) + (1 \times 12) + (24 \times 14) + (6 \times 16)$$
$$= 72 + 12 + 336 + 96$$
$$R_A = \frac{516}{24} = 21\tfrac{1}{2} \text{ tons}$$

Since the total load on the beam is 40 tons, the reaction at B is $40 - 21\frac{1}{2}$, i.e. $18\frac{1}{2}$ tons. The student is advised, however, to determine the reaction at B by taking moments about A and thereby to obtain a check on his working.

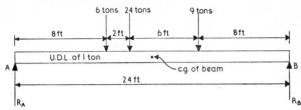

FIG. 5.8

EXAMPLE 1

A beam weighing 1,920 lb supports brickwork 9 in. thick weighing 120 lb/cu ft as indicated in Fig. 5.9. Calculate the reactions at the supports.

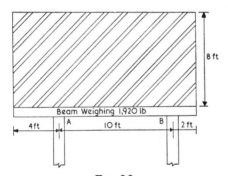

FIG. 5.9

Both the brickwork and the beam are uniformly distributed loads.

$$\text{Volume of brickwork} = 16 \times 8 \times \tfrac{3}{4} = 96 \text{ cu ft}$$
$$\text{Weight of brickwork} = 96 \times 120 = 11,520 \text{ lb}$$
$$\text{Weight of beam} = 1,920$$
$$\text{Total weight} = 13,440 \text{ lb}$$

The free-body diagram is shown in Fig. 5.10.

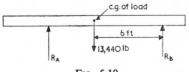

FIG. 5.10

Taking moments about B

$$10R_A = 13,440 \times 6$$
$$R_A = \frac{13,440 \times 6}{10} = 8,064 \text{ lb}$$
$$R_B = 13,440 - 8,064 = 5,376 \text{ lb}$$

(or R_B can be obtained by taking moments about A)

Overbalancing Problems

EXAMPLE 2

A rectangular block of stone 2 ft $\times$ 2 ft $\times$ 5 ft weighing 25 cwt rests on the ground (Fig. 5.11). Calculate the maximum force P which can be applied as shown without upsetting equilibrium.

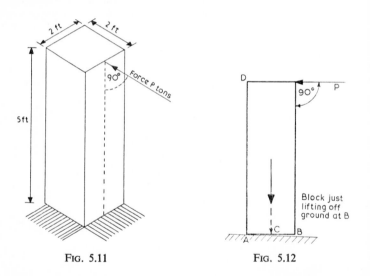

FIG. 5.11   FIG. 5.12

This problem can be viewed two-dimensionally as in Fig. 5.12. Equilibrium will be upset when the block just rises off the ground at B, the turning point being A. (It is assumed that sliding of the block will not occur. Sliding and frictional resistance are discussed in Chapter **19**.) When the block is just lifting off the ground, the overturning moment due to the force P is just balanced by the resisting moment due to the weight of the block, the block being balanced on the edge A. Since the inclination of AB to the horizontal is very slight, distances can be taken assuming the block is vertical.

Taking moments about A,

$$P \times \text{distance } AD = 25 \text{ cwt} \times \text{distance } AC$$

$$P \times 5 = 25 \times 1$$

$$P = 5 \text{ cwt}$$

Assuming a factor of safety of 2 against overturning is required, the maximum force P that should be applied is $2\frac{1}{2}$ cwt.

Another way of expressing factor of safety (F.S.) is—

$$\text{F.S. against overturning} = \frac{\text{resisting moment}}{\text{overturning moment}}$$

EXAMPLE 3

A long boundary wall 8 ft high and 18 in. thick is constructed of brickwork weighing 120 lb/cu ft. If the maximum wind pressure uniformly distributed over the whole height of the wall is 15 lb/sq ft, calculate the factor of safety against overturning neglecting any small adhesive strength between the brickwork and its base.

In wall problems it is customary to consider the equilibrium of a 1 ft run of wall (Fig. 5.13).

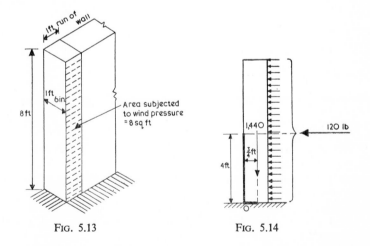

FIG. 5.13   FIG. 5.14

Weight of 1 ft run of wall	$= 8 \times 1\frac{1}{2} \times 1 \times 120$
	$= 1{,}440 \text{ lb}$
Wind pressure on 1 ft run of wall	$= 8 \times 1 \times 15$
	$= 120 \text{ lb}$

and this can be taken as acting at the centre of height of the wall for purposes of taking moments about O (Fig. 5.14).

$$\text{Resisting moment} = 1{,}440 \times \tfrac{3}{4}$$
$$= 1{,}080 \text{ lb-ft}$$
$$\text{Overturning moment} = 120 \times 4$$
$$= 480 \text{ lb-ft}$$
$$\text{F.S. against overturning} = \frac{1{,}080}{480} = 2 \cdot 25$$

EXAMPLE 4

A reinforced concrete roof slab is supported by two brick walls A and B (Fig. 5.15). Assuming the total load on the slab, including the weight of the slab is equivalent to 150 lb/sq ft of roof area, calculate the maximum distance x that the slab may overhang, if the factor of safety against overturning is 1·5.

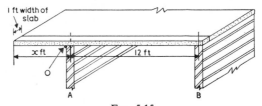

FIG. 5.15

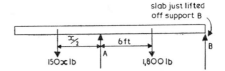

FIG. 5.16. FREE-BODY DIAGRAM

Actually, when the slab is on the point of overturning, the turning point will be the edge of the wall at O, but it is usual in these problems to take moments about the centre lines of the supports if the supports are not very wide.

Consider a strip of slab 1 ft wide. The load on 12 ft will be $12 \times 1 \times 150$, i.e. 1,800 lb, and the load on x ft will be $x \times 1 \times 150$, i.e. $150x$ lb.

When the slab is on the point of lifting, the turning point is A (Fig. 5.16).

$$\text{The resisting moment} = 1{,}800 \times 6 = 10{,}800 \text{ lb-ft}$$

$$\text{The overturning moment} = 150x \times \frac{x}{2} = 75x^2 \text{ lb-ft}$$

Since the factor of safety is to be 1·5

$$\frac{10,800}{75x^2} = 1·5$$

$$x^2 = \frac{10,800}{75 \times 1·5} = 96$$

$$x = \sqrt{96} = 9·8 \text{ ft}$$

EXAMPLE 5

Fig. 5.17 represents a uniform beam or slab of total weight 1,500 lb (100 lb per ft run). Calculate the tension in the tie and the reaction at *A*.

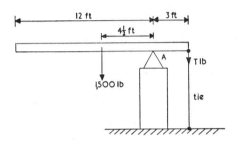

FIG. 5.17

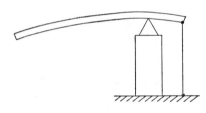

FIG. 5.18

Taking moments about *A*, *T* being the tension in the tie,

$$T \times 3 = 1,500 \times 4\tfrac{1}{2}$$
$$T = 2,250 \text{ lb}$$

The reaction at the support $= 1,500 + 2,250$
$$= 3,750 \text{ lb}$$

The downward pressure of the beam on the support at *A* also $= 3,750$ lb and there is no bending of the supporting column (Fig. 5.18).

The tie can be dispensed with by making a rigid joint between the column and beam as indicated in Fig. 5.19, but bending is now produced in the column and there is an overbalancing effect to be guarded against. One way of preventing overturning is to provide a base as shown in Fig. 5.19.

If it be assumed for the purposes of this example that both the vertical support and the horizontal base are 1 ft thick and weigh

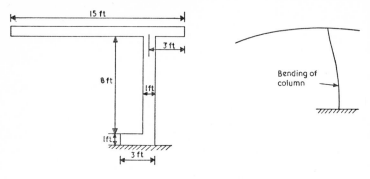

FIG. 5.19

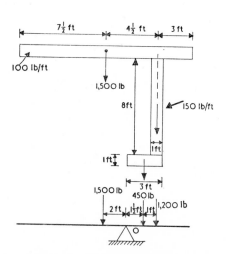

FIG. 5.20. FREE-BODY DIAGRAM

150 lb/ft run and that the other dimensions are as given in Fig. 5.20, the factor of safety against overturning can be calculated as follows—

Weight of horizontal member $= 100$ lb/ft $= 1,500$ lb
Weight of vertical member $= 8 \times 150 = 1,200$ lb
Weight of base $\qquad = 3 \times 150 = \quad 450$ lb

Taking moments about the overturning point (point *O*) the overturning moment is

$$1,500 \times 2 = 3,000 \text{ lb-ft}$$

The resisting moment is

$$(450 \times 1\tfrac{1}{2}) + (1,200 \times 2\tfrac{1}{2}) = 3,675 \text{ lb-ft}$$

$$\text{F.S. against overturning} = \frac{3,675}{3,000} = 1 \cdot 225$$

Note that the total pressure on the soil is equal to the total weight of the structure, i.e. $1,500 + 1,200 + 450$ which is 3,150 lb, but this pressure will not be uniform over the length of 3 ft. The greatest pressure will be at the point *O* in Fig. 5.20.

EXERCISE 5

1. Calculate the reactions at *A* and *B* due to the given point loads in Fig. 5.21 (*a*) to (*e*). The loads are in tons.

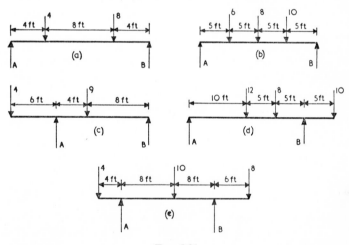

FIG. 5.21

2. Calculate the reactions at *A* and *B* due to the given system of loads in Fig. 5.22(*a*) to (*g*).

3. A beam *AB* carries two point loads and is supported by two beams *CD* and *EF* as shown in plan in Fig. 5.23. Neglecting the weights of the beams, calculate the reactions at *C*, *D*, *E* and *F*.

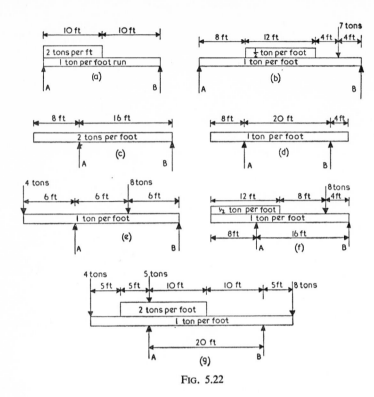

Fig. 5.22

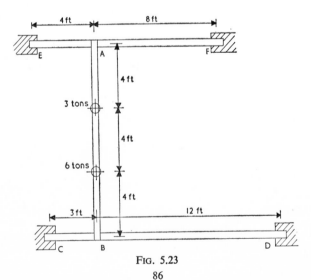

Fig. 5.23

4. A reinforced concrete bridge between two buildings spans 24 ft. The cross-section of the bridge is shown in Fig. 5.24. The brickwork weighs 120 lb/cu ft, the reinforced concrete weighs 150 lb/cu ft, and the stone coping weighs 100 lb per foot run. The floor of the bridge has to carry a uniformly distributed load of 100 lb/sq ft in addition to its own weight. Calculate the pressure on the supporting buildings from one end of each beam.

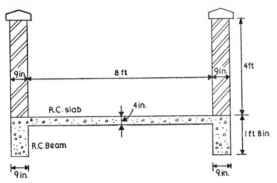

Fig. 5.24

5. Calculate the minimum holding down force at *B* and the reaction at *A* for the beam of Fig. 5.25. The beam itself weighs 3 cwt. If a factor of safety of 1·5 against overturning is required, calculate the length of side of a cube of concrete at *B* (concrete weighs 144 lb/cu ft).

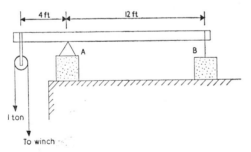

Fig. 5.25

6. A guy rope is anchored to the centre of the top face of a cube of concrete of 4 ft side (Fig. 5.26). The pull in the rope is 2,000 lb. Calculate the factor of safety against overturning. (Concrete weighs 144 lb/cu ft.)

7. A concrete cube of 4 ft side weighing 1¼ cwt/cu ft supports a structure as indicated in Fig. 5.27. Neglecting the weights of the members of the structure, calculate the factor of safety against overturning.

8. A concrete obelisk is 4 ft square and *h* ft high. Calculate the maximum value of *h* if there is to be a factor of safety against overturning of 2. The obelisk has to sustain a uniform wind pressure of 20 lb/sq ft on any one face and the concrete weighs 144 lb/cu ft.

9. A brick boundary wall 10 ft high has to sustain a uniform wind pressure of 15 lb/sq ft. Calculate the thickness of the wall so that there is a factor of safety of 2 against overturning. The brickwork weighs 120 lb/cu ft.

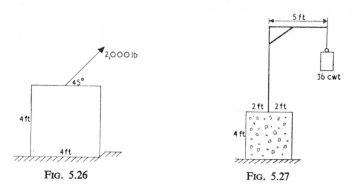

FIG. 5.26   FIG. 5.27

10. Concrete piers 3 ft square and 10 ft high support a roof frame as shown in Fig. 5.28. The concrete weighs 1¼ cwt/cu ft. Calculate the factor of safety against overturning of the piers.

11. A reinforced concrete retaining wall weighing 150 lb/cu ft resists an earth thrust equivalent to one force of 2,400 lb for every foot run of the wall (Fig. 5.29). Calculate the factor of safety against overturning of the wall.

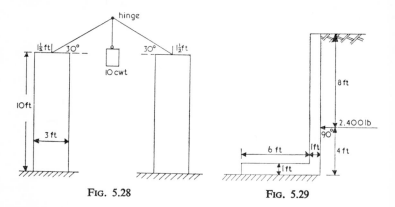

FIG. 5.28   FIG. 5.29

12. The horizontal and the vertical members of Fig. 5.30 weigh 100 lb per foot length; all members are 1 ft × 1 ft in cross-section and the total weights of all structures are equal. Calculate the factor of safety against overturning in each case.

13. A reinforced concrete roof slab has a total load, including its own weight of 120 lb/sq ft of roof area. The slab is supported by walls at *A* and *B* and carries a brick parapet 9 in. thick and 4 ft high weighing 120 lb/cu ft (Fig. 5.31). Calculate the factor of safety against overturning and the reactions at the supports *A* and *B*.

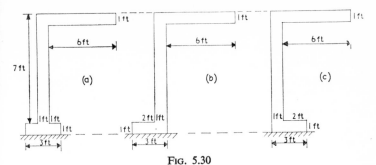

Fig. 5.30

14. Instead of the overhanging dimension of 8 ft in Question 13 and Fig. 5.31, substitute a dimension x ft. All other conditions are as in Question 13. Calculate the maximum distance x so that there is a factor of safety of 1·5 against overturning. (This problem involves a quadratic equation.)

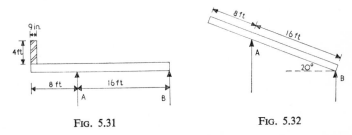

Fig. 5.31   Fig. 5.32

15. The roof slab shown in Fig. 5.32 is supported by walls at A and B. The total load on the slab, including its own weight, is 150 lb/sq ft of roof area. Calculate the factor of safety against overturning and the vertical reactions at A and B.

16. The vertical and horizontal portions of the structure in Fig. 5.33 weigh 100 lb per foot run. Calculate the factor of safety against overturning and calculate the reactions at A and B.

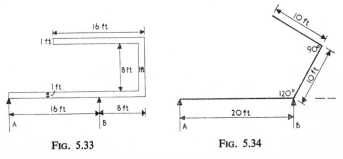

Fig. 5.33   Fig. 5.34

17. Fig. 5.34 represents the centre lines of a rigid structure weighing 100 lb/ft and supported at A and B. Calculate the reactions at A and B.

18. The rigid member *ABC* of Fig. 5.35 weighs 100 lb per foot of length. Calculate the factor of safety against overturning and the reactions at *B* and *C*.

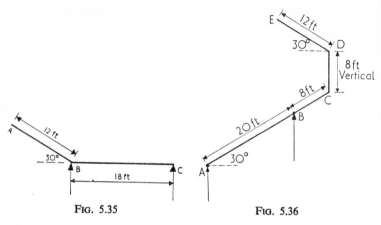

FIG. 5.35   FIG. 5.36

19. The member *ABCDE* of Fig. 5.36 weighs 200 lb per foot of length. Calculate the factor of safety against overturning and calculate the reactions at *A* and *B*.

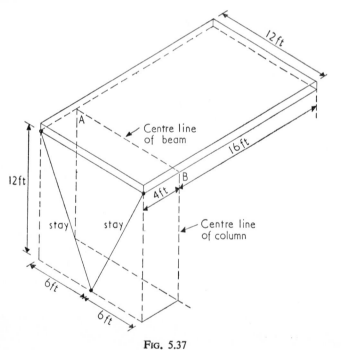

FIG. 5.37

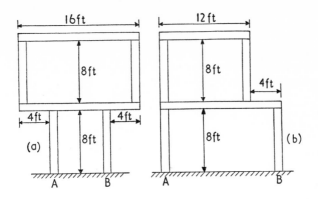

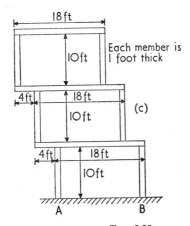

FIG. 5.38

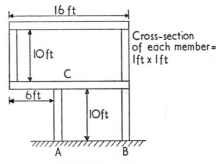

FIG. 5.39

20. A structure is simply supported by a beam *AB* and columns and by stay cables as shown in Fig. 5.37. The weight of the structure is equivalent to 150 lb/sq ft of roof area. Calculate the total load on beam *AB* and the tension in each stay. Assuming the stays are anchored to a concrete block, calculate the minimum weight of concrete necessary and the length of side of a cube of concrete, assuming a weight of 144 lb/cu ft.

21. Each member (vertical and horizontal) of the structures given in Fig. 5.38(*a*), (*b*) and (*c*) is 1 sq ft in cross-section and weighs 100 lb per foot of length. The joints are not rigid. Calculate the reaction of the soil at *A* and *B*. (Moments may be taken about the centre lines of the vertical members.)

22. Each member of the structure shown in Fig. 5.39 rests freely on another member. The members all weigh 100 lb per foot of length. Calculate the factor of safety against overturning about point *C*, and calculate the reaction of the soil at *A* and *B*. Moments may be taken about the centre lines of members.

CHAPTER 6

Resultant of Parallel Forces—
Couples—Centres of Gravity

Resultant of Parallel Forces

It was stated in Chapter 2 in connexion with concurrent forces that the resultant of a given number of forces is the single force which, when substituted for the given forces, has the same effect on the *state of equilibrium* of the body. This definition applies also to parallel forces.

Consider Fig. 6.1 which represents a beam of negligible weight supporting three vertical loads of 27, 36 and 54 cwt respectively.

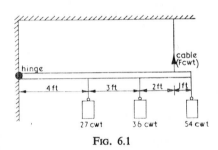

FIG. 6.1

The force in the vertical cable can be obtained by taking moments about the hinge, i.e.

$$F \times 9 \text{ ft} = (27 \times 4) + (36 \times 7) + (54 \times 10)$$
$$= 900 \text{ cwt-ft}$$
$$F = \frac{900}{9} = 100 \text{ cwt}$$

Now, if one force (the resultant) is substituted for the three downward loads without altering the state of equilibrium, its magnitude must be $27 + 36 + 54$, i.e. 117 cwt, and if the reaction in the cable is to remain as before, i.e. 100 cwt, the moment of the single resultant force about the hinge must equal the sum of the moments of the forces taken separately.

93

Referring to Fig. 6.2, moment of the resultant force about the hinge $= 117x$ cwt-ft.

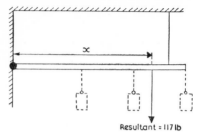

Resultant = 117 lb

Fig. 6.2

Moment of the forces about the hinge, taken separately

$$= (27 \times 4) + (36 \times 7) + (54 \times 10)$$
$$= 900 \text{ cwt-ft}$$

The moment of the resultant must therefore equal 900 cwt-ft therefore

$$117x = 900$$
$$x = \frac{900}{117} = 7\tfrac{9}{13} \text{ ft}$$

The resultant of the three forces is, therefore, a single force of 117 lb acting at $7\tfrac{9}{13}$ ft from the hinge. The reactions in the cable and at the hinge will be the same for this one force as for the three forces. It should be noted that the *bending effects* all along the beam due to the resultant is not the same as the bending effects due to the three loads and when calculating bending moments (Chapter 10) the student must take care that he does not use resultants wrongly.

In Fig. 6.3 a post of varying cross-section is subjected to pulls from three cables. The resultant of these three pulls is a force of 4 tons acting at x feet from the base A. Taking moments about A, the moment of the resultant is $4x$ tons-ft. The sum of the moments of the forces when taken separately is

$$(1 \times 10) + (2 \times 20) + (1 \times 30) = 80 \text{ cwt-ft}$$

therefore $\qquad\qquad 4x = 80$

whence $\qquad\qquad x = 20 \text{ ft}$

(Since the loads are symmetrically placed, the position of the resultant could have been obtained by inspection.)

The moment at the base of the post is the same whether we consider the forces separately or the resultant only, but when dealing with the top section of the post it would be wrong to consider the whole of the pull acting at 20 ft from the base as in Fig. 6.4. This would imply that there is no moment tending to break the post at section X–X. Fig. 6.3 is an example of "like" parallel forces, since

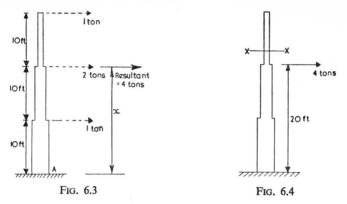

FIG. 6.3   FIG. 6.4

all the forces act in the same sense, that is, all the arrows representing the directions of the forces point in the same direction.

Unlike Parallel Forces

EXAMPLE 1

Calculate the magnitude and position of the resultant of the system of forces shown in Fig. 6.5 and determine where a fulcrum must be placed to maintain equilibrium. (Neglect the weight of the rod.)

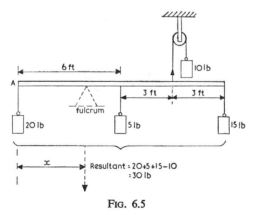

FIG. 6.5

This is an example of a system of *unlike parallel forces* since all the forces are not acting in the same sense. The total resultant force acting downwards $= 20 + 5 + 15 - 10 = 30$ lb. The moment of this resultant about *any point* must equal the algebraic sum of the moments of the separate forces. Taking moments about end A

$$30x = (5 \times 6) - (10 \times 9) + (15 \times 12)$$
$$= 30 - 90 + 180$$
$$x = \frac{120}{30} = 4 \text{ ft}$$

The fulcrum must therefore be placed at this point in order to maintain the rod in balance (and the reaction at the fulcrum $=$ 30 lb). The same answer would be obtained by taking moments about any point, as for example, the point B, 5 ft from A (see Fig. 6.6).

$$30x = (20 \times 5) + (5 \times 11) - (10 \times 14) + (15 \times 17)$$
$$= 100 + 55 - 140 + 255$$
$$x = \frac{270}{30} = 9 \text{ ft}$$

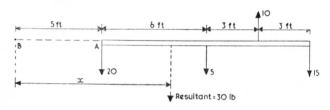

FIG. 6.6

The position of the resultant is therefore 9 ft from B or 4 ft from A.

Problems can often be simplified by working with a resultant instead of with a number of separate forces. This is demonstrated in the following example.

EXAMPLE 2

Calculate the resultant of the three downward forces of Fig. 6.7 then use the triangle of forces principle to determine the reaction in the cable and the reaction at the hinge.

The resultant of the three downward forces is 12 lb and, taking moments about the hinge,

$$12x = (6 \times 2) + (2 \times 4) + (4 \times 8)$$
$$x = \frac{52}{12} = 4\tfrac{1}{3} \text{ ft}$$

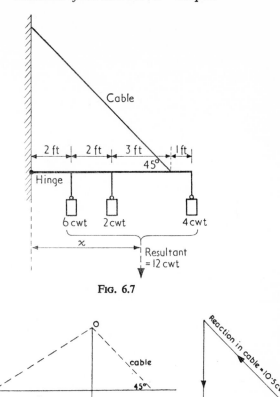

Fig. 6.7

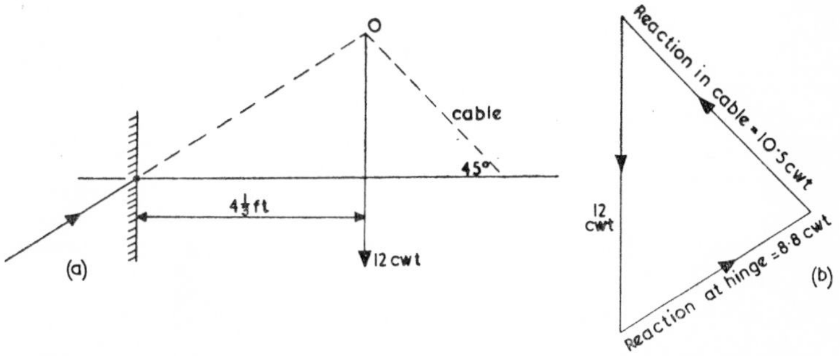

Fig. 6.8. (a) Free-body Diagram; (b) Force Diagram for Point O

Now, using the method of Chapter 3, page 36, the reactions can be found as shown in Fig. 6.8.

Couples

Two equal unlike parallel forces are said to form a *couple*.

Imagine a rod resting on a smooth table, as shown in Fig. 6.9, and assume that two equal unlike parallel forces of 4 lb are applied horizontally as shown. The rod will rotate in a clockwise direction and the moment causing this rotation is obtained by multiplying *one* of the forces by the distance *AB* between the two forces. The perpendicular distance *AB* is called the *arm of the couple*.

Therefore   moment of the couple $= 4\,\text{lb} \times 6\,\text{in.}$

$= 24\,\text{lb-in.}$

No matter about what point the moment is considered, the answer

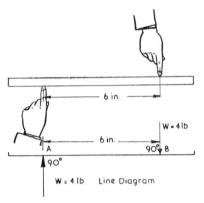

Fig. 6.9

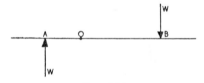

Fig. 6.10

Fig. 6.11

is equal to $W \times AB$. For example, taking moments about any
point O between the two forces (Fig. 6.10) the moment causing
rotation is $(W \times AO) + (W \times BO)$. This equals $W(AO + BO) =$
$W \times AB$.

In Fig. 6.11 the clockwise moment about O is $W \times AO$, and the
anticlockwise moment about O is $W \times BO$.

The net moment causing rotation is

$$W \times AO - W \times BO$$
$$= W(AO - BO)$$
$$= W \times AB$$

Note that a couple acting on a body produces rotation and the forces cannot be balanced by a single force. To produce equilibrium another couple of equal and opposite moment is required.

If one student applies a couple to a rod (or scale or pencil) resting on a smooth table, as indicated in Fig. 6.9, and another student

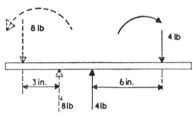

FIG. 6.12

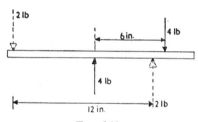

FIG. 6.13

tries to prevent rotation by holding one finger against the rod at any point, it will be discovered that the effort will be unsuccessful. If he applies two fingers, as indicated by the dotted lines in Fig. 6.12 or Fig. 6.13 equilibrium will result.

In Fig. 6.12,

Moment of clockwise couple = 4 lb × 6 in. = 24 lb-in.
Moment of anticlockwise couple = 8 lb × 3 in. = 24 lb-in.

In Fig. 6.13,

Moment of clockwise couple = 4 lb × 6 in. = 24 lb-in.
Moment of anticlockwise couple = 2 lb × 12 in. = 24 lb-in.

Fig. 6.14 represents a mast fixed at its base. The moment tending to break the mast at its base is

$$2(x + 3) - 2x \text{ cwt-ft} = 2x + 6 - 2x = 6 \text{ cwt-ft}$$

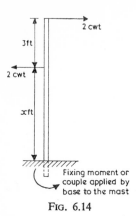

No matter what the distance x may be, the moment at the base will be 6 cwt-ft. This moment or couple is resisted by the fixing moment or couple applied by the base to the mast.

A knowledge of the principles of couples is useful in understanding beam problems (see Chapter 12).

Centres of Gravity

The centre of gravity of a body is a point in or near the body through which the resultant attraction of the earth acts for all positions of the body. For the purpose of taking moments to discover reactions, etc., the whole weight of a body can be *assumed* to act at its centre of gravity.

Fig. 6.14

As far as each of the problems in this book is concerned, the determination of the centre of gravity of a body is equivalent to determining the resultant of a number of like parallel forces.

Fig. 6.15 represents a thin sheet of tinplate with several small holes drilled in it. To one of these holes (hole A) is attached a

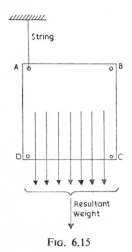

Fig. 6.15

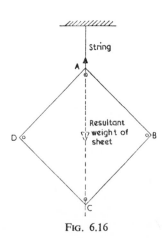

Fig. 6.16

string. It should be obvious that the position shown for the sheet in Fig. 6.15 is an impossible one. The sheet will swing round in a clockwise direction and come to rest as indicated in Fig. 6.16. Each particle of the sheet in Fig. 6.15 is attracted vertically downwards by the force of gravity and the parallel lines indicate the direction of the gravity forces. The resul-

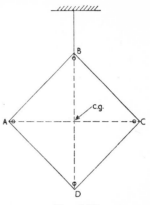

FIG. 6.17

tant of these parallel forces is the total weight of the sheet, and the sheet comes to rest in such a position that the line of the resultant weight and the line of the vertical reaction in the string form one continuous line.

If the string be now attached to point *B* the sheet will hang as in Fig. 6.17 and the intersection of the two lines *AC* and *BD* is called the centre of gravity of the body. (The actual position of the centre of gravity is in the thickness of the metal immediately behind the two lines *AC* and *BD*.)

The position of the centre of gravity of sheets of metal of various shapes can be obtained by the method shown in Fig. 6.18. The sheet is suspended from a pin and from the same pin is suspended a plumb line. The line of the string forming the plumb line can be marked on the sheet behind it with pencil or chalk. The sheet can now be suspended in a different position and another line marked The intersection of these two lines gives the position of the centre of gravity of the sheet.

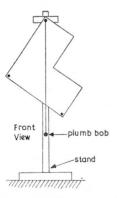

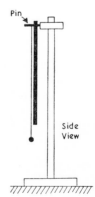

FIG. 6.18

The position of the centre of gravity of certain simple shapes is obvious by inspection (Fig. 6.19), e.g. the centre of gravity of a line or uniform rod is halfway along its length and the centre of gravity of a circle is at its centre.

If it were required to balance any of these shapes in a horizontal position by placing a pencil underneath, the point of application

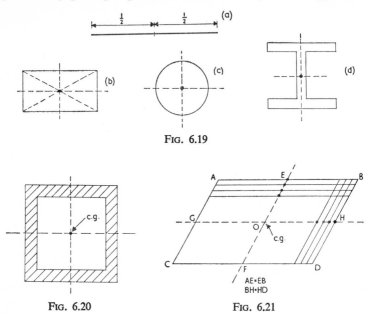

FIG. 6.19

FIG. 6.20   FIG. 6.21

of the pencil would be the centre of gravity of the sheet, and the reaction of the pencil would be equal to the weight of the sheet. Each of the shapes shown in Fig. 6.19 has at least two axes of symmetry and whenever a body has two axes of symmetry the centre of gravity is at the intersection of the axes.

The centre of gravity of a body need not necessarily be in the material of the body (see Fig. 6.20). Note that it is impossible to balance this shape on one point so that the sheet lies in a horizontal plane.

Centre of Gravity of a Parallelogram

Imagine that the thin sheet in the shape of a parallelogram, Fig. 6.21, is made up of an innumerable number of thin strips parallel to *AB*. Each strip may be regarded as a uniform rod and the centre of gravity of each strip is midway along its length. Line *EF* connects the mid-points of all the strips and the centre of gravity of the parallelogram must therefore be on this line. If the figure is divided into strips parallel to *BD* instead of parallel to *AB*, it can be shown similarly that the centre of gravity lies on line *HG*. The centre of gravity is therefore at point *O* where the lines *EF* and *HG* intersect.

Centre of Gravity of a Triangle

Fig. 6.22 represents a thin triangular sheet of uniform thickness. Divide the triangle into an innumerable number of strips parallel to *AB*. The centre of gravity of each strip is midway along its length, therefore the centre of gravity of the whole triangle lies on the line

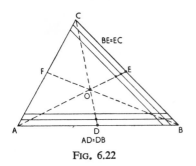

FIG. 6.22   FIG. 6.23

DC where $AD = DB$. Similarly, the centre of gravity lies on the line *EA* where $BE = EC$, and its actual position is at the intersection of the two lines *DC* and *AE*. A third line drawn from *B* to the mid-point *F* of line *AC* will also pass through the centre of gravity. A line drawn from an angle of a triangle to bisect the opposite side is called a *median*, therefore the centre of gravity of a triangle is at the intersection of its medians (Fig. 6.22). It can be proved by geometry that

$$DO = \frac{DC}{3}, \ EO = \frac{EA}{3} \ \text{and} \ FO = \frac{FB}{3}$$

Right Angled Triangle

The right angled triangle occurs frequently in structural problems and referring to Fig. 6.23 it is usually the distances *BG* and *BH* which are required. Again, it can be proved by geometry that

$$BG = \frac{BA}{3} \ \text{and} \ BH = \frac{BC}{3}$$

Semi-circle and Quadrant of Circle

The centres of gravity of many surfaces such as the semi-circle, parabola, etc., are best found by the methods of the calculus. The centre of gravity positions for a semi-circle and a quadrant of a circle are shown in Fig. 6.24.

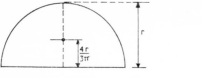

Fig. 6.24

Simple Geometrical Solids

The centre of gravity positions of a few simple solids are given in Fig. 6.25.

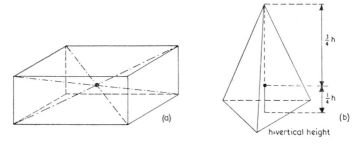

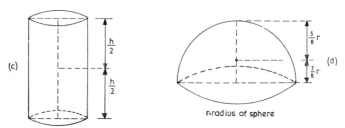

Fig. 6.25. (*a*) Cube or Rectangular Solid;
(*b*) Pyramid or Cone; (*c*) Cylinder; (*d*) Hemisphere

Compound Bodies

The following method applies if the compound body can be divided into several parts such that the centres of gravity and weights of the individual parts are known.

1. Divide the body into its several parts.
2. Determine the area (or volume) and weight of each part.
3. Assume the area (or volume or weight) of each part to act at its centre of gravity.

4. Take moments about a convenient point or axis to determine the centre of gravity of the whole body. The method is identical with that of determining the resultant of a number of forces, as explained earlier in the chapter.

EXAMPLE 3

A thin uniform sheet of material weighs w lb for each sq in. of its surface (Fig. 6.26). Determine the position of its centre of gravity.

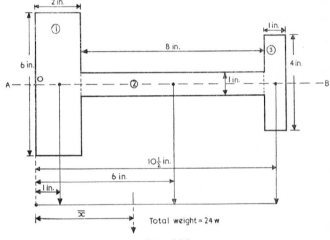

FIG. 6.26

Since the figure is symmetrical about line AB, its centre of gravity must lie on this line. The figure can be divided into three rectangles.

Area (1) $= 6 \times 2 = 12$ sq in., Weight $\qquad = 12w$ lb
Area (2) $= 8 \times 1 = 8$ sq in., Weight $\qquad = 8w$ lb
Area (3) $= 4 \times 1 = 4$ sq in., Weight $\qquad = 4w$ lb
Total area $\qquad = 24$ sq in., Total weight $= 24w$ lb

Let $\bar{x}$ be the distance from O of the centre of gravity of the whole figure. Take moments about this point.

$$24w\bar{x} = (12w \times 1) + (8w \times 6) + (4w \times 10\tfrac{1}{2})$$
$$= \quad 12w \qquad + 48w \qquad + 42w$$
$$= 102w$$
$$\bar{x} = \frac{102w}{24w} = 4\tfrac{1}{4} \text{ in.}$$

The centre of gravity is therefore on the line AB at $4\tfrac{1}{4}$ in. from the extreme left edge of the figure.

Note that the centre of gravity has been determined without knowing the actual weight of the material, and when a body is of uniform density throughout, its weight may be ignored and moments of areas or moments of volumes can be taken. The terms *centroid* and *centre of area* are frequently used in place of the *centre of gravity* when moments of areas are taken instead of moments of weights. (The position of the centroid of a section is of great importance in beam design for, as will be seen later, the portion of section above this centroid performs a different function to that portion of area below the centroid.)

EXAMPLE 4

Determine the position of the centre of gravity of the body shown in Fig. 6.27. The body has a uniform thickness of 1 ft and weighs 120 lb/cu ft.

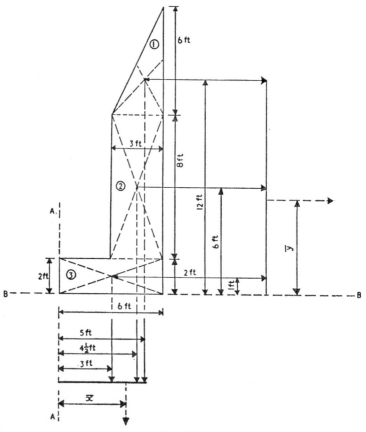

FIG. 6.27

Since the body is homogeneous (i.e. of uniform density) and is of uniform thickness throughout, its weight and thickness may be ignored and moments taken of areas—

$$\text{Area (1)} = \frac{3 \times 6}{2} = 9 \text{ sq ft}$$

$$\text{Area (2)} = 8 \times 3 = 24 \text{ sq ft}$$

$$\text{Area (3)} = 6 \times 2 = 12 \text{ sq ft}$$

$$\text{Total area} \qquad = 45 \text{ sq ft}$$

In centre of gravity problems it is usually convenient to choose two axes *A–A* and *B–B* at one extreme edge of the figure.

Let $\bar{x}$ be the horizontal distance of the centre of gravity of the whole figure from *A–A* and $\bar{y}$ be the vertical distance of the centre of gravity from axis *B–B*. The positions of the centre of gravity of the three separate parts of the figure are shown in Fig. 6.27.

Taking moments about axis *A–A*

$$45\bar{x} = (12 \times 3) + (24 \times 4\tfrac{1}{2}) + (9 \times 5)$$

$$= 36 + 108 + 45$$

$$\bar{x} = \frac{189}{45} = 4 \cdot 2 \text{ ft}$$

Taking moments about axis *B–B*

$$45\bar{y} = (12 \times 1) + (24 \times 6) + (9 \times 12)$$

$$= 12 + 144 + 108$$

$$\bar{y} = \frac{264}{45} = 5 \cdot 87 \text{ ft}$$

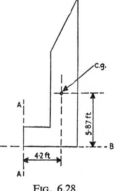

Fɪɢ. 6.28

The centre of gravity is in the position indicated by Fig. 6.28 and is within the thickness of the body halfway between the front and back faces

Use of the Link Polygon

Students who prefer a graphical method of solution to a calculation method can use the principle of the link polygon to obtain the position of the centre of gravity. The graphical solution of the previous problem is shown in Fig. 6.29, where the body is drawn to scale.

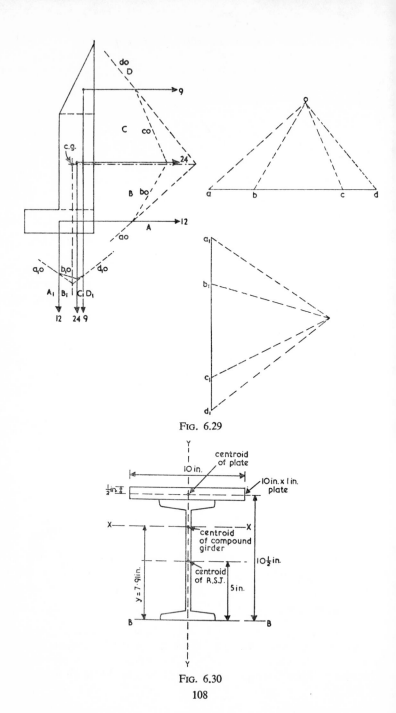

Fig. 6.29

Fig. 6.30

EXAMPLE 5

A compound girder is built up of a 10 in. × 5 in. R.S.J. with one 10 in. × 1 in. plate on the top flange only. The area of the steel joist alone is 8·85 sq in. Determine the position of the centroid of the compound girder (Fig. 6.30).

1. The compound section is symmetrical about the vertical axis Y–Y, so the centroid must lie on this line.

2. The addition of a plate to the top flange has the effect of moving the centroid (the X–X axis) towards that plate, and taking moments about line B–B at the lower edge of the section,

$$\text{Total area of section} \times y = (\text{area of R.S.J.} \times 5 \text{ in.})$$
$$+ (\text{area of plate} \times 10\tfrac{1}{2} \text{ in.})$$
$$(8\cdot85 + 10)y = (8\cdot85 \times 5) + (10 \times 10\tfrac{1}{2})$$
$$18\cdot85y = (44\cdot25) + (105)$$
$$= 149\cdot25$$
$$y = \frac{149\cdot25}{18\cdot85}$$
$$y = 7\cdot91 \text{ in.}$$

EXAMPLE 6

A reinforced concrete retaining wall weighs 150 lb/cu ft and the earth pressure, behind it is equivalent to one force of 2,400 lb for every foot length of the wall, acting at 4 ft from the base (Fig. 6.32). Calculate the factor of safety against overturning of the wall.

Method 1. From Fig. 6.31,

     Area (1) = 12 sq ft

     Area (2) = 6 sq ft

     Total   = 18 sq ft

It is not necessary to determine the actual position of the centre of gravity. Only the position of the vertical line in which the centre of gravity lies is required.

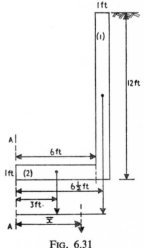

Take moments about axis A–A

$$18\bar{x} = (6 \times 3) + (12 \times 6\tfrac{1}{2})$$
$$\bar{x} = 5\tfrac{1}{3} \text{ ft}$$

Area of cross-section of wall is 18 sq ft, therefore the volume of one foot

FIG. 6.31

run of the wall is 18 × 1, i.e. 18 cu ft, and its weight is 18 × 150 or 2,700 lb.

Take moments about *O* (Fig. 6.32)

$$\text{Resisting moment} \quad = \quad 2,700 \times 5\tfrac{1}{3} = 14,400 \text{ lb-ft}$$

$$\text{Overturning moment} = \quad 2,400 \times 4 \ = 9,600 \text{ lb-ft}$$

$$\text{Factor of safety} \quad = \frac{14,400}{9,600} = 1\cdot5$$

Method 2. In problems of this description, it is just as convenient to take moments of the weights of the separate parts (Fig. 6.33) without determining the position of the centre of gravity.

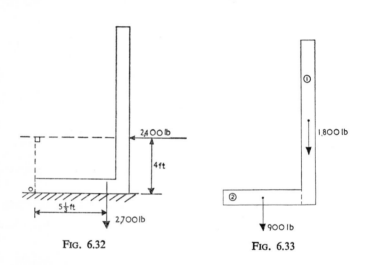

FIG. 6.32　　　　　　　　　　FIG. 6.33

$$\text{Weight of (1)} = 12 \times 1 \times 150 = 1,800 \text{ lb}$$

$$(2) = \ 6 \times 1 \times 150 = \ 900 \text{ lb}$$

$$\text{Resisting moment} = (900 \times 3) + (1,800 \times 6\tfrac{1}{2})$$

$$= 14,400 \text{ lb-ft, as before}$$

EXAMPLE 7

A steel beam weighing 1,400 lb carries brickwork 9 in. thick and weighing 120 lb/cu ft as shown in Fig. 6.34. Calculate the reactions at *A* and *B*.

One way of obtaining the answer is to calculate the position of the centre of gravity of all the loads and to assume the total weight

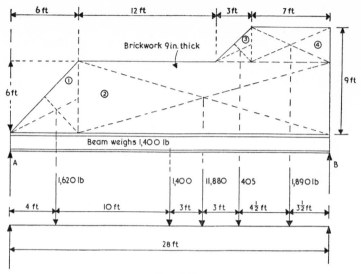

Fig. 6.34

to act at this point. In this case, however, it is quicker and simpler to take moments of the weights of the individual parts.

$$\text{Weight of (1)} = 6 \times \tfrac{6}{2} \times \tfrac{3}{4} \times 120 = 1{,}620 \text{ lb}$$

$$(2) = 22 \times 6 \times \tfrac{3}{4} \times 120 = 11{,}880 \text{ lb}$$

$$(3) = 3 \times \tfrac{3}{2} \times \tfrac{3}{4} \times 120 = 405 \text{ lb}$$

$$(4) = 7 \times 3 \times \tfrac{3}{4} \times 120 = 1{,}890 \text{ lb}$$

$$\text{Weight of beam} = 1{,}400 \text{ lb}$$

$$\text{Total weight} = 17{,}195 \text{ lb}$$

Taking moments about B

$$28\,R_A = (1{,}890 \times 3{\cdot}5) + (405 \times 8) + (11{,}880 \times 11) \\ + (1{,}400 \times 14) + (1{,}620 \times 24)$$

$$R_A = 199{,}015 \div 28 = 7{,}107{\cdot}7 \text{ lb}$$

Since the total load $= 17{,}195$ lb
$$R_B = 17{,}195 - 7{,}107{\cdot}7 = 10{,}087{\cdot}3 \text{ lb}$$

As a check, moments can be taken about A to determine R_B

EXAMPLE 8

A circular plate of steel of uniform thickness and 30 in. diameter has a circular hole of 10 in. diameter (Fig. 6.35). The centre of the hole is 8 in. from the centre of the plate. Determine the position of the centre of gravity of the plate.

The centre of gravity will lie on an axis of symmetry *B–B* as shown in Fig. 6.35.

$$\text{Area of unpierced plate} = \pi \times 15^2 = 225\pi$$
$$\text{Area of hole} \qquad = \pi \times 5^2 \ = \ 25\pi$$
$$\text{Actual area of pierced plate} = 200\pi$$

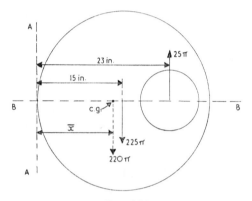

FIG. 6.35

Let $\bar{x}$ be the distance of the centre of gravity from axis *A–A*. The moment of the plate about axis *A–A* if there were no hole would be $225\pi \times 15$. Now this moment includes the moment of the piece of metal which has been taken away when forming the hole, therefore we must deduct this latter moment.

therefore $200\pi\bar{x} = (225\pi \times 15) - (25\pi \times 23)$

Dividing throughout by π

$$200\bar{x} = 3,375 - 575$$
$$\bar{x} = \frac{2,800}{200} = 14 \text{ in.}$$

SUMMARY

The resultant of a number of parallel forces is the algebraic sum of the forces. Its position can be found by taking moments about *any point* and moment of resultant equals the algebraic sum of moments of the individual forces.

A couple consists of two equal unlike parallel forces. The distance between the forces is called the arm of the couple, and the moment of a couple equals one of the forces multiplied by the arm of the couple.

The centre of gravity of a body is a point in or near the body through which the resultant weight of the body acts. When dealing with areas, the terms "centroid" and "centre of area" are frequently used.

EXERCISE 6

Problems involving calculation of centroids may also be found in Exercise 11.

1. For each of the structures shown in Fig. 6.36(*a*), (*b*) and (*c*) determine the

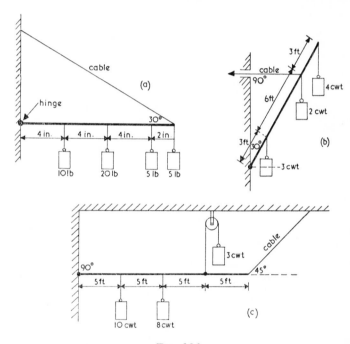

FIG. 6.36

position of the resultant of the vertical loads then, by using the triangle of forces, determine the tension in the cable and the reaction at the hinge. Neglect the weight of the rod.

2. The weights of the structures shown in Fig. 6.37(*a*), (*b*), (*c*) and (*d*) may be neglected. In each case the reaction at *A* is horizontal, and *B* is a hinge. Determine the position of the resultant of the vertical loads then, by applying the principle of the triangle of forces, determine the reactions at *A* and *B*.

3. The roof truss of Fig. 6.38 is supported on rollers at *B* and the reaction at *B* is therefore vertical. Determine the resultant of the four wind loads, then use the triangle of forces to determine the reactions at *A* and *B*.

4. Fig. 6.39 shows a system of three weights connected together by rigid bars. Determine the position of the centre of gravity of the system with respect to point *A*, ignoring the weight of the bars.

5. Bodies of weights 4, 6, 8 and 12 lb are situated at the corners *A*, *B*, *C*, *D* of a square of length of side 8 in. Calculate the position of the centre of gravity of the system with respect to point *A*.

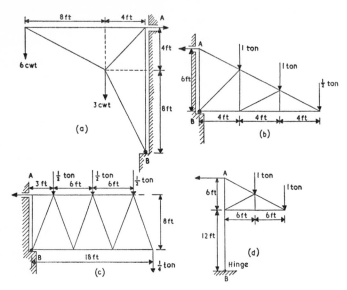

Fig. 6.37

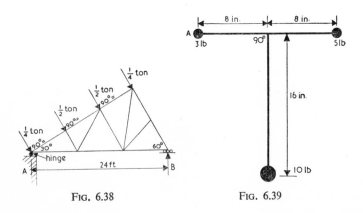

Fig. 6.38   Fig. 6.39

6. Reduce the system of forces shown in Fig. 6.40 to a couple. Determine the arm and moment of the couple.

7. Each of the shapes shown in Fig. 6.41(*a*), (*b*), (*c*) and (*d*) is symmetrical about a vertical axis. Calculate the distance from the base, of the centre of gravity.

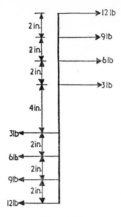

FIG. 6.40

8. In Fig. 6.42(*a*) to (*h*) take point *P* as the intersection of the *A–A* and *B–B* axes and calculate the position of the centre of gravity with respect to these axes. ($\bar{x}$ is the distance of the c.g. from the vertical axis *A–A* and $\bar{y}$ is the distance of the c.g. from the horizontal axis *B–B*.)

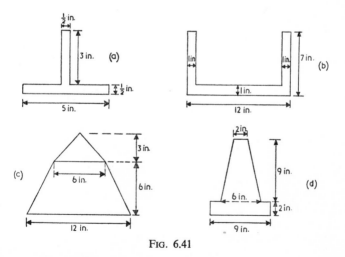

FIG. 6.41

9. A circular disc has two holes as indicated in Fig. 6.43. Calculate the distance from *A* of the centre of gravity.

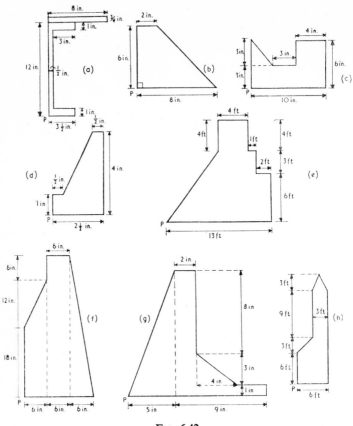

FIG. 6.42

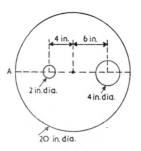

FIG. 6.43

116

10. Determine with respect to point *P*, the position of the c.g. of each of the shapes in Fig. 6.44(*a*), (*b*) and (*c*). ($\pi = 3 \cdot 142$)

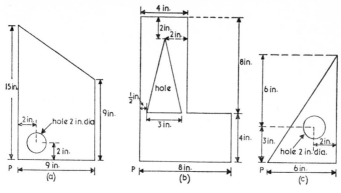

Fig. 6.44

11. The horizontal forces on the walls shown in Fig. 6.45(*a*), (*b*) and (*c*) represent the forces on a 1 ft run of wall. All the walls weigh 120 lb/cu ft. Calculate the factor of safety against overturning of the walls. (*Note:* only the position of the vertical line in which the c.g. is situated need be calculated.)

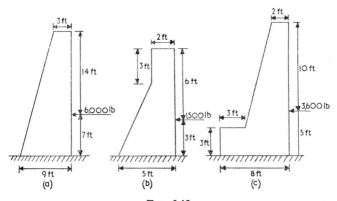

Fig. 6.45

12. The walls shown in Fig. 6.46(*a*) and (*b*) weigh 120 lb/cu ft. Calculate the value of *P* in lb per foot run of wall, if there is to be a factor of safety of 2 against overturning.

13. Fig. 6.47 shows the cross-section of a masonry buttress which is subject to an inclined thrust of 5,000 lb. Assuming that a 4 ft length of the buttress is effective in resisting the thrust and that the buttress weighs 120 lb/cu ft calculate the factor of safety against overturning.

14. A triangular sign board weighing 50 lb is supported in the manner indicated in Fig. 6.48. Calculate the reactions at *A* and *B*.

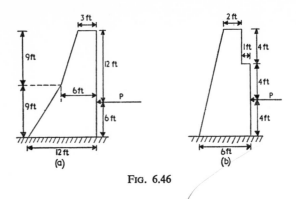

FIG. 6.46

15. Brickwork 9 in. thick and weighing 120 lb/cu ft is supported by a beam spanning from *A* to *B* (Fig. 6.49). Calculate the reactions at *A* and *B* due to the brickwork.

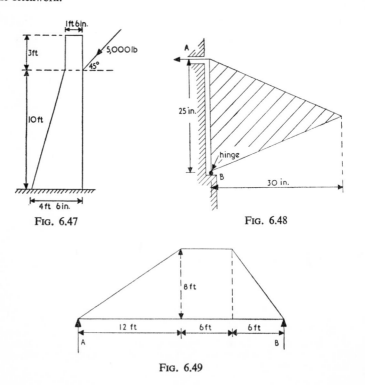

FIG. 6.47   FIG. 6.48

FIG. 6.49

CHAPTER 7

Framed Structures

A FRAME is a structure built up of three or more members which are normally considered as being hinged at the various joints. Any loads which are applied to the frame are usually transmitted to it at the joints, so that the individual members are in pure tension or compression.

A very simple frame is shown in Fig. 7.1. It consists of three individual members hinged at the ends to form a triangle, and the only applied loading consists of a vertical load of W at the apex. There are also, of course, reactions at the lower corners.

Under the action of the loads the frame tends to take the form shown in broken lines, i.e. the bottom joints move outward putting the member C in tension, and the members A and B in compression. Members A and B are termed *struts* and member C is termed a *tie*.

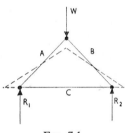

FIG. 7.1

Perfect and Imperfect Frames (all joints hinged).

A perfect frame is one which has just sufficient members to prevent the frame from being unstable.

An imperfect frame is one which contains too few members to prevent collapse.

Fig. 7.2 shows examples of perfect frames. Fig. 7.3 shows two

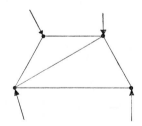

FIG. 7.2

119

examples of imperfect frames. In each of the two cases in Fig. 7.3 the frames would collapse as suggested by the broken lines; the addition of one member in each case would restore stability and produce perfect frames as in Fig. 7.2.

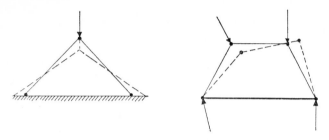

FIG. 7.3

Redundant Frames

A redundant frame is one which contains more than the number of members which would constitute a perfect frame.

Fig. 7.4, for example, shows a perfect frame, and Fig. 7.5 (the same frame with the addition of member *AB*) a redundant frame

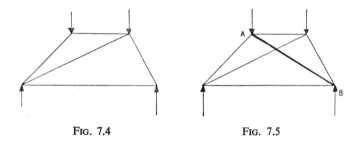

FIG. 7.4   FIG. 7.5

Note: A redundant member is not necessarily a member having no load. The member *AB* (Fig. 7.5), for example, will be stressed, and will serve to create a stronger frame than that in Fig. 7.4, but the redundant frame (having one member more than is necessary to produce stability) can not be solved by the ordinary methods of statics.

Number of Members in a Perfect Frame

The simplest perfect frame consists of three members in the form of a triangle as in Fig. 7.6. The frame also has three joints or node points, *A*, *B* and *C*.

If *two* more members are added to form another triangle as in Fig. 7.7, then *one* more joint has been added.

So long as triangles only are added, then the frame will remain a perfect frame.

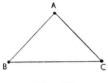

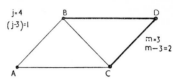

FIG. 7.6   FIG. 7.7

If J = number of joints, and m = number of members, then

$$2(J - 3) = m - 3$$
$$2J - 6 = m - 3$$
$$2J = m - 3 + 6$$
$$2J = m + 3 \text{ or } m = 2J - 3$$

i.e. number of members to form a perfect frame =

(twice the number of joints) — 3

or

$$\text{number of joints} = \frac{\text{number of members} + 3}{2}$$

The frames shown in Fig. 7.8 all comply with this requirement, i.e.

$$\frac{\text{the number of members} + 3}{2} = \text{the number of joints}$$

and

number of members = (twice number of joints) — 3

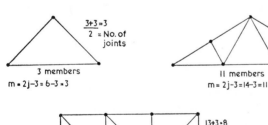

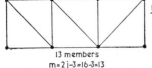

FIG. 7.8

The frames shown in Fig. 7.9 do not comply with this requirement, i.e. there are more than $2J - 3$ members, and the frames contain one or more redundant members.

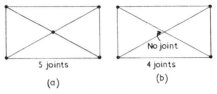

FIG. 7.9

In Fig. 7.9(*a*) the number of members is 8, which is more than $(2 \times 5) - 3$. Similarly, in Fig. 7.9(*b*) the number of members is 6, which is greater than $(2 \times 4) - 3$.

Stress Diagrams or Force Diagrams

Consider the simple perfect frame shown in Fig. 7.10. The known forces are the load at the apex and the two equal reactions of 1 ton.

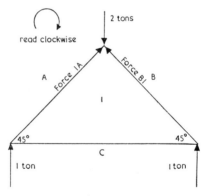

FIG. 7.10

In describing the loads, it is convenient to use Bow's Notation (see Chapter 2). Reading clockwise, the load at the apex, of 2 tons, is " load *AB*," the reaction at the right support is "load *BC*," and the reaction at the left support is "load *CA*." Similarly, the spaces *inside* the frame are usually denoted by numbers so that the load or total stress in the horizontal member is denoted by "force *C*1" or "force 1*C*."

As explained in Chapter 2, the forces or total stresses in the two

inclined members can be obtained by considering the equilibrium
of the joint at the apex (Fig. 7.11).

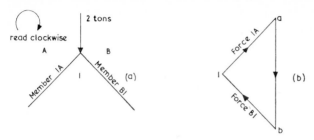

FIG. 7.11. (*a*) READING CLOCKWISE THE FORCES ARE *AB*, *B*1 AND 1*A*;
(*b*) FORCE DIAGRAM: NOTE THAT THE ARROWS "FOLLOW EACH OTHER"
ROUND THE TRIANGLE

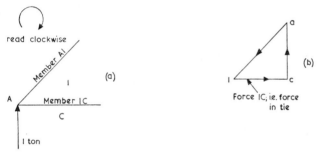

FIG. 7.12. JOINT AT LEFT-HAND REACTION;
(*b*) IS THE FORCE DIAGRAM

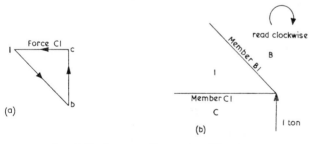

FIG. 7.13. JOINT AT RIGHT-HAND REACTION;
(*a*) IS THE FORCE DIAGRAM

The load in the horizontal tie member can be obtained either by
considering the joint at the left reaction, Fig. 7.12, or the joint at the
right reaction, Fig. 7.13.

Force Diagrams

The three triangle of forces diagrams drawn separately for the three joints may, for convenience, be superimposed upon each other to form in one diagram the means of determining all unknown forces. This resultant diagram, which is called a force diagram, or a stress diagram, is shown in Fig. 7.14.

Note that no arrows are shown on the combined force diagram. The directions of the arrows in the frame diagram are obtained by considering each joint as in Figs. 7.11 to 7.13. One must consider

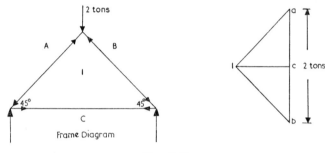

Fig. 7.14

each joint to be the centre of a clock and the letters are read clockwise round this centre. Thus, having drawn the combined diagram, consider say, the joint at the left reaction (Fig. 7.12). Reading clockwise round this joint, the inclined member is $A1$. On the force diagram, the direction from a to 1 is downwards to the left, therefore the arrow is placed in the frame diagram as shown, near the joint. The tie is member $1C$ and 1 to c on the force diagram is a direction left to right so the arrow is placed in this direction on the frame diagram.

Considering the joint at the apex (Fig. 7.11), the left hand inclined member is member $1A$ (not $A1$ as was the case when the joint at the left hand reaction was being considered). From the force diagram 1 to a is upwards to the right and this fixes the direction of the arrow on the frame diagram. Similarly, for the same joint, the other inclined member is $B1$. From the force diagram b to 1 is upwards towards the left. (Study the force diagrams and the directions of the arrows in Figs. 7.11 to 7.13.)

Note the directions of the arrows indicating compression (strut) and tension (tie) respectively (Fig. 7.14). These arrows represent the directions of the internal resistances in the members. Member $A1$ is a strut, which means that it has shortened as a result of the force in it. If the force were removed, the member would revert to its original length (i.e. it would lengthen) and the arrows indicate the attempt of the member to revert to its original length.

Member $C1$ is a tie and has therefore been stretched. The arrows indicate the attempt of the member to revert to its original (shorter) length.

The forces in the various members may be entered as shown in Table 7.1.

TABLE 7.1

Member	Force or stress in tons	Type
$A1$	1·4	strut
$B1$	1·4	strut
$C1$	1·0	tie

The principles described in the previous example may be applied to frames having any number of members and the work of determining the values of all the unknown forces may be enormously simplified by drawing *one* combined force diagram as shown in Fig. 7.15(*b*), and for this example the operations are explained in detail.

1. Starting from force AB (Fig. 7.15(*a*)) the *known* forces AB, BC, CD, DE, EF, FG and GA, working clockwise round the frame, are set down in order and to scale as ab, bc, cd, de, ef, fg and ga in Fig. 7.15(*b*). (Since the loading is symmetrical each of the reactions FG and GA is 2 tons.)

2. Point 1 on the force diagram is found by drawing b–1 parallel to $B1$, and g–1 parallel to $G1$. Point 1 lies at the intersection of these lines.

3. Point 2 on the force diagram is found by drawing c–2 parallel to $C2$ and 1–2 parallel to 1–2 from the frame (node 2). The point 2 is the intersection of these two lines.

4. Point 3 on the force diagram is found in the same manner by drawing 2–3 parallel to 2–3, and g–3 parallel to $G3$ from the frame, point 3 being the intersection.

5. The remaining points 4 and 5 are found in the same way as above, though in this case, as the frame is symmetrical and forces $E5$ and 4–5 are the same as $B1$ and 1–2, etc., only half the diagram need have been drawn.

6. The directions of the arrows may now be transferred to the frame diagram (Fig. 7.15(*a*)) by working clockwise around each node point.

Taking node 1 for example: moving clockwise; force *AB* is known to be downward, and *ab* ($\frac{1}{2}$ ton) is read downward on the force diagram. The next force in order (still moving clockwise round

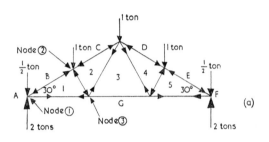

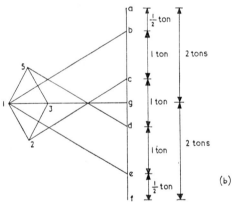

FIG. 7.15. (*a*) FRAME DIAGRAM; (*b*) FORCE OR STRESS DIAGRAM

the joint) is force *B* 1, which as *b*–1 on the force diagram acts to the left and downwards. Thus force *B*1 must act towards node 1 as indicated in Fig. 7.15(*a*). The next force in order (still moving clockwise) is 1*G*. 1–*g* on the force diagram acts from left to right, and thus the arrow is put in on the frame diagram acting to the right from this node (point 1).

7. Node 2: *BC* is known to act downward. The next force (moving clockwise) is *C*2, which, as *c*–2 in the force diagram acts downward to the left, thus must act towards node 2. The arrow is shown accordingly; the next force (still moving clockwise) is 2–1, and as 2–1 on the force diagram acts upward to the left, this must act toward the node 2, as shown by the arrow.

8. When all nodes have been considered in this way, it will be seen that each member of the frame in Fig. 7.15(*a*) has two arrows, one at each end of the member. As explained earlier, these arrows indicate, not what is being done to the member, but what the member is doing to the nodes at each end of it. Thus a member with arrows thus ↔ is in compression, i.e. it is being compressed and is reacting by pressing outward.

Similarly, two arrows thus →—← indicate tension in the member.

9. The *amounts* of all the forces *B*1, *C*2, 1–2, etc., are now scaled from the force or stress diagram, and the amounts and types of force can be tabulated as in Table 7.2.

TABLE 7.2

Member	Force or stress in tons	Type
*B*1	3	strut
*C*2	2·5	strut
*D*4	2·5	strut
*E*5	3·0	strut
*G*1	2·6	tie
*G*3	1·75	tie
*G*5	2·6	tie
1–2	0·9	strut
2–3	0·9	tie
3–4	0·9	tie
4–5	0·9	strut

It should be noted that constructing a force diagram involves considering each joint of the frame in turn and fixing the position of one figure on the force diagram by drawing two lines which intersect. No joint can be dealt with unless *all except two* of the forces meeting at the joint are known. This is why node 1 was taken as the first joint since, of the four forces meeting at this point, only two (*B*1 and 1*G*) are unknown. Solving this joint gives the forces in the members *B*1 and 1*G*. Node 2 can now be dealt with since only two forces, *C*2 and 2–1, are unknown. Node 3 cannot be dealt with before node 2 because, although the force in the member $G1$ is known, there are still three unknown forces, 1–2, 2–3, and $3G$.

Frame Containing a Member Having no Force

The external loads and the two equal reactions are set off to scale as shown in Fig. 7.16(*b*).

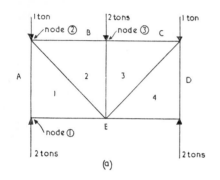
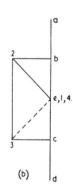

Fig. 7.16

Starting with node 1 the two unknown forces are $A1$ and $1E$.

From *a* on the force diagram a vertical line must be drawn (parallel to $A1$) and point 1 must lie on this vertical line where it meets a horizontal line drawn parallel to member $1E$. The point 1 must therefore be on the same point as *e* and force $1E = 0$.

Considering node 2, point 2 is found by drawing 1–2 to intersect *b*–2.

Point 3 is found by drawing *c*–3 and 3–2 on the force diagram, node 3.

Since the frame and loading are symmetrical there is no need to draw further lines, but in this simple example, one more line, shown dotted, completes the force diagram.

Further Example of Symmetrical Frame and Loading

By inspection, each reaction is 4 tons, and the force diagram for half the truss is shown in Fig. 7.17.

Frame with Unsymmetrical Loading

When the loading or/and the frame is unsymmetrical, *every* joint must be considered when drawing the force diagram. Fig. 7.18 is an example. (The reactions are calculated as described in a previous chapter.)

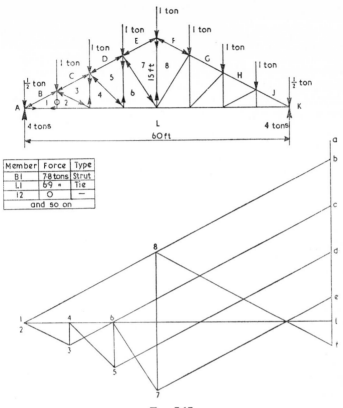

Member	Force	Type
B1	7·8 tons	Strut
L1	6·9 "	Tie
12	O	—
and so on		

FIG. 7.17

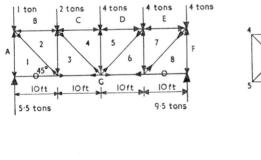

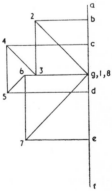

FIG. 7.18

129

Frame with Loads Suspended from the Bottom Chord of the Frame in Addition to Loads on the Top Chord

The reactions in Fig. 7.19 are calculated in the usual manner and are 4 tons at the left support and 5 tons at the right support. The vertical load line is then drawn as follows: *a–b* is 2 tons down; *b–c* is 4 tons down. The next force is the reaction *CD* of 5 tons,

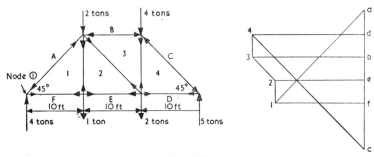

FIG. 7.19

therefore from *c* to *d* is measured upwards a distance equal to 5 tons. The next load is *DE* and is 2 tons down, therefore *d–e* represents this load on the force diagram. Similarly, *e–f* represents the load of 1 ton (*EF*) and finally *f–a* represents the vertical reaction *FA* of 4 tons.

The remaining force diagram can now be drawn in the usual manner, e.g. starting with node 1, two lines *a–1* and *f–1* are drawn to intersect at the point 1, and so on.

Frame Cantilevering over one Support

Fig. 7.20 shows a frame cantilevering 6 ft over the left support. By calculation, the reactions are found to be 15 cwt and 8 cwt respectively. The load line is drawn as explained in the previous example, *a–b*, *b–c*, *c–d*, *d–e* (all downwards), *e–f* upwards (8 cwt), *f–g* downwards (3 cwt), *g–a* upwards (15 cwt).

Cantilever Frames

In Fig. 7.21 there is no need to determine the reactions before starting on the force diagram. The loads are first plotted in order, *a–b*, *b–c*, *c–d*, *d–e*. Starting with node 1, *b–1* and *1–a* fix the position of point 1 on the force diagram, and so on, finishing with node 7, i.e. 6–7 and 7–a. Since member 7A is in compression, the reaction at the bottom support will be equal in value to the force in the member, therefore *f* is at the same point as 7. The reaction at the top is given by the line *e–f* on the force diagram.

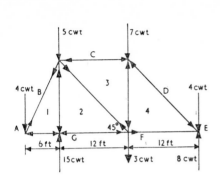
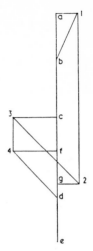

Fig. 7.20

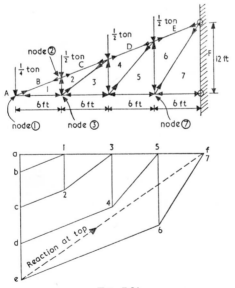

Fig. 7.21

131

French Roof Truss

The French truss shown in Fig. 7.22 has a special difficulty regarding the drawing of the force diagram. The force diagram is, however, drawn in the usual manner to begin with as follows—

Node 1: point 1 is found by drawing *b*–1 parallel to *B*1 and *l*–1 parallel to *L*1.

Nodes 2 and 3 are similarly dealt with without difficulty.

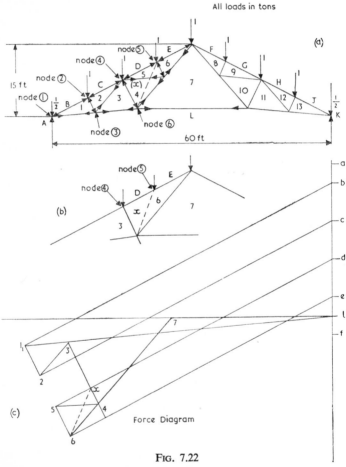

Fɪɢ. 7.22

The next node to consider is either node 4 or 6, but difficulty arises as there are still three unknown members at each node.

The usual manner of getting over this difficulty is to assume members 4–5 and 5–6 to be replaced temporarily by an imaginary member x–6, as shown in the small sketch, Fig. 7.22. (This substitution is justifiable because it can be proved that the force in member $E6$ is the same value whether the two members 4–5 and 5–6 are present or only the one member x–6.)

Node 4: point x may now be found on the force diagram by drawing d–x to intersect 3–x.

Node 5: point 6 may be found by drawing e–6 to intersect x–6. The two members 4–5 and 5–6 are now replaced.

Node 5: point 5 is found by drawing 6–5 to intersect 5–d.

Node 4: point 4 is found by drawing 5–4 to intersect 3–4.

The remainder of the force diagram may now be drawn without further difficulty, e.g. point 7 is fixed by drawing 4–7 to intersect l–7.

Frames Subjected to Inclined Loads

The frames dealt with in the preceding examples have all carried purely vertical loads, and so the end reactions have also been vertical.

Sometimes roof trusses have to be designed to withstand the effect of wind, and this produces loads which are assumed to be applied to the truss (via the purlins) at the panel points, in such a way that the panel loads are acting normal to the rafter line. As the inclined loads have a horizontal thrust effect on the truss as well as a vertical thrust effect, it follows that at least one of the reactions will have to resist the horizontal thrust effect.

It was stated in Chapter 3, that, when a truss is subjected to inclined loads, the usual assumptions are either that (*a*) one of the reactions is vertical, or (*b*) the horizontal components of the two reactions are equal. The method of determining such reactions by the use of the link polygon has been described in Chapter 3, and the student is advised to re-read the relevant sections.

When only symmetrical inclined loads have to be considered and one of the reactions is assumed to be vertical as in Fig. 7.23 the reactions can be found more easily by the method described below than by the link polygon.

If the four loads are considered to be replaced temporarily by the resultant R, then only three loads act on the truss, i.e. R, R_L and R_R. The three loads must act through one point for equilibrium, and the loads R and R_R obviously act through point x, the point of intersection of the vertical reaction R_R and the resultant inclined load R. As R_L must also act through point x, the direction of R_L is found by joining point A to point x.

The direction of all three loads is thus known, together with the magnitude of the resultant R, so the amounts of R_L and R_R may be found graphically as in Fig. 7.23.

The resultant R is set down to scale (b to c) and the point d is found by drawing in the direction of R_R from c and the direction of R_L from b to their intersection point d.

This vector diagram *bcd* is, of course, the triangle of forces for

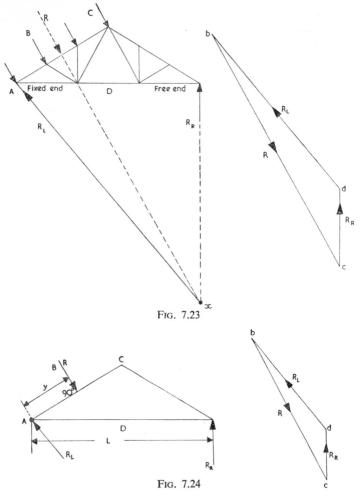

FIG. 7.23

FIG. 7.24

the loads, and $cd =$ reaction R_R to scale, and $db =$ reaction R_L to scale. From these three points, b, c, and d, the force diagram for the frame can be drawn in the usual way.

Vertical Reaction by Calculation

The vertical reaction can also be calculated by taking moments about the other end of the truss. For example, from Fig. 7.24, taking moments about A

$$R_R \times L = R \times y$$

and

$$R_R = \frac{R \times y}{L}$$

Point d can now be found by setting down the resultant load R (line bc) followed by the vertical reaction R_R as calculated to give the point d. Reaction R_L will then be found by scaling force db.

EXAMPLE

When the two reactions have been found, either graphically or by calculation, the forces in the individual bars may be found by drawing a force diagram, as in Fig. 7.25.

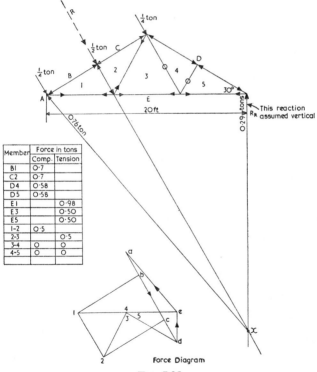

Member	Force in tons	
	Comp.	Tension
B1	0·7	
C2	0·7	
D4	0·58	
D5	0·58	
E1		0·98
E3		0·50
E5		0·50
1-2	0·5	
2-3		0·5
3-4	0	0
4-5	0	0

Force Diagram

FIG. 7.25

The resultant load R (inclined) is produced to intersect the vertical reaction R_R at the point x. The direction of left hand reaction R_L is then found by joining x to A.

The two reactions and the three inclined loads are thus now all known, and may be set down as in Fig. 7.25 in the order *ab*, *bc*, *cd* (inclined), *de* (vertical), and *ea* parallel to R_L.

The points 1, 2, 3, 4, 5 on the force diagram are then found in the usual way, as shown in Fig. 7.25.

Note, that there is no force in members 3–4 and 4–5 from this system of loading.

Further examples are shown in Figs. 7.26 and 7.27.

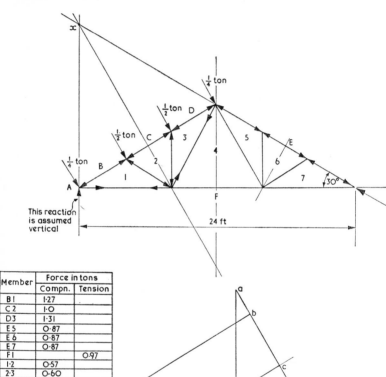

Member	Force in tons	
	Compn.	Tension
B1	1·27	
C2	1·0	
D3	1·31	
E5	0·87	
E6	0·87	
E7	0·87	
F1		0·97
1·2	0·57	
2·3	0·60	
3·4		1·0
No force in 4·5, 5·6, 6·7, F4 and F7		

Force Diagram

FIG. 7.26

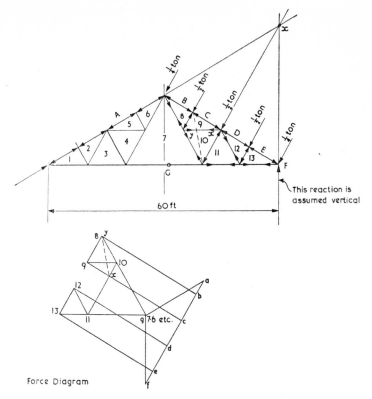

FIG. 7.27

EXERCISE 7

Questions 1 to 7. Determine the forces in the members of the frames shown in Figs. 7.28 to 7.34.

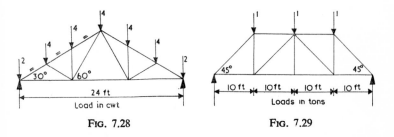

FIG. 7.28

FIG. 7.29

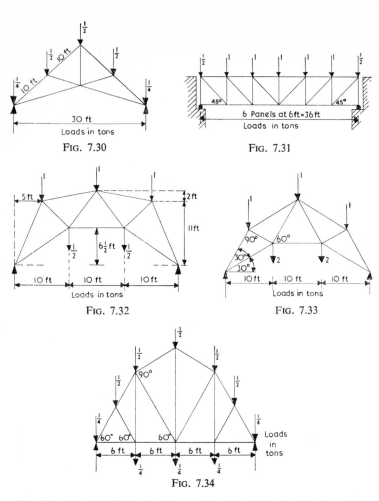

FIG. 7.30

FIG. 7.31

FIG. 7.32

FIG. 7.33

FIG. 7.34

Questions 8 to 16. Determine the reactions, then determine the forces in the members of the frames shown in Figs. 7.35 to 7.43

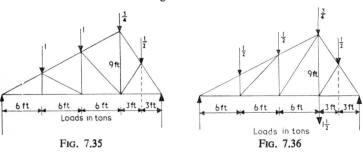

FIG. 7.35

FIG. 7.36

138

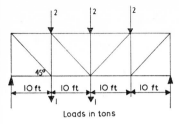

Loads in tons

FIG. 7.37

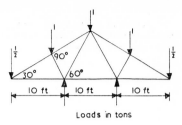

Loads in tons

FIG. 7.38

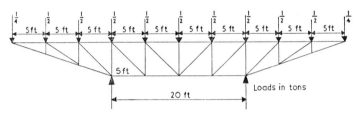

Loads in tons

FIG. 7.39

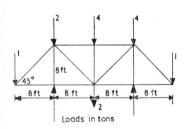

Loads in tons

FIG. 7.40

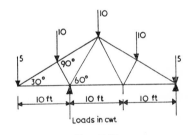

Loads in cwt

FIG. 7.41

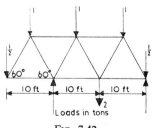

Loads in tons

FIG. 7.42

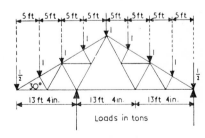

Loads in tons

FIG. 7.43

139

17. A lattice roof girder, upstanding above the top floor ceiling level, supports loads as shown in Fig. 7.44. Determine the forces in the members.

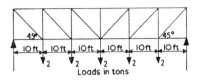

FIG. 7.44

Questions 18 to 20. Determine the forces in the members of the cantilever frames shown in Figs. 7.45 to 7.47. Also determine the values and directions of the reactions at the supports.

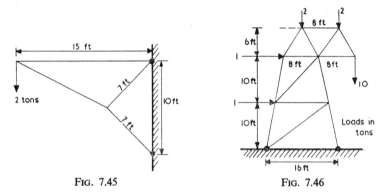

FIG. 7.45   FIG. 7.46

21. A framed structure is supported at *A* and *B* in such a manner that the reaction at *A* is horizontal. Calculate the values of the two reactions and determine the forces in the members of the frame (Fig. 7.48). Loads are in cwt.

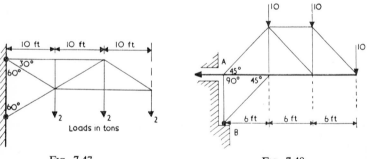

FIG. 7.47   FIG. 7.48

Questions 22 to 24. One of the reactions to each of the frames shown in Figs. 7.49 to 7.51 is vertical, as shown. Determine the reactions and the forces in the members of the frames.

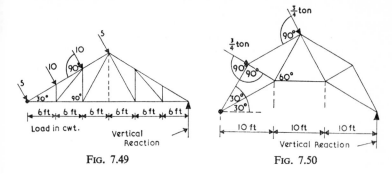

FIG. 7.49   FIG. 7.50

25. Repeat Question 22 (Fig. 7.49), assuming that the two supports resist equally the total horizontal component of the inclined forces.

26. Determine the reactions and the forces in the members of the frame shown in Fig. 7.52, assuming that the two supports resist equally the total horizontal component of the inclined forces.

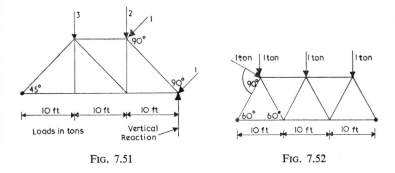

FIG. 7.51   FIG. 7.52

Note: Further practice may be obtained by drawing force diagrams for the frames given in Exercise 3 (Chapter 3), Questions 33 to 40.

CHAPTER 8

Calculation Methods for Frames

THE previous chapter has shown how the forces in the various members of loaded frames may be determined by drawing a force diagram for the frame. When the forces in *all* the members have to be found, the force diagram is usually the most convenient method, but on occasions it is necessary to determine the force in a single individual member, and in cases of this type it is normally more convenient to calculate the amount of the force.

Method 1; Method of Sections

Consider the *N* girder shown in Fig. 8.1; it is required to calculate the force in the member 1–2 of the bottom boom.

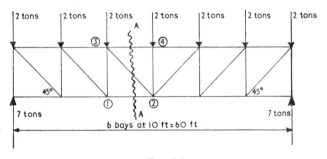

Fig. 8.1

1. Imagine the girder to be cut completely through, along the section *A–A*—a section passing through the member 1–2 concerned and two other members, 3–4 and 3–2.

2. Consider the portion of truss to the right of line *A–A* to be removed. The portion to the left of line *A–A* would then, of course, collapse, because three forces (the forces in members 1–2, 3–2 and 3–4) which were necessary to retain equilibrium had been removed.

3. If now, three forces *x*, *y* and *z*, equal respectively to force 1–2, force 3–4 and force 3–2 are now applied to the portion of frame concerned, as shown in Fig. 8.2, then the portion of frame will

remain in equilibrium under the action of the 7 tons reaction, the three 2 ton loads, and the forces x, y and z.

4. Three of these forces (x, y and z) are as yet unknown in amount and direction, but the force in member 1–2, i.e. force x, is to be determined at this stage, and it will be seen that the other two

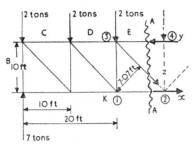

FIG. 8.2

unknown forces (y and z) intersect at and pass through the point 3 so that they have no moment about that point.

5. Thus, taking moments about the point 3, the portion of frame to the left of A–A is in equilibrium under: the moments of the two applied loads, the moment of the reaction, and the moment of the force x.

The moment of the reaction is a clockwise one of (7×20), i.e. 140 tons-ft.

The moments of the two loads are anticlockwise about point 3 and = (2×20) + (2×10), i.e. 60 tons-ft.

For equilibrium the moment of force x about point 3 (i.e. $10x$) must = $140 - 60$, i.e. 80 tons-ft anticlockwise.

Therefore $10x = 80$, whence $x = 8$ tons, and the arrow must act in the direction shown in Fig. 8.2 (in order that the moment of force x about point 3 is anticlockwise).

The member 1–2 is therefore in tension (pulling away from joint 1).

Note. It will be seen that, in general, the rule must be: take a cut through three members (which include the one whose force is to be determined) and take moments about the point through which the lines of action of the other two forces intersect.

To determine the force in the member 3–4:

Take moments about the point 2 where forces x and z intersect.

Moment of reaction $\qquad = (7 \times 30)$
$\qquad\qquad\qquad\qquad\qquad = 210$ tons-ft clockwise
Moments of applied loads $= (2 \times 30) + (2 \times 20) + (2 \times 10)$
$\qquad\qquad\qquad\qquad\qquad = 120$ tons-ft anticlockwise

Therefore

Moment of force y $= 210 - 120$

$= 90$ tons-ft anticlockwise

Therefore

$$10y = 90$$

$$y = 9 \text{ tons}$$

and, for the moment to be anticlockwise about point 2, the arrow must act towards the joint 3, therefore member 3–4 is a strut.

It should be noted that this particular method has its limitations. It would not appear to apply, for example, to member 3–2 (force z) for no point exists through which forces x and y intersect, as x and y are, in fact, parallel to each other.

However, when force y has been calculated, the force z may be found by taking moments about point 1, including the known value of force y (member 3–4).

Note: force y is 9 tons and is anticlockwise about point 1.

Moment of the reaction about point 1

$$= (7 \times 20) = 140 \text{ tons-ft}$$

Moments of the applied loads and the force in member 3–4

$$= (2 \times 20) + (2 \times 10) + (9 \times 10) = 150 \text{ tons-ft}$$

Therefore

moment of force z about point 1

$$= 150 - 140 = 10 \text{ tons-ft clockwise}$$

Therefore

$$7 \cdot 07z = 10$$

$$z = 1 \cdot 41 \text{ tons}$$

The arrow must act as shown in Fig. 8.2, therefore member 3–2 is a tie.

It should be noted that these arrows must be considered in relation to the nearest joints of that portion of the frame which remains after the imaginary cut through the three members has been made. These results should be checked by the student by drawing a force diagram for the entire frame.

EXAMPLE 1

Calculate the forces in the members marked 2–3, 1–6 and 2–6 of the frame shown in Fig. 8.3.

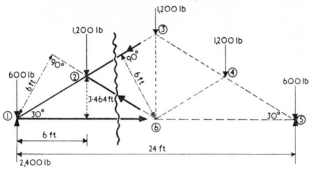

FIG. 8.3

Member 2–3: Take moments about point 6

Moment of reaction	$= 2{,}400 \times 12$
	$= 28{,}800$ lb-ft clockwise
Moment of applied loads	$= (600 \times 12) + (1{,}200 \times 6)$
	$= 14{,}400$ lb-ft anticlockwise

Moment of force in member 2–3 $= 28{,}800 - 14{,}400$
$= 14{,}400$ lb-ft anticlockwise

Therefore

Force 2–3 $\times$ 6 ft $= 14{,}400$

Force 2–3 $= 2{,}400$ lb (strut)

Member 1–6: Take moments about point 2

Moment of reaction	$= 2{,}400 \times 6$
	$= 14{,}400$ lb-ft clockwise
Moment of loads	$= 600 \times 6$
	$= 3{,}600$ lb-ft anticlockwise

Force 1–6 $\times$ 3·464 ft (anticlockwise) $= 14{,}400 - 3{,}600$

Force 1–6 $= \dfrac{10{,}800}{3{\cdot}464} = 3{,}118$ lb (tie)

Member 2–6. Take moments about point 1

Moment of reaction	$= 0$
Moment of loads	$= 1{,}200 \times 6$
	$= 7{,}200$ lb-ft clockwise

Force 2–6 $\times$ 6 (anticlockwise) $= 7{,}200$

Force 2–6 $= 1{,}200$ lb

The student is again reminded that, for determining whether members are struts or ties, the arrows as shown in Fig. 8.3 must be considered as acting towards or away from the nearest joint in that portion of the frame which remains after the *cut* has been made.

Method of Sections Applied to Girders with Parallel Flanges

The application of this method may be simplified considerably when the frame concerned has parallel flanges. Consider, for example, the Warren girder shown in Fig. 8.4.

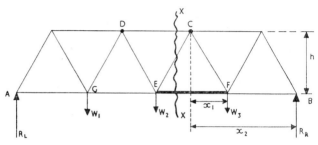

Fig. 8.4

In using the method of sections to find the force in member *EF*, the cut would be made through the section *X–X*, and moments taken about the point *C*.

Taking moments about *C* to the right,

$$(\text{Force in } EF) \times h = \text{moments of forces } R_R \text{ and } W_3$$
$$= (R_R \times x_2) - (W_3 \times x_1)$$
$$\text{Force in } EF = \frac{(R_R \times x_2) - (W_3 \times x_1)}{h}$$

But the value $(R_R \times x_2) - (W_3 \times x_1)$ is obviously the bending moment at *C*, considering the girder as an ordinary beam as shown in Fig. 8.5.

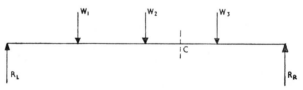

Fig. 8.5

So the rule may be given as follows—

To calculate the force in any top or bottom boom member of a girder of this type, calculate the bending moment at the node point opposite to the member and divide by the vertical height of the girder, e.g.

$$\text{Force in } EF = BM \text{ at point } C \div h$$

$$\text{Force in } DC = BM \text{ at point } E \div h$$

$$\text{Force in } GE = BM \text{ at point } D \div h$$

Note: This simplification of the method is sometimes known as the method of moments.

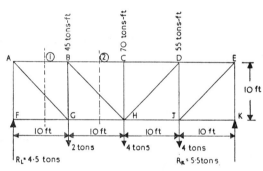

FIG. 8.6

EXAMPLE 2 (Fig. 8.6)

By calculation, the reactions are—

$$R_L = 4\cdot5 \text{ tons and } R_R = 5\cdot5 \text{ tons}$$

$$BM \text{ at } B \text{ and } G \ = (4\cdot5 \times 10) \qquad\qquad = 45 \text{ tons-ft}$$

$$BM \text{ at } C \text{ and } H \ = (4\cdot5 \times 20) - (2 \times 10) = 70 \text{ tons-ft}$$

$$BM \text{ at } D \text{ and } J \ = (5\cdot5 \times 10) \qquad\qquad = 55 \text{ tons-ft}$$

Therefore

$$\text{Force in } AB = \frac{BM \text{ at } G}{h} = \frac{45}{10} = 4\cdot5 \text{ tons}$$

(Section 1. The two other members meet at *G*)

$$\text{Force in } FG = \frac{BM \text{ at } A}{h} = \frac{0}{10} = 0$$

(Section 1. The two other members meet at A)

$$\text{Force in } BC = \frac{BM \text{ at } H}{h} = \frac{70}{10} = 7 \text{ tons}$$

(Section 2. The other two members meet at H)

$$\text{Force in } GH = \frac{BM \text{ at } B}{h} = \frac{45}{10} = 4 \cdot 5 \text{ tons}$$

(Section 2. The other two members meet at B)

$$\text{Force in } CD = \frac{BM \text{ at } H}{h} = \frac{70}{10} = 7 \text{ tons}$$

$$\text{Force in } HJ = \frac{BM \text{ at } D}{h} = \frac{55}{10} = 5 \cdot 5 \text{ tons}$$

$$\text{Force in } DE = \frac{BM \text{ at } J}{h} = \frac{55}{10} = 5 \cdot 5 \text{ tons}$$

$$\text{Force in } JK = \frac{BM \text{ at } E}{h} = \frac{0}{10} = 0$$

Method of Resolution of Forces

The forces in the individual members of loaded frames may also be determined by considering the various forces acting at each node

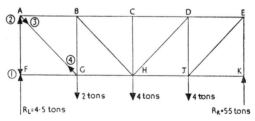

FIG. 8.7

point. This method is particularly useful for dealing with those members not so easily tackled by the method of sections, e.g. the vertical members of the frame dealt with in Example 2, Fig. 8.6. The diagram is again shown as Fig. 8.7.

Consider the node F:

There is a load of 4·5 tons *upward* at F. Obviously, member AF must itself counteract this(as FG—a horizontal member, cannot resist vertical force). Hence the force in member AF must equal 4·5 tons, and it must, at the node point F, be acting downwards in opposition to the reaction R_L, as shown by the arrowhead 1. This shows member *AF* to be a strut, and the other arrowhead 2 may be put in, acting towards *A*.

Consider the node *A*:

It is now known that a force of 4·5 tons acts upwards at this point (arrowhead 2). Again, member *AB*, being horizontal, cannot resist a vertical load, so member *AG* must resist the upward 4·5 tons at *A*. Thus the force in *AG* must act downwards at *A*, and the arrow 3 may be placed in position. The amount of force *AG* must be such that its vertical component equals 4·5 tons as in Fig. 8.8.

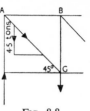

FIG. 8.8

Thus
$$\frac{4·5}{\text{force } AG} = \sin 45° = 0·7071$$

Therefore
$$\text{force in } AG = \frac{4·5}{0·7071} = 6·36 \text{ tons}$$

and *AG* is in tension, so the arrow 4 may be drawn in.

The load of 6·36 tons acting down and to the right at *A* tends to pull point *A* to the right, horizontally. Thus the force in member *AB* at *A* must *push* point *A* to the left for equilibrium (arrow 5, showing member *AB* to be a strut); thus arrow 6 may be placed as shown in Fig. 8.9. The amount of force in *AB* is such that it counteracts the horizontal component of force 6·36 tons (arrow 3).

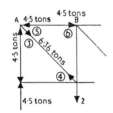

FIG. 8.9

FIG. 8.10

Thus, as in Fig. 8.10,

$$\frac{\text{Force in } AB}{6·36} = \cos 45° = 0·7071$$

Thus force $AB = 6·36 \times 0·7071 = 4·5$ tons compression, as was seen by the method of moments.

Consider the node *G*:

It has already been seen that there is no force in member *FG*, since the bending moment is zero at the opposite point *A*. Thus, as there is a force of 6·36 tons at *G*, acting upwards and to the left, the force in *BG* must act in such a way that it counteracts the resultant of the vertical forces at *G*. These vertical forces are—

(*a*) the vertical resultant upward of the 6·36 tons (i.e. 4·5 tons ↑);
(*b*) the downward applied load of 2 tons ↓ .

Their resultant is obviously 2·5 tons upward, so member *BG* must act downwards to the extent of 2·5 tons (arrows 7 and 8 may thus

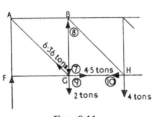

FIG. 8.11

be placed) and *BG* is thus a strut with a force of 2·5 tons (Fig. 8.11). Also, as *AG* pulls to the *left* at *G* to the extent of 4·5 tons (the horizontal component of the force *AG*) then member *GH* must pull to the *right* to the extent of 4·5 tons (arrow 9), and member *GH* is seen to be a tie with a force of 4·5 tons. This again agrees with the result obtained by the method of moments.

This process may be continued from each node to the next, and although its application is admittedly somewhat more laborious than the drawing of a force diagram, the student-reader is strongly recommended to practise this method; its use most definitely results in a better and more complete understanding of the forces acting at each node, and by its use struts and ties are more easily distinguished.

EXERCISE 8

Use calculation methods to determine the forces in the members of the frames of Exercise 7, Questions 2, 4, 10, 11, 13, 15, 17, 18, 19 and 21.

CHAPTER 9

Stress, Strain and Elasticity

Stress

WHEN a member is subjected to load of any type, the many fibres or particles of which the member is made up, transmit the load throughout the length and section of the member, and the fibres doing this work are said to be in a state of stress.

There are different types of stress, but the principal kinds are compressive stress and tensile stress.

Tensile Stress

Consider the steel bar shown in Fig. 9.1 having a cross-sectional area of A sq in. and pulled out at each end by loads W. Note that the total load in the member is W tons (not $2W$ tons). There would be no load at all in the member if only one load W was present as the member would not be in equilibrium.

FIG. 9.1

At *any* plane such as X–X taken across the section, there exists a state of stress between the fibres on one side of the plane and those on the other. Here the stress is tensile by nature—the fibres on one side exerting stress to resist the tendency of being pulled away from the fibres on the other side of the plane. This type of resistance to the external loads is of course set up along the whole length of the bar and not at one plane only, just as in a chain, resisting forces are set up by every link.

In this particular case (Fig. 9.1), if the loads act through the centroid of the shape, the stress is provided equally by the many fibres and each square inch of cross-section provides the same resistance to the "pulling apart" tendency.

151

This is known as *direct* or *axial* stress and the total amount of stress generated (that is, the total amount of resistance) is equal to the total load *W* tons (or lb, etc.). In order to assess whether the stress is a safe one for the material it is common to refer to the *intensity of stress* or *unit stress* (i.e. stress per unit area) as a unit of assessment.

Intensity of Stress

Fig. 9.2 represents a bar of cast steel which is thinner at the middle of its length than elsewhere, and which is subjected to an

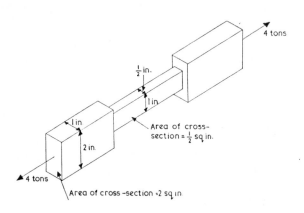

FIG. 9.2

axial pull of 4 tons. If the bar were to fail in tension, it would be due to the bar snapping where the amount of material is a minimum. The total stress tending to cause the bar to fracture is 4 tons at all cross-sections, but whereas 4 tons is being resisted by a cross-sectional area of 2 sq in. for part of its length it is being resisted by only ½ sq in. at the middle portion of the bar. The intensity of stress or unit stress is greatest at this middle section and is at the rate of 8 tons per sq in. of cross-section. At other points along the bar, 4 tons is resisted by 2 sq in. and the intensity of stress is equivalent to 2 tons per sq in. of cross-section.

In cases of *direct* tension, therefore, the

$$\text{intensity of stress} = \frac{\text{applied load}}{\text{area of cross-section of member}}$$

The term intensity of stress (or unit stress) is the correct one but it is common to omit the words "intensity of" and to speak about the "stress" being so many tons per sq in. or lb per sq ft, etc.

$$\text{Thus tensile stress} = \frac{\text{load}}{\text{area}} = \frac{W}{A}$$

EXAMPLE 1

A bar of steel 3 sq in. in cross-sectional area is being pulled with an axial force of 18 tons. Calculate the stress (i.e. intensity of stress) in the steel.

Since 3 sq in. of cross-section is resisting 18 tons it means that each sq in. is resisting 6 tons. In other words,

$$\text{stress} = \frac{W}{A} = \frac{18 \text{ tons}}{3 \text{ sq in.}} = 6 \text{ tons/sq in.}$$

Compressive Stress

Fig. 9.3 shows a similar member to that of Fig. 9.1 but with two axial forces of W tons each acting inwards towards each other and thus putting the bar into a state of compression.

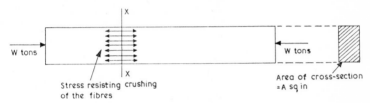

FIG. 9.3

Again, at any plane section such as $X–X$ there is a state of stress between the fibres, but this time the stress which is generated is resisting the tendency of the fibres to be crushed together. Once more the stress is shared equally between the fibres, and the unit stress, or stress intensity per unit of area is

$$\frac{\text{load}}{\text{area}}, \text{ i.e. } \frac{W}{A} \text{ tons/sq in.}$$

EXAMPLE 2

A brick pier is 3 ft square and 10 ft high and weighs 120 lb/cu ft. It is supporting an axial load from a column of 90 tons (Fig. 9.4). The load is uniformly spread over the top of the pier so the arrow shown merely represents the resultant of the

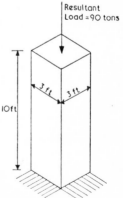

FIG. 9.4

load. If the load actually acted on a point of the brickwork there would be a high intensity of stress at the top of the pier, immediately under the load.

Calculate (*a*) the stress in the brickwork immediately under the column; (*b*) the stress at the bottom of the pier.

(*a*) Area of cross-section = 9 sq ft.

90 tons on 9 sq ft is equivalent to 10 tons on each square foot,

$$\text{or Stress} = \frac{90 \text{ tons}}{9 \text{ sq ft}} = 10 \text{ tons/sq ft}$$

(*b*) Weight of pier = $3 \times 3 \times 10 \times 120 = 10,800$ lb = 4·82 tons

$$\text{Total load} = 90 + 4\cdot82 = 94\cdot82 \text{ tons}$$

$$\text{Stress} = \frac{94\cdot82 \text{ tons}}{9 \text{ sq ft}} = 10\cdot54 \text{ tons/sq ft}$$

EXAMPLE 3

A 3 in. × $\frac{3}{8}$ in. mild steel plate is attached to a $\frac{3}{8}$ in. thick gusset plate with two rivets as shown in Fig. 9.5. The holes drilled to receive the rivets were $1\frac{13}{16}$ in. diameter. The axial pull on the plates is 6 tons. Calculate the maximum stress in the 3 in. wide plate.

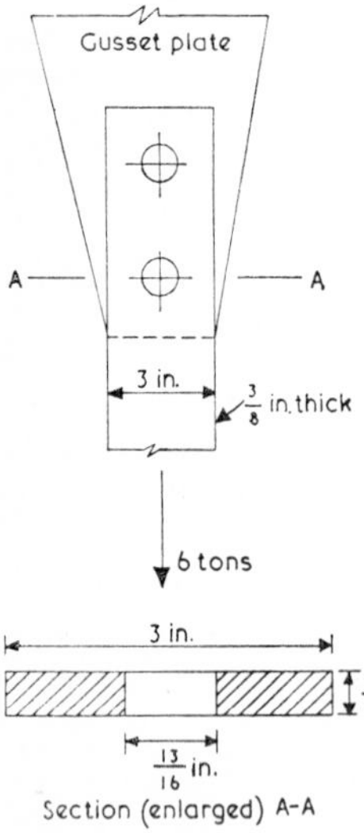

The plate is weakest at section *A–A* since it contains a hole. Although the hole is filled with the rivet, the rivet cannot be assumed to transmit the tension. An enlarged cross-section at *A–A* is shown in Fig. 9.5. The area of metal resisting the pull is shown shaded, and equals

$$(3 \times \tfrac{3}{8}) - (\tfrac{13}{16} \times \tfrac{3}{8}) = 1\cdot125 - 0\cdot305$$
$$= 0\cdot82 \text{ sq in.}$$

$$\text{Tension stress} = \frac{6 \text{ tons}}{0\cdot82 \text{ sq in.}}$$
$$= 7\cdot32 \text{ tons/sq in.}$$

FIG. 9.5

When investigating the strength of this connexion, the shear stresses in the rivets must also be considered. Rivets are dealt with in Chapter 17.

Strength of Materials and Factor of Safety

In Examples 1 and 2 the stress in the steel was calculated as 6 tons/sq in. and the stress in the brickwork as 10 (or 10·54) tons/ sq ft. Two questions now arise—

(*a*) is it safe to allow these materials to be stressed to this extent, or
(*b*) can higher stresses be allowed so that smaller members can be used, thus economizing in material?

Strength of Steel

There are many types of steel but the type used principally in structures is known as *mild* or *structural steel* (see British Standard Specification (B.S.S.) No. 15). If a bar of this steel, one square inch in cross-sectional area, is subjected to a gradually increasing pull in a testing machine, it is found that the bar breaks when the pull reaches about 30 tons. In other words the *failing stress* or *ultimate stress* is 30 tons/sq in. Referring to Example 1, this means that the bar 3 sq in. in cross-sectional area would require about 90 tons to cause it to fail in tension. The bar, however, is only supporting 18 tons, therefore it is amply strong and a smaller bar would suffice. The question now is: How small can the bar be? It would be obviously unwise to make it of such dimensions that the stress is 27 tons/sq in., because the bar would be very near its failing strength. (The strength of different batches of mild steel might vary between 28 and 33 tons/sq in.) Other factors argue against using too high a stress for design purposes. The actual total stress in the bar might be more (or even less) than the calculated value, due to assumptions made during the calculation stage. For example, the calculations may be based on the presence of a perfect hinge at a certain point in the structure. If the construction is such that there is a certain amount of fixity at the so-called hinge the actual stresses in the members might be somewhat different from the calculated stresses. Structural engineering is not an exact science, and calculated values of reactions, stresses, etc., whilst they may be mathematically correct for the theoretical structure, may be only approximate as far as the actual behaviour of the structure is concerned. In addition, the behaviour of mild steel at its *yield point* (see page 165) is a very important limiting factor to its safe design stress.

Working Stress

The maximum stresses allowed in materials (called permissible stresses, or design stresses, or working stresses) are specified in British Standard Specifications, Codes of Practice, and Building By-laws such as those of the London County Council (L.C.C.). The present permissible or working stress for ordinary mild steel subjected to tension is 9 to 9·5 tons/sq in., therefore a pull of 18 tons (see example) would require a bar 2 sq in. in cross-section. It was stated above that mild steel fails when a stress of about 30 tons/sq in. is reached. If working stress is 9 tons/sq in., the factor of safety against failure by tension is

$$\frac{\text{failing (ultimate) stress}}{\text{working stress}} \simeq \frac{30}{9} \simeq 3\tfrac{1}{3}$$

This may appear at first glance to be a high factor of safety, but for reasons which are discussed on page 166, the practical factor of safety is less than this theoretical value of $3\tfrac{1}{3}$. (Other materials, such as timber and bricks, which are not so uniform as steel is, may have higher factors of safety than $3\tfrac{1}{3}$.)

PERMISSIBLE STRESS FOR STEEL IN COMPRESSION: Steel is equally as strong in compression as it is in tension and if a structural member is very short compared with its cross-sectional dimensions, the permissible stress is nearly 9·5 tons/sq in. When a compression member (strut or column) is long and slender, it is liable to fail by buckling and in this case the permissible stress may be much less than 9·5 tons/sq in. This subject is discussed more fully in Chapter 16.

PERMISSIBLE STRESS FOR BRICKWORK IN COMPRESSION: The permissible stress depends on—

(*a*) the type of brick;
(*b*) the strength of the mortar;
(*c*) the slenderness of the wall or pier.

A very short pier of strong engineering bricks may have a working stress of 40 tons or more per square foot and a very short pier of good "building" bricks may have a working stress of 16 tons or more per square foot.

PERMISSIBLE COMPRESSIVE STRESSES FOR CONCRETE: The permissible stresses may range in the case of short piers or foundation blocks from about 50 to 20 tons/sq ft, depending on the proportion of cement to aggregates. Further details are given in Chapter 16, and it is hoped in a companion volume to this book.

PERMISSIBLE STRESSES FOR TIMBER: The stresses depend on the type of timber and the type of stress to which the timber is subjected. For example, timber in tension may be permitted 1,500 to 1,200 lb/sq in. and in compression in "short" posts about 1,000 to 800 lb/sq in. For permissible compressive stresses in "long" posts see Chapter 16.

Types of Stress

It is only in cases of direct tension and compression (and shear) where the applied load is resisted equally by every square inch of cross-section of the member that the stress (or to be more exact the intensity of stress) equals the load divided by the area of cross-section of the member.

For example, Fig. 9.6(*a*) shows a beam bending as the result of an applied load *W*. The stress in the beam fibres is not uniform and cannot be obtained by dividing the load by the area of cross-section of the beam. In Fig. 9.6(*b*) the load *W* causes bending stress in the portion *AB* of the member and portion *BC* is subjected to bending and compression (combined stress). Similarly, in Fig. 9.6(*c*) the

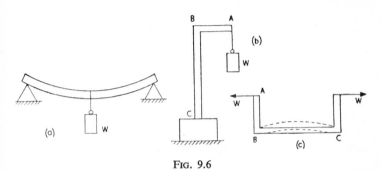

Fig. 9.6

portion *AB* is subjected to bending, whilst portion *BC* is subjected to combined tension and bending. Methods of calculating bending and combined stresses, etc. are given in Chapters 18 and 19.

Questions 1 to 18 of Exercise 9 may now be attempted.

Elasticity and Strain

All materials alter slightly in shape when they are stressed. A member which is subjected to tension stress increases in length and its cross-section becomes slightly smaller. Similarly, a compression member becomes shorter and slightly larger in cross-section. The very slight alteration in cross-section of building members is not as a rule important and only the alterations in length will be considered in this book.

Elastic Materials

Everyone is familiar with the properties of the material called elastic. When a tension force is applied to a piece of elastic it becomes longer, and when the force is removed, the material reverts to its original length. This property is common to some building materials such as steel, although under its normal working loads the amount of elongation is usually too small to be detected by the unaided eye. Another property of elastic materials is that the alteration in length is directly proportional to the load. For example, if in a given member

> 1 ton produces an extension of $\frac{1}{100}$ in.
> 2 tons will produce an extension of $\frac{2}{100}$ in.
> 3 tons will produce an extension of $\frac{3}{100}$ in.

and so on, provided the *elastic limit* of the material is not exceeded.

This law (alteration in length is proportional to the force) was first stated by Robert Hooke (1635–1703) and is therefore known as Hooke's Law. Hooke was a mathematician and scientist and a contemporary of Sir Christopher Wren.

Although all materials alter in length when stressed, materials which are not elastic do not obey Hooke's Law. That is, the alterations in length are not directly proportional to the load. Structural steel and timber are almost perfect elastic materials.

Strain

Just as it is convenient to represent the stress in a member as load per unit area, so it is convenient to represent the alteration in length of a member in terms of alteration per unit length.

$$\text{The } \frac{\text{alteration in length}}{\text{original length}} \text{ is called the strain}$$

Tension Strain.

$$\text{Tension strain} = \frac{\text{amount of elongation}}{\text{original length}}$$

In Fig. 9.7 the strain $= \delta$ in./L in. δ is a Greek symbol called delta which is frequently used to denote small alterations in length.

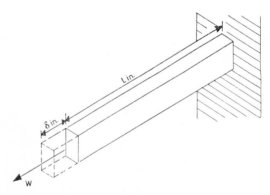

Fig. 9.7

If in Fig. 9.7 $L = 80$ in. and $\delta = 0\cdot06$ in.

Then   Tension strain $= \dfrac{\delta}{L} = \dfrac{0\cdot06}{80} = 0\cdot00075$

Note that strain is a ratio or number.

COMPRESSIVE STRAIN.

EXAMPLE 4

A timber specimen 3 in. × 3 in. in cross-section and 12 in. long when tested in a compression machine shortened by 0·0078 in. due to a load of 4 tons (Fig. 9.8). Calculate the strain.

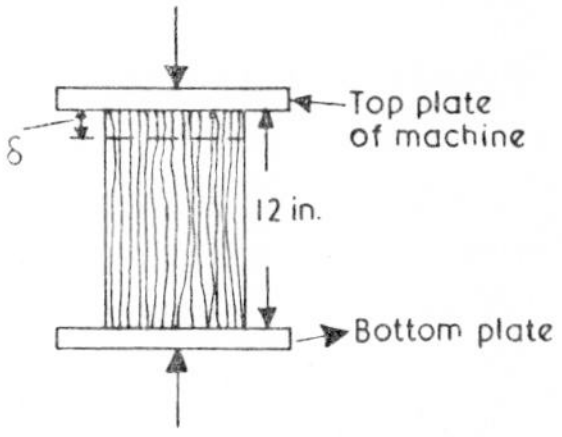

Compression strain

$= \dfrac{\text{amount of shortening}}{\text{original length}} = \dfrac{\delta}{L}$

$= \dfrac{0\cdot0078 \text{ in.}}{12 \text{ in.}} = 0\cdot00065$

FIG. 9.8

Note that the load of 4 tons which is responsible for the strain does not enter into its calculation.

Modulus of Elasticity

Let us assume that we require a general formula by the use of which we can determine the amount of elongation (or shortening) in any member composed of an elastic material. Assume for example that the material is rubber. By carrying out experiments on pieces of rubber of different lengths, different areas of cross-section and different qualities, the following facts would be demonstrated—

1. Increase in the load W produces proportionate increase of elongation (Hooke's Law), therefore W is one term of the required formula.

2. Increase in length L of the member means increase in elongation. It will be found that the elongation is directly proportional to the length of the member, i.e. for a given load and a given area of cross-section a member 20 in. long will stretch twice as much as a member of the same material 10 in. long. L is therefore a term in the formula.

3. It is harder to stretch a member of large cross-sectional area A than a member of small cross-sectional area. Experiments will show that the elongation is inversely proportional to the area, i.e. for a given load and a given length a member 1 sq in. in cross-sectional area will stretch only half as much as a member $\frac{1}{2}$ sq in. in area. A is therefore a term in the formula.

4. Rubber can be obtained of different qualities, i.e. of different

stiffnesses. Other conditions being constant (i.e. length, area, etc.) it is more difficult to stretch a "stiff" rubber than a more flexible rubber. Let us represent this quality of stiffness by the symbol E, then the greater the value of E, i.e. the greater the stiffness of the material, the smaller will be the elongation; other conditions (length, load and area) being constant.

The formula for elongation (or shortening) of an elastic material can now be expressed as

$$\delta = \frac{WL}{AE}$$

W and L are in the numerator of the fraction, because the greater their values, the greater the elongation. A and E are in the denominator of the fraction because the greater their values (i.e. the greater the area and the greater the stiffness) the less will be the elongation.

The symbol E in the above formula represents the stiffness of a given material (i.e. a measure of its elasticity), and if we can express this stiffness in certain definite units, the formula can be used to determine elongations of members of structures. Now if $\delta = WL/AE$, by transposing the formula, $E = WL/A\delta$ and the value of E for different materials can be obtained experimentally by compression or tension tests.

The foregoing explanation is lengthy and the subject has been treated in such a manner in the hope that the student will appreciate the meaning of modulus of elasticity (E) instead of thinking of it as a term in some more or less incomprehensible formula.

The usual more concise treatment of the subject is as follows: In an elastic material stress is proportional to strain,

Therefore, $\dfrac{\text{stress}}{\text{strain}} = $ a constant value

This value is called the modulus (i.e. measure) of elasticity of the material and is denoted by E.

Therefore $\dfrac{\text{stress}}{\text{strain}} = E$

But $\text{stress} = \dfrac{\text{load}}{\text{area}} = \dfrac{W}{A}$

And $\text{strain} = \dfrac{\text{alteration in length}}{\text{original length}} = \dfrac{\delta}{L}$

Therefore $\dfrac{W}{A} \Big/ \dfrac{\delta}{L} = E$

Whence $E = \dfrac{WL}{A\delta}$

The modulus of elasticity is often called Young's modulus, after the scientist Thomas Young (1773–1829). Note that modulus of elasticity is expressed in lb per sq in. or tons per sq in. This is because stress is load per unit area and strain is a number.

Therefore $\dfrac{\text{stress}}{\text{strain}}\left(\dfrac{\text{lb or tons per sq in.}}{\text{a number}}\right) = E\,(\text{lb or tons per sq in.})$

Fig. 9.9 indicates in essentials the manner of testing a block of

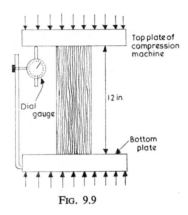

FIG. 9.9

timber $2\frac{1}{2}$ in. $\times$ 4 in in cross-section and 12 in. high. In the actual experiment four gauges (reading to $\frac{1}{1000}$ of an inch) were used, one at each corner, and the average of the four readings was taken for each increment of load. A gauge was used at each corner because possible small inequalities in the top and bottom surfaces of the timber might result in unequal shortening of the timber block. The following readings (Table 9.1), which have been slightly adjusted for purposes of clearer explanation, were recorded as the compressive load was gradually increased:

TABLE 9.1

	Load on specimen W	Shortening of specimen δ
1	0 lb	0 in.
2	4,000 lb	0·004 in.
3	8,000 lb	0·008 in.
4	12,000 lb	0·012 in.
5	16,000 lb	0·016 in.

Now $E = \dfrac{WL}{A\delta}$, where $L = 12$ in. and $A = 10$ sq in.

From reading 2, $E = \dfrac{4,000 \times 12}{10 \times 0.004} = 1,200,000$ lb/sq in.

From reading 3, $E = \dfrac{8,000 \times 12}{10 \times 0.008} = 1,200,000$ lb/sq in.

From reading 4, $E = \dfrac{12,000 \times 12}{10 \times 0.012} = 1,200,000$ lb/sq in.

From reading 5, $E = \dfrac{16,000 \times 12}{10 \times 0.016} = 1,200,000$ lb/sq in.

It will be noted that E is a constant value, and it is this value which is taken as the modulus of elasticity for the timber. Since modulus denotes measure, E is a measure of the elasticity (or stiffness).

The results of the experiment can be plotted as shown in Fig. 9.10. In an actual experiment results might not be as uniform as given on page 161, but the resultant graph would approximate very closely to a straight line.

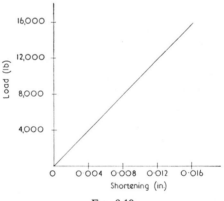

Fig. 9.10

EXAMPLE 5

A post of timber similar to that tested as described on page 161 is 6 in. square and 10 ft high. How much will the post shorten when an axial load of 21,600 lb is applied?

The modulus of elasticity of this type of timber we know to be 1,200,000 lb/sq in.

$$A = 36 \text{ sq in.}, \quad L = 10 \text{ ft} = 120 \text{ in.}$$

Therefore

$$\delta = \frac{WL}{AE} = \frac{21,600 \times 120}{36 \times 1,200,000} = 0.06 \text{ in.}$$

This problem demonstrates that if the modulus of elasticity of a material is known, the amount a given member will shorten (or lengthen) under a given load can be calculated.

Experiment on Mild Steel

A bar of mild steel $\frac{1}{2}$ in. diameter was gripped in the jaws of a testing machine and subjected to a gradually increasing pull (Fig. 9.11). A gauge was attached to two points on the bar 10 in. apart (gauge length = 10 in.) and the following readings were recorded (Table 9.2). (The elongations given in the table have been slightly adjusted as such complete accuracy is not possible in the testing of materials.)

The area (A) of a $\frac{1}{2}$ in. diameter circle is 0·196 sq. in.

$$L = 10 \text{ in.}$$

From reading 2,

$$E = \frac{WL}{A\delta} = \frac{1,000 \times 10}{0.196 \times 0.0017}$$

$$= 30,000,000 \text{ lb/sq in.}$$

$$= 13,400 \text{ tons/sq in.}$$

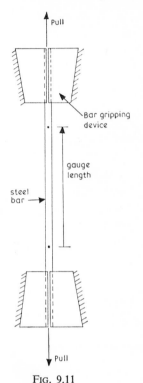

FIG. 9.11

From reading 3, $E = \dfrac{WL}{A\delta} = \dfrac{2,000 \times 10}{0.196 \times 0.0034} = 30,000,000$ lb/sq in.

and so on.

The constant value of E in this case is 30,000,000 lb/sq in. or 13,400 tons/sq in.

Note that the modulus of elasticity of steel is much greater than that of timber. Steel, of course, is much harder to stretch than is timber.

EXAMPLE 6

A tie bar in a roof truss is of similar steel to that tested as described above. The bar is 3 in. by $\frac{3}{8}$ in. in cross-section and 12 ft long. How much will the bar stretch due to a pull of 8 tons?

TABLE 9.2

	Load (lb)	Elongation (in.)
1	0	0
2	1,000	0·0017
3	2,000	0·0034
4	3,000	0·0051
5	4,000	0·0068
6	5,000	0·0085

We know that E for this type of steel is 13,400 tons/sq in.

$$L = 144 \text{ in.}$$

Therefore
$$\delta = \frac{WL}{AE} = \frac{8 \times 144}{3 \times \frac{3}{8} \times 13,400}$$
$$= 0·077 \text{ in.}$$

Values of E used for Design Purposes

STEEL. It would be inconvenient to test specimens every time a designer required to calculate the extension or shortening of a structural member. Fortunately, the properties of mild steel do not vary much from batch to batch and the value of E to be used for design purposes is usually specified as 13,000 tons/sq in. When calculations are carried out in pounds, 30,000,000 lb/sq in. is often taken as the value of E. This is equivalent to 13,400 tons/sq in. and for practical purposes it does not matter much whether 13,000 tons/sq in. or 30,000,000 lb/sq in. is assumed.

TIMBER. Timber is more variable than steel and different types of timber have different values of E. For most practical purposes, however, it is sufficient to use the average values given in handbooks or quoted in by-laws. For example, the L.C.C. By-laws give the following values (Table 9.3):

TABLE 9.3

	Class of timber	
	A	B
Modulus of elasticity (mean)	1,600,000 lb/sq in.	1,200,000 lb/sq in.
Modulus of elasticity (minimum)	1,000,000 lb/sq in.	750,000 lb/sq in.

"The mean value of E shall only be used for rafters and joists and in all other cases the minimum value of E shall be used."

Class A timber is defined as Douglas fir, or longleaf pitch pine or shortleaf pitch pine.

Class B timber is defined as Canadian spruce, European larch, red pine, western hemlock, whitewood.

CONCRETE. Concrete is not an elastic material in the same sense as is steel, but for reinforced concrete calculations, a value of E of 2,000,000 lb/sq in. is usually assumed.

Behaviour of Mild Steel in Tension: Yield Point

On page 164 results were given for a tension test on a mild steel bar $\frac{1}{2}$ in. in diameter. The highest load recorded was 5,000 lb and if the load is taken off, the bar will revert to its original length. On reloading, the bar will again elongate, and on unloading the elongation will disappear, and so on.

If the load is gradually increased beyond 5,000 lb the bar will continue to stretch proportionately to the applied load until a loading of about 7,500 to 8,500 lb is reached. (These loads on a bar $\frac{1}{2}$ in. in diameter are equivalent to stresses of about 17 tons/sq in. and 19 tons/sq in. respectively.) At about this point the steel reaches its elastic limit (i.e. it ceases to behave as an elastic material) and begins to stretch a great amount compared with the previous small elongations. This stretching takes place without the application of any further load and the steel is said to have reached its *yield point*. After a short time the steel recovers a little and ceases to stretch. Additional load can now be applied, but the steel has been considerably weakened and stretches a great deal for each small increment of load. Finally, at about a stress of 30 tons/sq in. the bar breaks, and just before it breaks, it *waists* at the point of failure as indicated in Fig. 9.12. If the two fractured ends are placed together and the distance between the original gauge points is measured it will be found that the total elongation is 20 per cent or more of the original length.

Fig. 9.13 shows a graph which has been constructed from the results of a test on a $\frac{1}{2}$ in. diameter bar, the gauge length being 10 in.

Actually, the limit of proportionality (stress proportional to strain) is reached a little before the yield point, but for most practical purposes it is quite justifiable to consider the limit of proportionality, the elastic limit and the yield point to be identical. In addition, referring to Fig. 9.12, the bar reduces considerably in cross-section just before it fails, and some load can be taken off the bar so that the actual load which causes failure is less than the maximum recorded load. This is indicated on the graph by the dotted line.

The failing stress (about 30 tons/sq in.) is calculated on the original cross-sectional area of the bar and not on the final reduced cross-section.

To sum up: Mild steel reaches its *yield point* and loses its valuable elastic properties at a stress of about 17 to 19 tons/sq in. Up to this point elongations are small but any further increase in load results in large elongations. If the load is removed from steel after

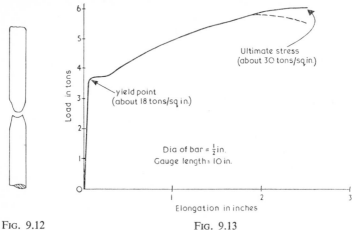

FIG. 9.12   FIG. 9.13

it has been loaded beyond its yield point, the steel will not revert to its original length. The elongation which remains is called *permanent set*.

It was stated on page 156 that the factor of safety of steel against failure is about $3\frac{1}{3}$, i.e.

$$\frac{30 \text{ tons per sq in.}}{9 \text{ tons per sq in.}}$$

It should be obvious, however, that it would be unwise to load steel beyond its *yield point* because the resulting large changes in length would cause cracking of plaster, brickwork, etc. In addition, the steel would be in an unstable state, so it would appear that the yield stress is more suitable than the ultimate (i.e. failing) stress on which to base the working stress.

Assuming a yield stress of about 18 tons/sq in. and a working stress of 9 tons/sq in. the factor of safety is therefore about 2.

Stresses in Composite Members

When a structural member is made up of two members of different materials of equal length and connected together so that each member shortens or lengthens the same amount when load is applied, the intensities of stress in the two members will be in the same ratio as their elastic moduli, e.g.

$$\frac{\text{stress in material } A}{\text{stress in material } B} = \frac{E \text{ for material } A}{E \text{ for material } B}$$

Note. E_A/E_B is called the *modular ratio*.

EXAMPLE 7

A reinforced concrete column is 12 in. square and 10 ft high and it contains four bars of mild steel, each bar being of 1 in. diameter (Fig. 9.14). The column

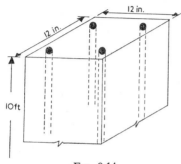

FIG. 9.14

is supporting an axial load of 131,600 lb. Calculate the stresses in the two materials and the amount the column will shorten. Take E for steel as 30,000,000 lb/sq in. and E for concrete as 2,000,000 lb/sq in.

Since the steel is gripped tightly by the surrounding concrete, both materials shorten the same amount (δ). The strain in the concrete δ/L is therefore equal to the strain in the steel.

Now, $$\frac{\text{stress}}{\text{strain}} = E$$

Therefore $$\text{strain} = \frac{\text{stress}}{E}$$

$$\text{Strain in concrete} = \frac{\text{stress in concrete}}{E \text{ for concrete}} = \frac{\text{stress } (c)}{E_c}$$

$$\text{Strain in steel} = \frac{\text{stress in steel}}{E \text{ for steel}} = \frac{\text{stress } (s)}{E_s}$$

Since the strains are equal, it follows that

$$\frac{\text{stress } (s)}{E_s} = \frac{\text{stress } (c)}{E_c}$$

or
$$\frac{\text{stress } (s)}{\text{stress } (c)} = \frac{E_s}{E_c}$$

$$\frac{\text{stress } (s)}{\text{stress } (c)} = \frac{30,000,000}{2,000,000} = 15$$

i.e. the stress in the steel is 15 times the stress in the concrete.

Area of one 1 in. diameter bar $= 0.7854$ sq in.

Area of four 1 in. diameter bars $= 3.1416$ sq in.

Therefore

Area of concrete $\qquad = 144 - 3.1416$ sq in.

$\qquad = 140.8584$ sq in.

Let $\qquad x$ lb/sq in. $=$ stress in the concrete

then $\qquad 15x$ lb/sq in.$=$ stress in the steel

Load taken by the concrete $\qquad =$ stress $\times$ area

$\qquad = 140.8584x$ lb

Load taken by the steel $\qquad = 3.1416 \times 15x$ lb

$\qquad = 47.124x$ lb

Load taken by column $\qquad = 140.8584x + 47.124x$

$\qquad = 187.9824x$ lb

But the load on the column $\qquad = 131,600$ lb

Therefore $\qquad 187.98x = 131,600$ lb

$\qquad x = 700$ lb/sq in. (slide rule)

And stress in steel $\qquad = 700 \times 15$

$\qquad = 10,500$ lb/sq in.

To calculate the amount of shortening of the column consider one material only, e.g. the shortening of the concrete is due to the load carried by the concrete.

$$\frac{\text{stress}}{\text{strain}} = E$$

Therefore
$$\frac{700}{\text{strain}} = 2,000,000$$

$$\text{strain} = \frac{700}{2,000,000}$$

But
$$\text{strain} = \frac{\delta}{L}$$

where $\qquad\qquad L = 10 \text{ ft} = 120 \text{ in.}$

$$\frac{\delta}{120} = \frac{700}{2,000,000}$$

$$\delta = \frac{700 \times 120}{2,000,000} = 0\!\cdot\!042 \text{ in.}$$

The same result would be obtained by making calculations with respect to the steel.

It should be noted that the method by which the above problem has been solved, although correct for determining the stresses in the two materials, is not nowadays used for designing reinforced concrete columns subject to axial loads. The steel is permitted a much higher stress than that based on the modular ratio, and examples of design of reinforced concrete columns are given in Chapter 16.

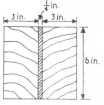

Fig. 9.15

EXAMPLE 8

Two 6 in. × 3 in. × 10 ft long timber members are reinforced with a plate of steel 6 in. × ¼ in. × 10 ft (Fig. 9.15), the three members being adequately bolted together. The permissible stresses for the timber and steel if used independently are 800 and 18,000 lb/sq in. E for the timber is 1,500,000 lb/sq in. and E for the steel is 30,000,000 lb/sq in. Calculate the permissible tensile load for the composite member, and the amount of elongation due to this load.

$$\text{Area of timber} = 36 \text{ sq in.}$$

$$\text{Area of steel} = 6 \times \tfrac{1}{4} = 1\tfrac{1}{2} \text{ sq in.}$$

At first glance it might appear that the safe load $= (36 \times 800) + (1\tfrac{1}{2} \times 18,000)$. It must be remembered, however, that the stresses in the two materials will be in the ratio

$$\frac{E_s}{E_t}, \text{ i.e. } \frac{30,000,000}{1,500,000}$$

i.e. 20/1 so that if the stress in the timber is taken as 800 lb/sq in., the stress in the steel will be 20 × 800, i.e. 16,000 lb/sq in. Therefore,

$$\begin{aligned}
\text{safe load for timber} &= 36 \times 800 &&= 28,800 \text{ lb} \\
\text{safe load for steel} &= 1\tfrac{1}{2} \times 16,000 &&= 24,000 \\
\text{Total safe load} &= && 52,800 \text{ lb}
\end{aligned}$$

To obtain the elongation of the composite member, consider either the timber or the steel, e.g.

$$\text{stress in timber} = 800 \text{ lb/sq in.}$$

$$\text{strain} = \frac{\text{stress}}{E} = \frac{800}{1,500,000}$$

$$\frac{\delta}{120} \text{ in.} = \frac{800}{1,500,000}$$

Therefore $$\delta = \frac{800 \times 120}{1,500,000} = 0.064 \text{ in.}$$

SUMMARY

Intensity of Tensile Stress, or more briefly, stress, is obtained by dividing the applied load by the area of cross-section of the member, i.e.

$$\text{tensile stress} = \frac{W}{A}$$

$$\text{Similarly, compressive stress} = \frac{W}{A}$$

The permissible or working stress for a material depends on the nature of the material, the type of stress and the use of the material in the building as, for example, whether it is used in a long column or in a short column.

Factor of Safety = failing or ultimate stress of the material divided by the working stress.

$$\text{Tension or Compression Strain} = \frac{\text{alteration in length}}{\text{original length}}$$

In elastic materials stress is proportional to strain providing the elastic limit of the material is not exceeded.

Modulus of Elasticity or Young's modulus is a measure of the resistance of an elastic material to being stretched or shortened. The greater the value of E, the more difficult it is to cause shortening or lengthening of the material.

$$E = \frac{\text{stress}}{\text{strain}}$$ and is measured in pounds per square inch or tons per square inch.

$$\left(E = \frac{WL}{A\delta}\right)$$

When two materials A and B are combined,

$$\frac{\text{stress }(A)}{\text{stress }(B)} = \frac{E(A)}{E(B)}$$

EXERCISE 9

1. A steel tie bar 4 in. × $\frac{3}{8}$ in. in cross-section is transmitting a pull of 13·5 tons. Calculate the stress in the bar.

2. Calculate the safe tension load for a steel bar 3 in. × ¼ in. in cross-section, the working stress being 9·5 tons/sq in.

3. A tie bar is 3 in. wide and it has to sustain a pull of 10 tons. Calculate the required thickness of the bar if the permissible stress is 9 tons/sq in.

4. A bar of steel circular in cross-section is 1 in. in diameter. It sustains a pull of 6 tons. Calculate the stress in the bar.

5. Calculate the safe load for a bar of steel 1½ in. in diameter if the working stress is 9·5 tons/sq in.

6. A bar of steel, circular in cross-section, is required to transmit a pull of 4 tons. If the permissible stress for the steel is 9 tons/sq in. calculate the required diameter of the bar.

7. A hollow steel tube 4 in. external diameter and 3 in. internal diameter is subject to a tensile load of 40 tons. Calculate the stress in the steel.

8. A timber tension member is 4 in. square in cross-section. Calculate the safe load for the timber if the permissible stress is 1,200 lb/sq in. Calculate the diameter of a steel bar which would be of equal strength to the timber member. Permissible stress is 9 tons/sq in.

9. A steel tie bar 3 in. wide and ⅜ in. thick has a hole $\frac{13}{16}$ in. diameter drilled in it for connexion purposes. Calculate the safe pull for the member if the working stress is 9 tons/sq in.

10. A tie bar of the shape shown in Fig. 9.16 has a uniform thickness of ½ in. and has a hole each end $\frac{13}{16}$ in. diameter. Calculate the width x so that the bar is equally strong throughout its length. Calculate the safe pull for the bar if the permissible stress is 9 tons/sq in.

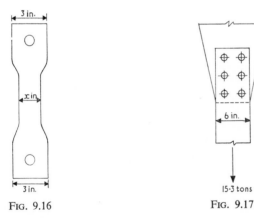

FIG. 9.16   FIG. 9.17

11. A tie bar of steel 6 in. wide is connected to a gusset plate by six rivets as shown in Fig. 9.17. The diameter of each rivet hole is $\frac{13}{16}$ in. Calculate the required thickness of the bar if the working stress is 9·5 tons/sq in.

12. A short brick pier 13½ in. square has a permissible stress of 20 tons/sq ft. Calculate the safe axial load for the pier.

13. Calculate the cross-sectional dimensions of a square brick pier to support an axial load of 36 tons, if the permissible stress for the brickwork is 16 tons/sq ft.

14. L.C.C. By-laws require test cubes of Grade III concrete (1 : 2 : 4 nominal mix) to have a crushing strength at 28 days after mixing of 2,250 lb/sq in. The same By-laws specify working stresses of 600 lb/sq in. for short concrete columns

and 39 tons/sq ft for concrete foundations. Calculate the factor of safety in each case.

15. A short specimen of deal timber 2 in. square in cross-section failed in a compression machine at a load of 7 tons. The permissible stress for such timber is 800 lb/sq in. Calculate the factor of safety.

16. A steel stanchion carrying a load of 87·75 tons is to be provided with a square steel base plate to spread the load on to a concrete foundation block. Calculate the minimum length of side (in inches) of the base plate if the stress on the concrete must not exceed 39 tons/sq ft.

17. A steel column circular in cross-section is 6 in. in diameter and carries a load of 120 tons. Calculate (a) the compressive stress in the column; (b) the length of side of a square steel base plate to transmit the column load to a concrete foundation block. The permissible stress on the concrete is 39 tons/sq ft; (c) assuming the concrete base to weigh 15 tons, calculate the plan dimensions of the concrete foundation so that the stress on the soil does not exceed 2 tons/ sq ft.

18. The permissible tension stress on bolts is 6 tons/sq in. on the net section. The diameter at the root of the thread of a $\frac{3}{4}$ in. diameter bolt is 0·622 in. How many bolts in tension would be required to sustain a pull of 7·2 tons?

19. The following data were recorded during a tensile steel test—

Diameter of bar = 0·75 in. (Area = 0·44 sq in.)
Distance between gauge points = 8 in.
Elongation due to load of 5 tons = 0·007 in.
Load at yield point = 7·9 tons
Failing or ultimate load = 12·75 tons

Calculate, in tons/sq in., (a) the stress at yield point; (b) the ultimate stress; (c) the modulus of elasticity of the steel.

20. A steel bar 4 in. × $\frac{1}{2}$ in. in cross-section and 10 ft long is subjected to an axial pull of 13 tons. How much will it increase in length if the modulus of elasticity of the steel is 13,000 tons/sq in?

21. A mild steel bar is 1 in. in diameter and 2 ft long. If it stretches 0·01 in. under a load of 10,000 lb, calculate (a) the stress in tons/sq in.; (b) the strain; (c) the modulus of elasticity in tons/sq in.

22. A brass rod is 3 ft long and $\frac{3}{4}$ in. in diameter. It is subjected to a tensile force of 3 tons. Calculate (a) the stress; (b) the total amount of stretch. $E = 5,800$ tons/sq in.

23. A hollow steel tube 4 in. external diameter and 3 in. internal diameter and 10 ft long is subjected to a tensile load of 40 tons. Calculate the stress in the material and the amount the tube stretches if Young's modulus is 12,500 tons/ sq in.

24. During an experiment on a timber specimen 3 in. × 3 in. in cross-section, a shortening of 0·009 in. was recorded on a gauge length of 12 in. when a load of 8,100 lb was applied. Calculate the modulus of elasticity of the timber. Using this value of E, determine the amount of shortening of a timber post 6 in. square and 8 ft high due to an axial load of 28,800 lb.

25. Assuming the permissible stress for a timber post 6 in. square and 9 ft high is 920 lb/sq in., calculate the safe axial load for the post. How much will the post shorten under this load, assuming E to be 1,600,000 lb/sq in?

26. Three separate members of steel, copper and brass are of identical dimensions and are equally loaded. Young's moduli for the materials are: steel, 13,000 tons/sq in.; copper, 6,500 tons/sq in.; brass, 5,800 tons/sq in. If the steel member stretches 0·005 in. calculate the amount of elongation in the copper and brass members.

27. During a compression test, a block of concrete 4 in. square and 8 in. long (gauge length = 8 in.) shortened 0·008 in. when a load of 33,600 lb was applied. Calculate the stress and strain and Young's modulus for the concrete.

28. A reinforced concrete column 13 in. square and 10 ft high contains four $\frac{7}{8}$ in. diameter steel bars and supports an axial load of 162,080 lb. Calculate the stresses in the concrete and steel assuming E for steel is 30,000,000 lb/sq in. and E for concrete is 2,000,000 lb/sq in. Calculate the shortening of the column under the load.

29. A tension member is made of timber and steel firmly fixed together side by side. The cross-sectional area of the steel is 2 sq in. and that of the timber is 6 sq in. and the length of the member is 10 ft. If the maximum permissible stresses for the steel and timber when used separately are 20,000 lb/sq in. and 1,200 lb/sq in. respectively, calculate the safe load which the member can carry and the increase in length due to the load. Young's modulus for steel is 30,000,000 lb/sq in. and for timber is 1,200,000 lb/sq in.

30. A structural member made of wood is 5 in. × 4 in. in cross-section. It is required to carry a tensile force of 60,000 lb and is to be strengthened by two steel plates 5 in. wide bolted to the 5 in. sides of the wood. Calculate the thickness of steel required if the permissible stresses for the steel and wood are 20,000 and 800 lb/sq in. respectively. Assume that Young's modulus for the steel is 25 times that for the wood.

31. A timber post 6 in. square has two steel plates 6 in. × $\frac{1}{4}$ in. bolted to it on opposite sides along the entire length of the post. Calculate the stresses in the timber and steel due to a vertical axial load of 76,800 lb. If the post is 10 ft high calculate the amount of shortening under the load. E for steel is 30,000,000 lb/sq in. and E for timber is 1,500,000 lb/sq in.

32. A metal bar consists of a flat strip of steel rigidly fixed alongside a flat strip of brass. The brass has a cross-sectional area of 1·5 sq in. and the steel 0·5 sq in. The compound bar was placed in a tensile testing machine and the extension measured by means of an extensometer fixed over a 10 in. gauge length. The extension was recorded as 0·005 in. Calculate the load applied to the bar and the stress in each material.

$$E \text{ for brass } = 5,000 \text{ tons/sq in.}$$
$$E \text{ for steel } = 13,000 \text{ tons/sq in.}$$

CHAPTER 10

Bending Moment and Shearing Force

WHEN a beam is loaded, the applied loads have a tendency to cause failure of the beam, and whether or not the beam *actually* does fail depends obviously upon the extent or amount of loading and on the size and strength of the beam in question.

It is necessary to provide a beam that will safely carry the estimated loading with a reasonable factor of safety, and which will at the same time be light enough for economy and shallow enough to avoid unnecessary encroachment upon headroom.

In order to calculate the stresses that loading will induce into the fibres of a beam's cross-section, and to compare them with the known safe allowable stress for the material of which the beam is made, it is necessary to study the ways in which loading *punishes* a beam, and to assess the degree of *punishment*.

Loading tends to cause failure in two main ways—

1. By bending the beam to an excessive amount, as shown in Fig. 10.1.
2. By "shearing" the beam across its cross-section, as shown in Fig. 10.2.

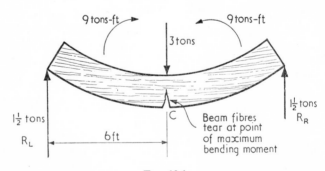

FIG. 10.1

These two tendencies to failure or collapse do of course occur simultaneously, but for a clearer understanding of each they will be considered separately.

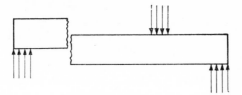

FIG. 10.2

Bending Moment

The degree of punishment in bending is measured as bending moment, and the amount of bending tendency is dependent obviously upon the loads and upon the distance between them.

For example, the beam shown in Fig. 10.1 tends to split in bending under the 3 ton load because the L.H. (left hand) reaction of 1½ tons, acting 6 ft to the left has a clockwise bending tendency of 1½ × 6 = 9 tons-ft, at the point where splitting of this type would most easily occur in this case.

If the beam had been of 20 ft span instead of only 6 ft the L.H. reaction (ignoring for a while the self weight of the beam) would still be only 1½ tons, but this time the bending tendency at the point of maximum stress would be 1½ × 10 = 15 tons-ft.

Reverting to the beam shown in Fig. 10.1, which we have seen has a clockwise bending tendency to the left of point *C* of 9 tons-ft, there is also an anticlockwise bending tendency to the right of *C* of 1½ × 6 = 9 tons-ft caused by the action of the R.H. (right hand) reaction. At *any point* along the span of a simple beam of this type supported at its ends the bending tendency to the left will always be clockwise, and that to the right anticlockwise but of the same amount. Thus at any point of such a beam the bending will be of the *sagging* type as shown in Fig. 10.3, and the fibres towards the lower face of the section will be subjected to tension.

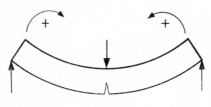

FIG. 10.3

There are types of beams that bend in the opposite way, for example a cantilever as shown in Fig. 10.4 has a *hogging* rather than a sagging tendency, and obviously the moments in this type must be anticlockwise to the left and clockwise to the right.

To distinguish between these two types of bending it is normal to describe sagging as positive, and hogging as negative.

From the foregoing example, which has been of the very simplest nature, it follows that bending moment may be described as the factor which measures the bending effect at any point of a beam's

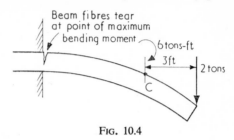

FIG. 10.4

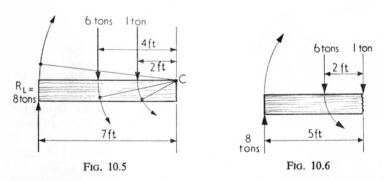

FIG. 10.5   FIG. 10.6

span due to a system of loading, and the bending moment in amount is found by taking the moments acting to the left *or* to the right of the point concerned. The beam discussed and shown in Fig. 10.1 had only one load acting to the left of the point *C* at which the bending moment was calculated; where there is more than one load on the portion of beam concerned—as for example in the portion of beam shown in Fig. 10.5—then taking moments to the left of point *C*, the reaction has a clockwise bending effect, and the two downward loads have anticlockwise bending tendency, so the net bending moment at *C* will be the difference between these two types of moment, or as it is most usually described "The algebraic sum of the moments to the left or to the right of the point."

Here, the L.H. reaction exerts a clockwise moment of 8 tons × 7 ft = 56 tons-ft about point *C*, and the downward loads exert moments in an anticlockwise direction of 6 tons × 4 ft = 24 tons-ft and 1 ton × 2 ft = 2 tons-ft, thus the bending moment at $C =$ + (8 × 7) — (6 × 4) — (1 × 2) = 56 — 24 — 2 = 30 tons-ft. The bending moment at the point of the 1 ton load in the above beam would be (8 tons × 5 ft) — (6 tons × 2 ft) = 40 — 12 = 28 tons-ft as shown in Fig. 10.6. Note that in this case the 1 ton load is ignored, as, passing through the point concerned, it does not exert a moment about that point.

Uniform Loading

The previous examples have been chosen so that all loads were point loads—that is to say the loading was considered to be applied

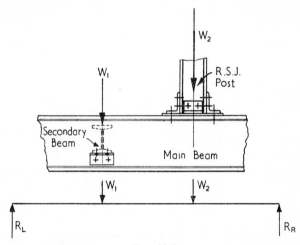

Fig. 10.7

at one definite point along the span. Loads in actual fact are rarely applied in this fashion to structural members, but many loads applied to beams approximate to point loading, and in design are considered as concentrated loads. The main beam shown in Fig. 10.7 for example carries the reaction from one secondary beam, and in addition has sitting on its top flange a short steel post; both these loads are applied to such a short length of the beam that they may be considered as point loads.

On the other hand, there are many cases where the loading is applied at a more or less uniform rate to the span of the beam. Such an example is found where a brick wall is carried on the top flange of a beam, or when a reinforced concrete slab sits upon a steel or R.C. beam.

It would be most uneconomical in design to treat such loads as being concentrated at their mid-point, since they do not punish the beam to anything like the same extent.

Where such uniform rate of loading occurs, as in the case of the portion of beam shown in Fig. 10.8 for example, only that portion

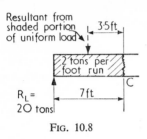

Resultant from shaded portion of uniform load

3·5 ft

2 tons per foot run

C

$R_L =$ 20 tons

7 ft

Fig. 10.8

of loading which lies to the left of the point C (shown shaded) need be considered when the moment at that point to the left is being calculated. The shaded portion of load is 2 tons × 7 = 14 tons, and its resultant lies halfway along its length (3·5 ft from C). Therefore the moment about C of the uniform load = 14 tons × 3·5 ft and the total bending moment at point C = (20 × 7) — (14 × 3·5) = 140 — 49 = 91 tons-ft.

Shearing Force

The effect of the reactions and other loads in causing bending moment has already been discussed briefly, and it has been observed that simple reactions (for example) cause much greater moment in long spans than in short ones.

In addition to bending, however, beams tend to shear or split vertically into two or more portions under load as shown in Fig. 10.9.

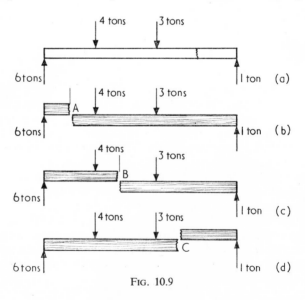

Fig. 10.9

Consider the portion of beam shown in Fig. 10.9(a). The loads tending to shear the beam are the two point loads acting downwards and the L.H. reaction acting upwards.

For simplicity of explanation the weight of the beam itself has been ignored.

Fig. 10.9(b) shows how the beam would tend to shear at point A. The only load to the left of A is the L.H. reaction (acting upwards) of 6 tons, and there is therefore a resultant force of 6 tons tending to shear the portion of beam to the left of A upwards as shown. Note that the loads to the right of A are 7 tons downward and re-action 1 ton upward, so that there is also a resultant of 6 tons tending to shear the portion of beam to the right of A downward.

This 6 tons upward to the left, and 6 tons downward to the right constitutes the shearing force at the point A.

It follows from the above that shear force may be described as the algebraic sum of the loads to the left or to the right of a point.

This type of shearing force, where the resultant shear is upwards to the left and downwards to the right, may be described as positive shear.

Consider now the point B as shown in Fig. 10.9(c). The resultant shear to the left is seen to be $6 - 4 = 2$ tons upward to the left, and $3 - 1 = 2$ tons downward to the right (again positive shear). At point C in Fig. 10.9(d), the shear to the left is $4 + 3 - 6 = 1$ ton down, and to the right = the R.H. reaction of 1 ton upward. This type of shear: down to the left and up to the right, is described as "negative shear."

The previous example of shear force ignored the weight of the beam and the only loading consisted of point loads. As shear force has been described as the algebraic summation of loads to the left (or to the right) of a point, then obviously the shear alters in such cases only where another point load occurs. When the loading is of a uniform nature however as in Fig. 10.10 then the shear force will vary at a uniform rate also, and a sudden jump in the value will only occur at the point of application of the one point load. The shear at point A (Fig. 10.10(a)) upward to the left will be for example 14 tons up $- 2$ tons down $= +12$ tons. Similarly the shear at point B (Fig. 10.10(b)) upward to the left is 14 tons up $- 4$ tons down $= 10$ tons (again positive).

The shear just to the left of C (Fig. 10.10(c)) $= 14 - 7 = 7$ tons positive, whilst just to the right of C when the 4 ton point load is included—it is 14 tons $- (7 + 4) = 3$ tons positive. Thus it will be seen that uniform loads cause gradual and uniform change of shear, whilst point loads bring about a sudden change in the value of the shear force.

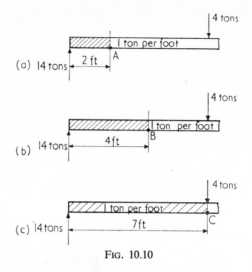

Fig. 10.10

Bending Moment and Shear Force Diagrams

Bending moment and shear force have been described in general terms and it will have been seen that the values of both vary at different points along the span.

It is often desirable to show this variation by means of a diagram which is really a graph, and these diagrams are called bending moment and shear force diagrams.

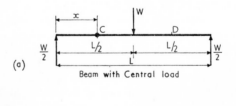

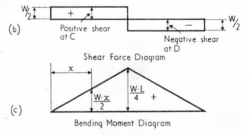

Fig. 10.11

The following examples will serve to show how the diagrams of this type may be constructed for simple and more complex cases.

Fig. 10.11(*a*) shows a simply supported beam of span *L* carrying one point load of *W* tons at the centre of the span. Since the loading is symmetrical the reactions must be equal to each other, and each reaction will be *W*/2 tons. Ignoring the self weight of the beam, at any point *C* at *x* ft from the left hand reaction, the shear force to the left will be simply the value of the L.H. reaction, i.e. *W*/2 tons upward to the left, and wherever point *C* lies between the L.H. end and the load, the shear will still be $+W/2$ tons.

Similarly at any point to the right of the load as at point *D*, the shear to the left of *D* is *W* tons downward and *W*/2 tons upward, which is equal to *W*/2 tons down to the left or *W*/2 tons up to the right (negative shear). These variations of the shear values are shown to scale on the shear force diagram (Fig. 10.11(*b*)). The vertical ordinate of the diagram at any point along the span shows the shear force at that point, and the diagram is drawn to two scales, a vertical scale of 1 in. = a suitable number of tons, and a horizontal scale of 1 in. = a suitable number of feet, being the same scale as that used in showing the span of the beam. Fig. 10.11(*c*) shows the variation of bending moment and constitutes a bending moment diagram.

Obviously the moment at each end is zero, and at any point *C* at *x* ft from the L.H. end the bending moment (summation of moments to the left) is simply $W/2 \times x = Wx/2$ tons-ft. This moment increases as *x* increases, and will reach a maximum amount of $W/2 \times L/2 = WL/4$ at the centre of span as shown.

Again the diagram is drawn horizontally to the same scale as the span of the beam, but this time vertically to a scale of 1 in. = a suitable number of tons-ft or tons-in., and the vertical ordinate at any point along the span represents the bending moment at that point.

Comparing the two diagrams, it will be seen that the bending moment everywhere on the span is positive, and that the shear force changes its type from positive to negative at the point along the span where the bending moment reaches its maximum amount.

Fig. 10.12 shows a simply supported beam loaded with one single non-central point load, at distance *a* from one end and at *b* from the other.

Taking moments about the L.H. end—

$$\text{R.H. reaction} \times L = W \times a$$

Thus　　　　R.H. reaction　　　$= Wa/L$

Similarly, taking moments about the R.H. end

$$\text{L.H. reaction} \times L = W \times b$$
$$\text{L.H. reaction} = Wb/L$$

At any point between the L.H. end and the point load, the shear.

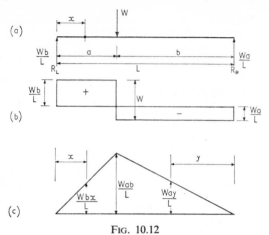

Fig. 10.12

to the left = the L.H. reaction = Wb/L (positive). Similarly, at any point between the load and the R.H. end, the shear to the right = the R.H. reaction of Wa/L (up to the right, thus negative shear). Thus the shear changes sign from positive to negative at the point load as in the previous example, and the S.F. diagram is as shown in Fig. 10.12(*b*).

As before, the bending moment is zero at the L.H. end, and at any point between that end and the load is equal to $R_L \times x = Wb/L \times x = Wbx/L$. This reaches a maximum value of Wab/L at the point load (where $x = a$). Also, at any point between the load and the R.H. end, at a distance of y from the R.H. reaction, the bending moment = R.H. reaction $\times y = Way/L$ and this also reaches a maximum at the point load (where $y = b$) of Wab/L.

The full bending moment diagram is thus a triangle with a maximum vertical height of Wab/L at the load, and the B.M. at any point along the span may thus be scaled from the diagram to the same scale which was used in setting up the maximum ordinate of Wab/L.

The next case will deal with a simply supported beam of span L carrying a uniformly distributed load of intensity w tons per foot run (Fig. 10.13). The span consists of L feet of load, and thus the total load is wL tons, and as the beam is symmetrical each reaction will be half of the total load and $R_L = R_R = wL/2$ tons.

Shear: The shear (up to the left) at a point just in the span and very very near to R_L is quite obviously simply the L.H. reaction of $wL/2$.

When the point concerned is, say, 1 ft from R_L however, the shear to the left (summation of loads to the left of the point) is then the

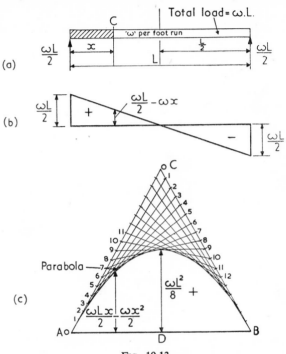

Fig. 10.13

algebraic sum of $wL/2$ upwards, and 1 ft of load (w) downwards $= wL/2 - w$.

Similarly when the point concerned is 2 ft from R_L

The shear up to the left

$$= \frac{wL}{2} \text{ upwards} - 2w \text{ (2 ft of load) downwards}$$

$$= \frac{wL}{2} - 2w$$

Putting this in general terms, the shear at any point C on the span at distance x from $RL = wL/2 - x$ ft of uniform load $= wL/2 - wx$. This will give a positive result wherever x is less than $L/2$, and a negative result where x exceeds $L/2$, so the shear will "change sign"

7—(T.779)

where $x = L/2$ (at the point of mid-span), and the S.F. diagram will be as shown in Fig. 10.13(b).

Referring again to Fig. 10.13(a), the bending moment at the L.H. end is again zero, and at a point 1 ft from R_L, the B.M. (summation of moment to the left) is simply the algebraic sum of

(*a*) the clockwise moment of the L.H. reaction ($wL/2 \times 1$);
(*b*) the anticlockwise moment from 1 ft of downward load $= w \times \frac{1}{2}$.

Thus the B.M. $= wL/2 - w/2$

If the bending moment is required at a point C, at x ft from R_L then the B.M. is the algebraic sum again of

(*a*) the clockwise moment of the L.H. reaction ($wL/2 \times x$);
(*b*) the anticlockwise moment of x ft of load (wx) . $x/2$.

$$\text{Thus the B.M.} = \frac{wLx}{2} - \frac{wx^2}{2}$$

This bending moment will be positive for any value of x, and will reach a maximum value when

$$x = L/2 \text{ (at mid-span) of } (wL/2 \times L/2) - \tfrac{1}{2}w(L/2)^2$$
$$= \frac{wL^2}{4} - \frac{wL^2}{8}$$
$$= \frac{wL^2}{8}$$

It should be most carefully noted that the maximum B.M. is $wL^2/8$, where w is the amount of uniform load per foot.

Sometimes it is more convenient to think in terms of the *total load* W (capital W), and in this case $W = wL$, and the maximum B.M. in terms of the total load will then be

$$\frac{wL \times L}{8} = \frac{WL}{8}$$

If the values of this B.M. at points along the span are plotted as a graph, the resulting B.M. diagram will be a parabola with a maximum ordinate of $wL^2/8$ or $WL/8$ as shown in Fig. 10.13(c). Where the diagram has to be drawn, it will be necessary only to draw a parabola having a central height of $WL/8$, and any other ordinates at point away from the centre may be scaled or calculated as desired. The construction of the parabola is clearly shown in Fig. 10.13(c). D is the mid-point of span AB, and the triangle ACB is drawn, of *twice* the height of the required parabola. The sides AC and BC

are each divided into any convenient number of parts (18 as shown in this case). Point 1 on *AC* is then joined to point 1 on *BC*, point 2 on *AC* joined to point 2 on *BC*, etc., as shown, and the parabola becomes clearly visible.

The student is advised at this stage to study carefully the shear force diagrams already drawn. From them, certain rules for drawing S.F. diagrams may be derived.

It will be noted that these diagrams are drawn on a horizontal base, and that upward loads (reactions) are projected upward on this base. Also at the point loads, the S.F. diagram drops vertically by the amount of the point load.

Where a uniform load occurs however, the S.F. diagram slopes down at a uniform rate, dropping for each foot of span an amount

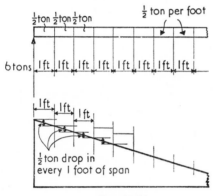

FIG. 10.14

equal to the amount of uniform load per foot as shown in Fig. 10.14. It will also be observed that in every case, the bending moment has been a maximum at the point where the shear force changes its sign. (Sometimes referred to as the point of zero shear.)

Bearing this in mind, it is common practice among students to draw the shear force diagram simply to discover where the maximum B.M. occurs. This is quite unnecessary, as will be seen from consideration of the two cases shown in Figs. 10.15 and 10.16.

In Fig. 10.15, the L.H. reaction is 11 tons, and the shear force will change sign at the point of maximum B.M. where the downward loads starting from the L.H. end just equal 11 tons.

From *A* to *C*, the downward uniform load is 4 ft at $\frac{1}{2}$ ton per ft $= 2$ tons. Then at the point load, there is a further drop of 7 tons, making a drop in the shear diagram from *A* to *C* of 9 tons.

Thus if *D* is the point of maximum B.M. (zero shear) then the portion of load shown shaded must $= 11 - 9 = 2$ tons, so that the downward loads up to D equal the L.H. reaction.

Thus, if the distance from C to D is x, then x ft at $\frac{1}{2}$ ton per ft must equal 2 tons: $\frac{1}{2}x = 2$. Thus $x = 4$ ft, and the maximum B.M. occurs at $4 + 4 = 8$ ft from R_L.

Similarly in the case shown in Fig. 10.16 the load from the L.H. end up to and including the 7 ton point load $= (4 \times \frac{1}{2}) + 7 = 9$

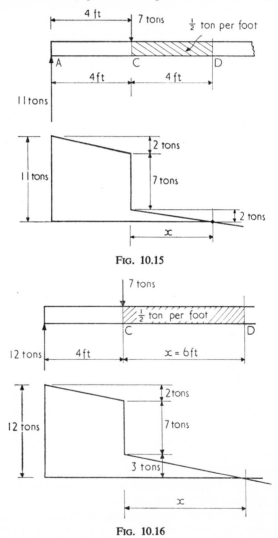

FIG. 10.15

FIG. 10.16

tons. Therefore a further $12 - 9 = 3$ tons of load is required beyond C to D, the point of maximum B.M.

Thus $$x \times \tfrac{1}{2} = 3 \text{ tons}$$

and $$x = \frac{3}{\tfrac{1}{2}} = 6 \text{ ft}$$

and the maximum B.M. occurs at point D which is $4 + 6 = 10$ ft from the L.H. end.

It will be seen that where the maximum B.M. occurs at a point on the span where the loading is uniform, the position of this point is such that the sum of the downward loads from the L.H. end exactly equals the L.H. reaction.

Similarly of course, the downward loads taken from the R.H. end will equal the R.H. reaction at this point.

When the loading includes point loading however, as it does in the example shown in Fig. 10.17, it may well be that the point at

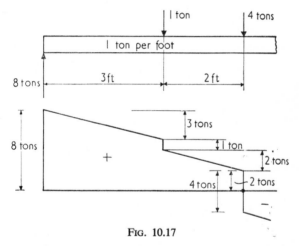

Fig. 10.17

which the bending moment is a maximum coincides with the position of a point load—and in the beam illustrated in Fig. 10.17 the maximum value occurs at the 4 ton load.

Summing up the loads (starting from the L.H. end) it will be seen that just to the left of the 4 ton load they are $(5 \times 1) + 1 = 6$ tons, that is just less than R_L.

Immediately to the right of the 4 ton load they add up to $(5 \times 1) + 1 + 4 = 10$ tons which is more than R_L.

The rule for finding the position of the maximum bending moment may therefore be stated as follows: Add the downward loads together, starting from one reaction to the point where they equal (or suddenly become greater than) that reaction. This is the point of zero shear, and the point of maximum B.M.

Cantilevers

A beam which is supported at one end only by being firmly built into a wall or which is held horizontally at one end only by other means, is called a cantilever. Fig. 10.18 shows such a cantilever *AB* having a length of L ft and loaded with one point load of W tons at the free end *B*.

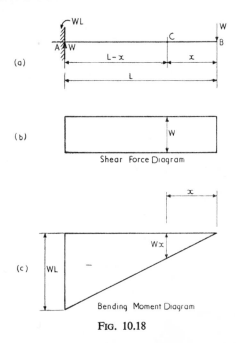

Fig. 10.18

The only downward load is W tons, so for equilibrium the L.H. upward reaction will also be W tons, but in addition, to prevent the beam from rotating, the wall or other form of restraint at the fixed end *A* must exert a moment of WL in an anticlockwise direction.

The shear at any point *C* between *A* and *B* (sum of the loads to the left or to the right of *C*) will be W tons down to the right, or W tons up to the left. This is positive shear, and the value remains the same at all points along the span, so that the shear force diagram is a rectangle as shown in Fig. 10.18(*b*).

The bending moment (taken as the moments to the right) at any point C, distance x ft from the free end B will be the downward load of W multiplied by x ft.

Thus the bending moment at any point $= Wx$ tons-ft. This is a negative or hogging bending moment, and its value varies directly as the value of x varies, so that the B.M. diagram will be a triangle as shown in Fig. 10.18(*c*).

The maximum value will occur at the fixed end when $x = L$, and its amount is WL tons-ft.

Note: The previous rule (page 187) for finding the position of maximum B.M. will not apply to cantilevers. In the case of cantilevers the maximum B.M. will always occur at the fixed end.

Fig. 10.19 shows a cantilever with a uniformly distributed load of w tons/ft run. The total load will be $w \times L = wL$ tons, and the upward reaction at A will also be wL tons.

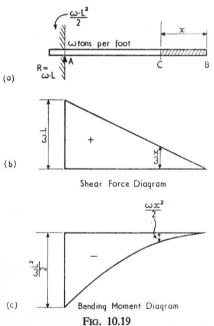

FIG. 10.19

The moment of the downward load wL about the support $A = wL \times L/2 = wL^2/2$ tons-ft.

Thus the wall (or other form of restraint) at A must exert an anti-clockwise moment of $wL^2/2$ on the beam to prevent its rotating under the couple formed by the upward reaction and the resultant of the downward load.

The shear at any point C at distance x from the free end will be the portion of load to the right of $C = x$ ft at w tons/ft $= wx$ tons (positive shear).

This varies at the same rate as x varies, and so the shear force diagram will be a triangle having a maximum value at the reaction (where $x = L$) of wL tons, as shown in Fig. 10.19(b).

Similarly the bending moment at C will be the moment (clockwise) of the portion of load to the right of $C = (wx) \, x/2 = wx^2/2$ tons-ft (negative or sagging moment).

This again reaches a maximum value at the fixed end A where $x = L$ of $wL^2/2$ tons-ft, and the rate of increase will be found to form a parabola as shown in the bending moment diagram in Fig. 10.19(c).

Note: If the total load W is used instead of the value of the load per ft run (w), then $W = wL$, and the maximum bending moment will be $WL/2$ tons-ft.

EXAMPLE 1

Draw the bending moment and shear force diagrams for the cantilever shown in Fig. 10.20 showing all important values.

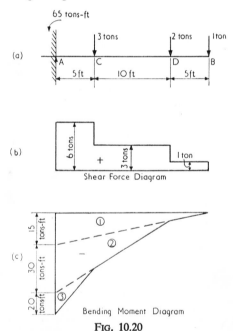

FIG. 10.20

Shear:

At any point between A and C, the shear downward to the right is the sum of the three downward loads = 6 tons positive.

Similarly between *C* and *D* the shear is the sum of the two loads to the right = 3 tons positive. Between *D* and the free end *B* the shear is the single load of 1 ton positive.

This is shown in the shear force diagram constructed in Fig. 10.20(*b*).

Bending moment:

The bending moment diagram is most easily drawn by treating the three loads separately; the 1 ton load produces a bending moment of $1 \times 20 = 20$ tons-ft at *A* and the B.M. diagram for this load alone is the triangle 1 shown in Fig. 10.20(*c*).

The 2 ton load causes a B.M. at *A* of $2 \times 15 = 30$ tons-ft, and the B.M. diagram for this load alone is the triangle 2.

Finally, the 3 ton load causes $3 \times 5 = 15$ tons-ft B.M. at *A* and the B.M. diagram for this load is the triangle 3.

As in fact all three loads are on the beam at the same time, then the final B.M. diagram is the sum of the three triangles 1, 2 and 3 as shown in Fig. 10.20(*c*).

EXAMPLE 2

Draw the bending moment and shear force diagrams for the beam loaded as shown in Fig. 10.21(*a*) showing all important values.

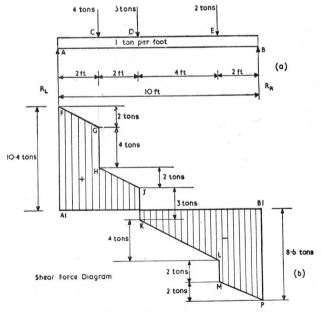

FIG. 10.21

Taking moments about A—

$$R_R \times 10 = (1 \times 10 \times 5) + (4 \times 2) + (3 \times 4) + (2 \times 8)$$
$$= 50 + 8 + 12 + 16 = 86$$
$$R_R = 86/10 = 8 \cdot 6 \text{ tons}$$

Thus $\qquad R_L = 10 + 4 + 3 + 2 - 8 \cdot 6 = 10 \cdot 4 \text{ tons}$

Note: It should be obvious to the reader by now that the shear diagrams represent all point loads as vertical lines—upward in the case of reactions, and downward in the case of downward loads.

Also downward uniform loads are shown as sloping lines (gradual change in the value of the shear force) and therefore the shear diagram may be plotted quickly from a horizontal base by merely plotting the loads in this way as they occur.

The horizontal base is shown as line *A*1–*B*1 in Fig. 10.21(*b*). The procedure is as follows—

1. Draw up from *A*1 the vertical reaction R_L of 10·4 tons (*A*1–*F*).

2. Draw the gradual change of 2 tons between *A* and *C* as the sloping line *F*–*G*.

3. Draw *G*–*H* of 4 tons vertically downward to represent the sudden change of shear at the 4 ton load at point *C*.

4. Draw the gradual change of 2 tons between *C* and *D* as the sloping line *H*–*J*.

5. Draw *J*–*K* of 3 tons vertically downward to represent the sudden change of shear at the 3 ton load at point *D*.

6. Draw the gradual change of 4 tons between *D* and *E* as the sloping line *K*–*L*.

7. Draw *L*–*M* of 2 tons vertically downward to represent the sudden change of shear at the 2 ton point load at *E*.

8. Draw the gradual change of 2 tons between *E* and *B* as the sloping line *M*–*P*.

9. Finally draw the vertical right hand reaction of 8·6 tons upward from *P* to join the horizontal base at *B*1.

Fig. 10.21(*b*) shows the construction of this shear force diagram, and the final diagram with its important values is shown in Fig. 10.22.

Bending moment:

The bending moment at any point or the maximum bending moment may be calculated in the usual way by taking moments to the left or to the right of that point, but if the final B.M. diagram is required (as it is in this example) then it is best drawn by constructing (*a*) the B.M. diagram for the uniform load, and (*b*) the B.M. diagram for the point loads alone and adding the two diagrams together.

The B.M. diagram for the uniform load is shown in Fig. 10.23(*a*) and the diagram for the point loads alone in Fig. 10.23(*b*).
The two diagrams are added as shown in Fig. 10.23(*c*).

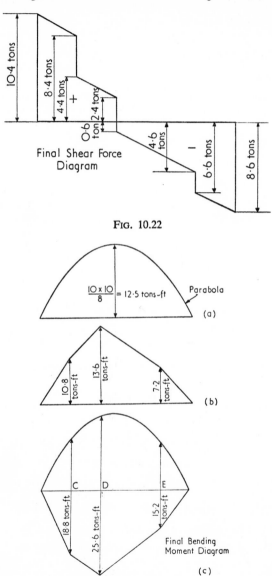

FIG. 10.22

FIG. 10.23

The reactions for the point loads alone are 5·4 tons at the L.H. support and 3·6 tons at the R.H. support.

$$\text{B.M. at } C = (10\cdot4 \times 2) - (2 \times 1) = 18\cdot8 \text{ tons-ft}$$
$$\text{B.M. at } D = (10\cdot4 \times 4) - (4 \times 2) - (4 \times 2)$$
$$= 25\cdot6 \text{ tons-ft (max.)}$$
$$\text{B.M. at } E = (8\cdot6 \times 2) - (2 \times 1) = 15\cdot2 \text{ tons-ft.}$$

EXAMPLE 3

Draw the shear force diagram for the beam shown in Fig. 10.24, and calculate the value of the maximum B.M. Determine also the B.M. at a point *c* at 5 ft from the L.H. reaction.

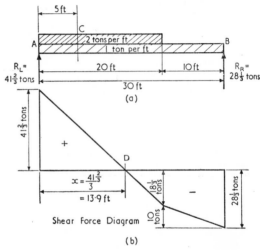

FIG. 10.24

Taking moments about A:

$$R_R \times 30 = (1 \times 30 \times 15) + (2 \times 20 \times 10)$$
$$= 450 + 400 = 850$$

Thus $R_R = 850/30 = 28\cdot34 \text{ tons}$

Thus $R_L = 30 + 40 - 28\cdot34 = 41\cdot66 \text{ tons}$

Maximum B.M. will occur at x ft from A where

$$x \times 3 \text{ tons per ft} = \text{L.H. reaction of } 41\cdot66$$

Thus $$x = \frac{41\cdot66}{3} = 13\cdot9 \text{ ft}$$

Maximum bending moment at D

$$= (41 \cdot 66 \times 13 \cdot 9) - (41 \cdot 66 \times 6 \cdot 95)$$
$$= (579) - (289 \cdot 5)$$
$$= 289 \cdot 5 \text{ tons-ft}$$

Or taking moments to the right,
Maximum bending moment at D

$$= (28 \cdot 33 \times 16 \cdot 1) - (16 \cdot 1 \times 8 \cdot 05) - (12 \cdot 2 \times 3 \cdot 05)$$
$$= 455 - (129 \cdot 5 + 37 \cdot 2)$$
$$= 455 - 166 \cdot 5 = 289 \cdot 5 \text{ tons-ft.}$$

Bending moment at C, 5 ft from R_L

$$\text{B.M.} = (41 \cdot 66 \times 5) - (5 \times 3 \times 2 \cdot 5)$$
$$= 208 \cdot 3 - 37 \cdot 5$$
$$= 170 \cdot 8 \text{ tons-ft}$$

If a bending moment diagram is required, bending moment values may be calculated at several points of the span and these values drawn to scale vertically from a horizontal line representing the span of the beam. By joining the tops of these lines a bending moment diagram is obtained.

Example 4

Draw the shear force diagram for the loaded beam shewn in Fig. 10.25, and determine the position and amount of the maximum bending moment.

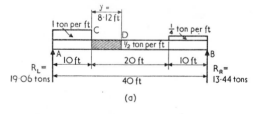

(a)

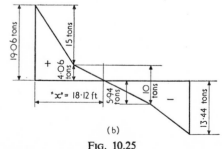

(b)

Fig. 10.25

Taking moments about R_L

$$40\,R_R = (\tfrac{1}{2} \times 40 \times 20) + (1 \times 10 \times 5) + (\tfrac{1}{4} \times 10 \times 35)$$

$$= 400 + 50 + 87{\cdot}5 = 537{\cdot}5$$

$$R_R = \frac{537{\cdot}5}{40} = 13{\cdot}44 \text{ tons}$$

Position of maximum B.M.:

At point C, 10 ft from L.H end, downward load from L.H. end = 15 tons. Maximum B.M. will occur where this has increased to 19·06 tons. Thus the maximum B.M. will occur at point D where the amount of load between C and D (shown shaded) = 19·06 − 15 = 4·06 tons.

Thus distance $Y \times \tfrac{1}{2}$ ton/ft = 4·06

Therefore
$$Y = \frac{4{\cdot}06}{\tfrac{1}{2}} = 8{\cdot}12 \text{ ft}$$

Maximum B.M. occurs at D at 18·12 ft from L.H. end

$$\text{Maximum B.M.} = (19{\cdot}06 \times 18{\cdot}12) - (15 \times 13{\cdot}12)$$
$$- (8{\cdot}12 \times \tfrac{1}{2} \times 4{\cdot}06)$$
$$= 345{\cdot}36 - (196{\cdot}8 + 16{\cdot}48)$$
$$= 132{\cdot}1 \text{ tons-ft}$$

Check on maximum B.M. taking moments to the right of D

$$\text{Maximum B.M.} = (13{\cdot}44 \times 21{\cdot}88) - (\tfrac{3}{4} \times 10 \times 16{\cdot}88)$$
$$- (11{\cdot}88 \times \tfrac{1}{2} \times 5{\cdot}94)$$
$$= 294{\cdot}07 - (126{\cdot}6 + 35{\cdot}28)$$
$$= 132{\cdot}2 \text{ tons-ft}$$

Example 5

Draw the shear force and bending moment diagrams for the beam shown in Fig. 10.26, and determine the position and amount of the maximum bending moment.

Taking moments about A

$$R_R \times 6 = (4 \times 2) + (5 \times 4) + (2 \times 8) = 8 + 20 + 16 = 44$$

Thus
$$R_R = \frac{44}{6} = 7\tfrac{1}{3} \text{ tons}$$

and
$$R_L = 11 - R_R = 3\tfrac{2}{3} \text{ tons}$$

The shear force diagram is as shown in Fig. 10.25(b)

B.M. at the 4 ton load $= 3\frac{2}{3} \times 2 = 7\frac{1}{3}$ tons-ft $\qquad$ (+)

B.M. at 5 ton load $\quad = (3\frac{2}{3} \times 4) - (4 \times 2) = 6\frac{2}{3}$ tons-ft $\quad$ (+)

B.M. at R.H. reaction $= (2 \times 2) = 4$ tons-ft $\qquad$ (−)

The bending moment diagram is as shown in Fig. 10.26(c).

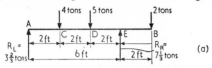

(a)

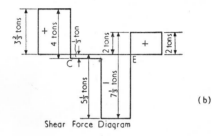

Shear Force Diagram

(b)

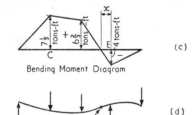

Bending Moment Diagram

(c)

(d)

Point of contraflexure

FIG. 10.26

Note that due to the overhanging of the R.H. end, part of the beam is subjected to negative bending moment, and this changes to positive moment at the point of contraflexure.

There are therefore two points of zero shear: one at *C* which marks the point of maximum positive moment, and one at *E* where the maximum negative moment occurs. The absolute maximum bending moment is thus $7\frac{1}{3}$ tons-ft at *C*, and the shape of the bent beam is as shown in Fig. 10.26(d).

EXAMPLE 6

Draw the shear force and bending moment diagrams for the beam shown in Fig. 10.27 and determine the position and amount of the maximum bending moment.

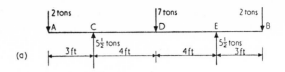

(a)

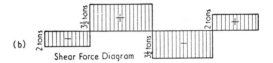

(b)

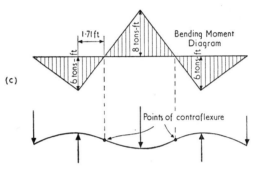

(c)

FIG. 10.27

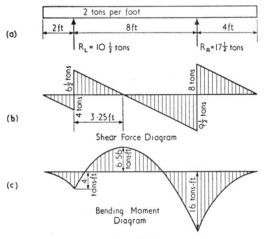

FIG. 10.28

Since the loading and the beam are symmetrical, the reactions are each equal to $5\frac{1}{2}$ tons.

$$\text{B.M. at } D = (5 \cdot 5 \times 4) - (2 \times 7)$$
$$= 22 - 14$$
$$= 8 \text{ tons-ft} \qquad (+)$$
$$\text{B.M. at } C = -2 \times 3$$
$$= -6 \text{ tons-ft} \qquad (-)$$

EXAMPLE 7

A beam 14 ft long carrying a uniformly distributed load of 2 tons per foot run cantilevers over both supports as shown in Fig. 10.28(*a*).

The shear force and bending moment diagrams are given in Fig. 10.28(*b*) and (*c*). The student can check that the reactions are $10\frac{1}{2}$ tons and $17\frac{1}{2}$ tons respectively. The maximum positive bending moment occurs at $5\frac{1}{4}$ ft from the left end of the beam and is:

$$(10\tfrac{1}{2} \times 3\tfrac{1}{4}) - (2 \times 5\tfrac{1}{4} \times 5\tfrac{1}{4}/2)$$
$$= (10\tfrac{1}{2} \times 3\tfrac{1}{4}) - (10\tfrac{1}{2} \times 2\tfrac{5}{8})$$
$$= 34 \cdot 125 - 27 \cdot 5625$$
$$= 6 \cdot 56 \text{ tons-ft approximately}$$

The maximum negative bending moment occurs over the right hand support and is $8 \text{ tons} \times 2 \text{ ft} = 16$ tons-ft.

By calculating several other bending moment values the diagram can be constructed as shown in Fig. 10·28(*c*).

EXAMPLE 8

A beam carries a triangular shaped load *ABC* of total amount 12 tons as indicated in Fig. 10.29. Determine the position and amount of the maximum bending moment.

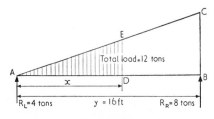

FIG. 10.29

The reaction at A can be found by assuming the whole of the load of 12 tons acting at the centroid of the triangle, $5\frac{1}{3}$ ft from end B.

$$16\, R_L = 12 \times 5\tfrac{1}{3}$$

$$R_L = 4 \text{ tons}$$

Therefore $R_R = 8$ tons

The shear force will be zero (and the bending moment will be its maximum value) at point D where the load of the shaded triangle ADE equals 4 tons, i.e. the reaction at A.

We can assume the load of 12 tons to be represented by the area ABC and the load of 4 tons to be represented by the area ADE. Triangles ADE and ABC are similar, and if x and y are two corresponding sides of two similar figures of areas X and Y,

then $$\frac{x^2}{y^2} = \frac{X}{Y}$$

Therefore $$\frac{x^2}{16^2} = \frac{4}{12}$$

$$x^2 = 85 \cdot 33$$

$$x = 9 \cdot 24 \text{ ft}$$

The centre of gravity of the load of 4 tons is at one-third of $9 \cdot 24$ ft from D, therefore the maximum bending moment is:

$$(4 \times 9 \cdot 24) - (4 \times 3 \cdot 08)$$

$$= 24 \cdot 64 \text{ tons-ft}$$

SUMMARY

Shear force at a point in the span of a beam may be described as the algebraic sum of the loads to the left or to the right of the point.

To determine the position of the maximum bending moment in a beam simply supported at its two ends, add together the downward loads starting from one reaction to the point where they equal (or suddenly become greater than) that reaction. This is the point of zero shear and the point of maximum bending moment.

The maximum bending moment is the algebraic sum of the moments of the loads and reaction acting to *one side* of the point of maximum bending moment.

The maximum bending moment in cantilevers will always occur at the fixed end and equals the sum of the moments of all the loads about the fixed end.

EXERCISE 10

Questions 1 to 14. Calculate the reactions, determine the position and amount of the maximum bending moment for the beams shown in Figs. 10.30 to 10.43.

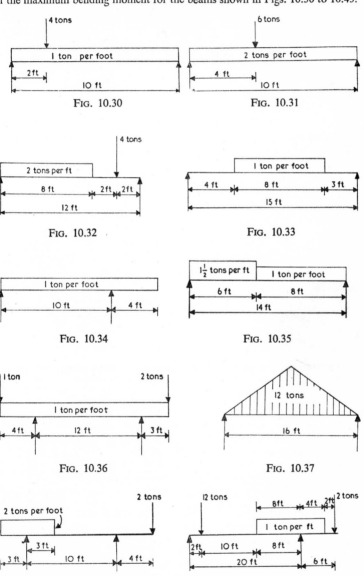

FIG. 10.30

FIG. 10.31

FIG. 10.32

FIG. 10.33

FIG. 10.34

FIG. 10.35

FIG. 10.36

FIG. 10.37

FIG. 10.38

FIG. 10.39

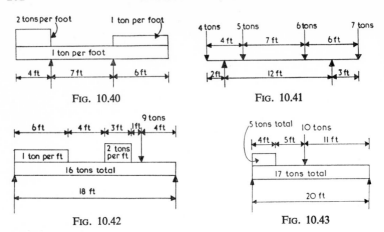

FIG. 10.40

FIG. 10.41

FIG. 10.42

FIG. 10.43

15. Fig. 10.44 shows the shear force diagram for a loaded beam. Sketch the beam, showing the loading conditions, and calculate the maximum positive and negative bending moments.

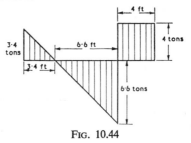

FIG. 10.44

16. A steel beam spans 16 ft, and carries on its whole length a brick wall 9 in. thick and 10 ft high. The brickwork weighs 120 lb/cu ft, and the self weight of beam and casing is estimated as being 0·57 tons. What is the maximum bending moment on the beam?

17. A steel beam is as shown in Fig. 10.45. The portion between supports A and B carries a uniform load of 1 ton/ft and there are point loads at the free ends as shown. What is the length L in feet between A and B if the B.M. at a point C midway between these supports is just zero?

18. For the beam loaded as shown in Fig. 10.46: (*a*) calculate the reactions; (*b*) determine the position and amount of the maximum positive and maximum negative B.M.s.

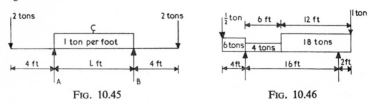

FIG. 10.45

FIG. 10.46

19. Referring to Fig. 10.47, calculate (*a*) end reactions; (*b*) position and amount of maximum B.M.

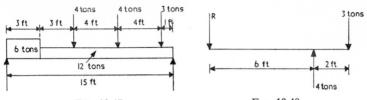

FIG. 10.47   FIG. 10.48

20. Calculate the maximum bending moment in Fig. 10.48.

21. Determine the position and amount of the maximum shear force and B.M. in Fig. 10.49.

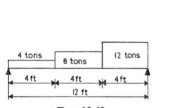

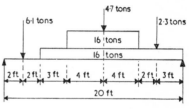

FIG. 10.49   FIG. 10.50

22. Referring to Fig. 10.50, (*a*) calculate the end reactions; (*b*) determine the position and amount of the maximum B.M.

23. For the cantilever loaded as shown in Fig. 10.51, calculate—(*a*) the B.M. at the 4 ton load; (*b*) the B.M. at the point *D*; (*c*) the maximum B.M.

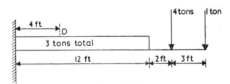

FIG. 10.51

24. Referring to Fig. 10.52, calculate the B.M. (*a*) at point 1, (*b*) at point 2, (*c*) at the support.

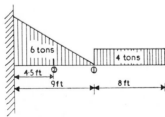

FIG. 10.52

25. A cantilever *AB* is rigidly fixed at *A* and carries a triangular load of 8 tons, as shown in Fig. 10.53. Determine, (*a*) the B.M. at point *C*, (*b*) the maximum B.M.

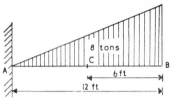

FIG. 10.53

26. Calculate the maximum bending moment for the cantilever shown in Fig. 10.54.

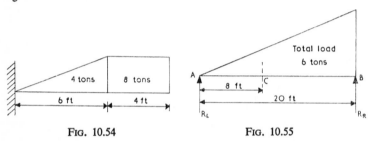

FIG. 10.54   FIG. 10.55

27. A steel joist simply supported at its ends carries a load of varying intensity as shown (Fig. 10.55). Determine—(*a*) the end reactions R_L and R_R; (*b*) the maximum B.M.; (*c*) the B.M. at point *C*.

28. A steel post cantilevers vertically carrying two point loads as shown in Fig. 10.56. Calculate the B.M. at (*a*) the 3·5 ton load; (*b*) the base; (*c*) 3 ft from the base.

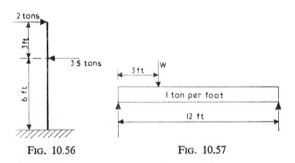

FIG. 10.56   FIG. 10.57

29. A steel beam loaded as shown in Fig. 10.57 has a maximum bending moment (occurring at the point load) of 36 tons-ft. What is the value *W* tons of the point load?

30. In the beam shown in Fig. 10.58, the maximum bending moment occurs at the supports R_L and R_R and the bending moment at the central 2 ton load is zero. What is the length in feet of the span L?

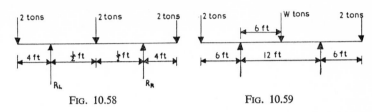

FIG. 10.58   FIG. 10.59

31. In the beam shown in Fig. 10.59, the maximum negative bending moment is twice the amount of the maximum positive bending moment. What is the value in tons of the central load W?

32. Calculate for the steel beam shown in Fig. 10.60: (a) the bending moment at point C; (b) the bending moment at point D; (c) the maximum bending moment.

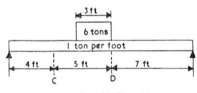

FIG. 10.60

33. Derive an expression for the beam as shown in Fig. 10.61 for (a) the maximum bending moment; (b) the B.M. at C.

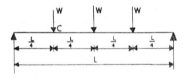

FIG. 10.61

CHAPTER 11

Properties of Sections—Moment of Inertia

THE previous chapter has been concerned with estimating the punishing forces and moments which loading induce in a beam. The beam itself must of course be made just strong enough to withstand these punishing effects with a reasonable factor of safety, and the strength of the beam or its degree of resistance to bending moment and shear force is built up in terms of—

(*a*) the shape and size of the beam's section;
(*b*) the strength of the particular material the beam is made of.

The final degree of "defence" or resistance will be measured in units which take into account both of these two factors, but for a clearer understanding they will be treated separately to begin with, and the present chapter deals with (*a*) only, and will show how the shape or profile of a beam's section affects its strength.

The properties which various sections have by virtue of their shape alone are—

1. Cross-sectional area.
2. Position of centre of gravity or centroid.
3. Moment of inertia.
4. Section modulus.
5. Radius of gyration.

The properties *section modulus* and *radius of gyration* will be considered later in Chapters 12 and 16 respectively.

The cross-sectional area should need no description and may be calculated with ease for most structural members.

Centres of gravity have been dealt with in Chapter 6. The position of the centre of gravity, or, more accurately, the centroid of the section, is of great importance in beam design for (as will be seen later), the portion of section *above* this centroid performs a different function from that portion of area *below* the centroid. It should be remembered that—

1. Where a shape has an axis of symmetry, the centroid lies on this axis.

2. Where a shape has two axes of symmetry then the centroid is at the intersection of the two axes.

Note that the two axes of symmetry marked $X–X$ and $Y–Y$ in Fig.
11.1(a) and (b) are also called *principal axes* of the sections.

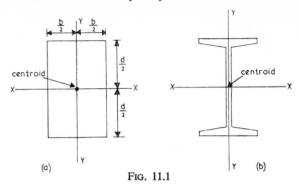

(a)

FIG. 11.1

Moment of Inertia

The moment of inertia or the second moment of area of a shape
is a property which measures the *efficiency* of that shape as regards
its resistance to bending.

Other factors besides shape enter of course into the building up
of a beam's resistance to bending moment; the material of which
a beam is made has a very obvious effect on its strength, but this is
allowed for in other ways, and the moment of inertia takes no regard of
the strength of the material; it measures only the manner in which the
geometric properties or shape of a section affect its value as a beam.

A beam such as the rolled steel joist shown in Fig. 11.2 may of
course in theory be used with the web vertical or with the web
horizontal, and it will offer much more resistance to bending when
fixed as in (a) than when as in (b).

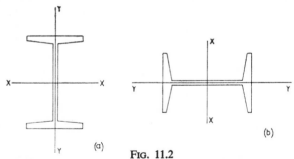

(a)   (b)

FIG. 11.2

This is because the moment of inertia about the $X–X$ axis of
bending is larger than the moment of inertia about the $Y–Y$ axis.

These axes ($X–X$ and $Y–Y$) are termed the "principal axes" and they are in fact axes which intersect at the centroid of the section concerned. It is mainly for this reason that we need to be able to calculate the position of the centroid, as without knowing its position we should be unable to determine the values of the moments of inertia.

It will normally be necessary then to calculate the moments of inertia about both these principal axes, and these are usually described as I_{xx} and I_{yy}, the moments of inertia about the X–X and Y–Y axes respectively.

The manner in which the " build up" of a shape affects its strength against bending must—to be understood completely—involve the use of calculus, but to the architectural student whose knowledge of

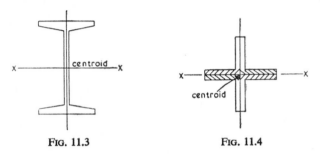

FIG. 11.3   FIG. 11.4

higher mathematics is usually limited, it may still be made reasonably clear from fairly simple considerations.

The term moment of inertia is itself responsible for a certain amount of confusion in the minds of architectural students. Inertia suggests laziness in some ways, whereas in fact the true meaning of inertia may be described as the resistance which a body makes to any forces or moments which attempt to change its shape (or its motion in the case of a moving body). A beam tends to change its shape when loaded, and inertia is the internal resistance with which the beam opposes this change of shape. The moment of inertia is a measure of the resistance which the section can supply in terms of its shape alone.

GOOD AND BAD BEAM SHAPES. In order to make the best use of the beam material the "shape" of the section has to be chosen with care. Certain shapes are better able to resist bending than others, and in general it may be stated that a shape will be more efficient when the greater part of its area is as far as possible away from its centroid.

The rolled steel joist (R.S.J.) shown in Fig. 11.3 for example has its flanges (which comprise the greater part of its area) well away from the centroid and the axis of bending X–X, and is in consequence an excellent shape for resisting bending.

Fig. 11.4 shows a shape built up by riveting together four angles. The bulk of its area (shown shaded) is situated *near to* the centroid, and the section is not a good one from the point of view of resistance to bending about the *X–X* axis.

If the same four angles are arranged as shown in Fig. 11.5 however, then the mass of the area has been moved away from the axis of bending *X–X*, and the section—which now resembles roughly an R.S.J. form is a good one, with a high resistance to bending.

When again the same four angles are used with a plate placed between them as in Fig. 11.6, the flanges are moved even further from the neutral axis, and the efficiency of the shape is much greater.

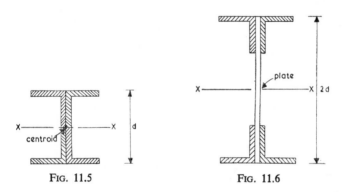

FIG. 11.5   FIG. 11.6

Large deep girders are built up in this way when very heavy loads have to be supported.

When a shape such as that shown in Fig. 11.5 is being designed, it will be found that doubling the area of the *flange* will approximately double the flange's efficiency, but doubling the depth *d* as in Fig. 11.6 will increase the efficiency by 4, i.e. 2^2. It may be said then that the efficiency of the flange varies directly as its area and as the square of its distance from the centroid.

MOMENT OF INERTIA OR SECOND MOMENT OF A SECTION. In order to measure the increase in efficiency of a section as its area and depth increase, the second moment of area or moment of inertia is calculated, and this property does in fact measure both the direct increase in area and the square of the increase in depth.

CALCULATION OF MOMENT OF INERTIA. To determine the moment of inertia of the rectangle shown in Fig. 11.7, it will be necessary to divide the shape into a number of strips of equal area as shown.

The area of each strip will be multiplied by the square of the distance of its centroid from the centroid of the whole section, thus in fact assessing its second moment or in other words forming a factor which measures its area directly and the square of its distance from the axis of bending.

The sum of all such products $a \times y^2$ will be the second moment or moment of inertia of the whole shape about the axis X–X.

Area $a \times y^2$ = second moment of area or moment of inertia of the shaded strip about axis X–X. The sum of all such products equals total I_{xx} of section.

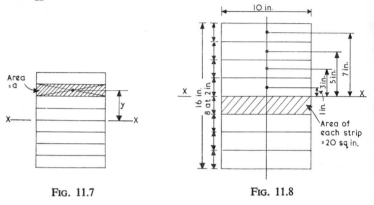

FIG. 11.7　　　　　　　FIG. 11.8

Assume a rectangle to be as shown in Fig. 11.8, 10 in. wide and 16 in. in depth. Fig. 11.8 shows the section divided into 8 strips each 2 in. deep, each strip having an area of 20 in.^{2}

The sum of all the products ay^2

$$= (2 \times 20 \times 7^2) + (2 \times 20 \times 5^2)$$
$$+ (2 \times 20 \times 3^2) + (2 \times 20 \times 1^2)$$
$$= 1{,}960 + 1{,}000 + 360 + 40$$
$$= 3{,}360 \text{ in.}^4 \text{ units}$$

This is the approximate value of the I_{xx}, or moment of inertia about the X–X axis, but the exact value of this factor will of course depend upon the number of strips into which the shape is divided. To obtain a more accurate result the same figure will now be divided into 16 strips as shown in Fig. 11.9.

The area of each of the 16 strips will now be 10 in.^{2} and the value of the second moment of area or I_{xx} will be

$$(2 \times 10 \times 7 \cdot 5^2) + (2 \times 10 \times 6 \cdot 5^2) + (2 \times 10 \times 5 \cdot 5^2)$$
$$+ (2 \times 10 \times 4 \cdot 5^2) + (2 \times 10 \times 3 \cdot 5^2) + (2 \times 10 \times 2 \cdot 5^2)$$
$$+ (2 \times 10 \times 1 \cdot 5^2) + (2 \times 10 \times 0 \cdot 5^2)$$
$$I_{xx} = 1{,}125 + 845 + 605 + 405 + 245 + 125 + 45 + 5$$
$$= 3{,}400 \text{ in.}^4 \text{ units}$$

This result (3,400 in.[4] units) based on 16 strips is very near to an exact value, but in fact the value increases and approaches the figure 3,413 in.[4] units as the number of strips increases to infinity. It can be shown that if b is the width of the rectangle and d is the depth, then the exact value of $I_{xx} = b \cdot d^3/12$ which in the case shown above is $\dfrac{10 \times 16^3}{12}$ or 3,413 in.[4] units.

The units of the answer are important, and it should be appreciated that as an area (in.[2]) has been multiplied by a distance squared (y^2),the

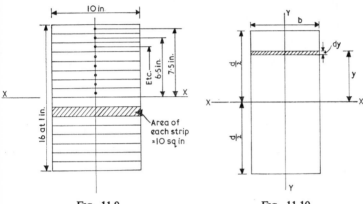

FIG. 11.9   FIG. 11.10

answer is the second moment of area or simply moment of inertia of the shape, and is measured in in.[4] units.

Exact value of $bd^3/12 = I_{xx}$ of rectangle: For those students who have an elementary knowledge of calculus, the foregoing approximate derivation of $bd^3/12$ will appear somewhat lengthy, and the exact value is obtained by integrating as follows. Consider a small strip of area of breadth b and depth dy at a distance of y from the neutral axis as shown in Fig. 11.10. The second moment of area of this strip (shown shaded) is

$$(\text{its area}) \times (y)^2 = b \cdot dy \cdot y^2 = b \cdot y^2 \cdot dy$$

The second moment of half of the rectangle is the sum of all such quantities $by^2 dy$ between the limits of $y = 0$ and $y = d/2$.

$$I_{xx} \text{ of half rectangle} = \int_0^{d/2} by^2 \, dy = {}_0^{d/2}\left[\frac{b \cdot y^3}{3}\right] = \frac{b \cdot d^3}{24}$$

Thus the I_{xx} of the complete rectangle $= \dfrac{bd^3}{24} \times 2 = \dfrac{b \cdot d^3}{12}$

Similarly of course, the I_{yy} of the rectangle $= \dfrac{d \cdot b^3}{12}$

The values of the moments of inertia of a number of common shapes are listed below for reference (Fig. 11.11).

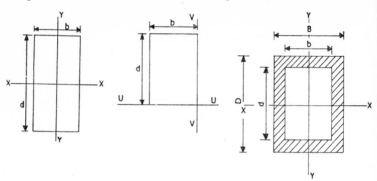

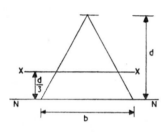

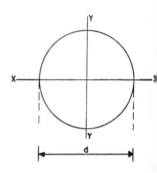

FIG. 11.11

Rectangle, about neutral axes:

$$I_{xx} = bd^3/12$$
$$I_{yy} = db^3/12$$

Rectangle, about one edge:

$$I_{uu} = bd^3/3$$
$$I_{vv} = db^3/3$$

Hollow rectangular shape:

$$I_{xx} = \tfrac{1}{12}(BD^3 - bd^3)$$
$$I_{yy} = \tfrac{1}{12}(DB^3 - db^3)$$

Triangle:

$$I_{xx} \text{ about neutral axis} = bd^3/36$$
$$I_{nn} \text{ about base} = bd^3/12$$

Circle:

$$I_{xx} = I_{yy} = \frac{\pi d^4}{64}$$

Principle of Parallel Axes

Fig. 11.12 shows a simple rectangular section of size $b \times d$. The I_{xx} of the rectangle is of course as previously shown $bd^3/12$. It will be seen however that there are times when the moment of inertia of the rectangle about some other parallel axis such as Z–Z is required, and the I_{zz} will obviously be greater than the I_{xx}, since larger distances are involved in the summation AH^2.

The rule for use in these cases may be stated as follows—

To find the moment of inertia of any shape about an axis Z–Z, parallel to the neutral axis X–X and at a perpendicular distance of

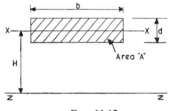

FIG. 11.12

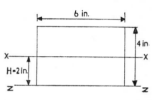

FIG. 11.13

H away from the neutral axis, the amount $A \cdot H^2$ (area of shape $\times$ distance H squared) must be added to I_{xx}.

For example, in the case of the rectangle shown in Fig. 11.13,

the $$I_{xx} = bd^3/12 = \frac{6 \times 4^3}{12} = 32 \text{ in.}^4 \text{ units}$$

The I_{zz} about the base (where $H = 2$ in.)

$$= I_{xx} + AH^2 = 32 + (24 \times 2^2)$$

$$= 32 + 96$$

$$= 128 \text{ in.}^4 \text{ units}$$

Note. This particular case could have been derived directly from the formula of $bd^3/3$ given in case 2 of Fig. 11.11.

$bd^3/3$ being in this example $\dfrac{6 \times 4^3}{3} = 128 \text{ in.}^4 \text{ units}$

Moments of Inertia of Steel Girder Shapes

The principle of parallel axes may be used to calculate the approximate values of the moments of inertia of joists and other structural sections. For example, the R.S.J. or B.S.B. (British

Standard Beam) shown in Fig. 11.14 consists of three rectangles, ignoring the tapering of the flanges, etc. It should be noted that for structural steel sections, the moments of inertia can be found tabulated in handbooks. Examples of such tables are given on pages 253 and 255 and the given moments of inertia take into

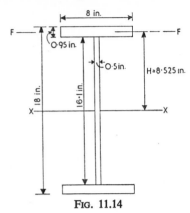

FIG. 11.14

account the tapering of the flanges, etc. Some examining bodies, however, require students to calculate the moments of inertia of shapes similar to Fig. 11.14 and so an 18 in. × 8 in. × 80 lb B.S.B. will be taken as an example.

In structural tables the average thickness of flange is given as 0·95 in. and the thickness of the web as 0·5 in.

The web has its centroid on the $X–X$ axis of the joist and the I_{xx} of the web thus equals

$$\frac{0·5 \times 16·1^3}{12} = 174 \text{ in.}^4$$

The moment of inertia of one flange about *its own axis* ($F–F$) is

$$\frac{8 \times 0·95^3}{12} = 0·57 \text{ in.}^4$$

and from the principle of parallel axes, the I_{xx} of the one flange is—

$$I_{xx} = 0·57 + (8 \times 0·95 \times 8·525^2)$$
$$= 553 \text{ in.}^4 \text{ approximately}$$

The total I_{xx} of the two flanges plus the web is—

$$\text{Total } I_{xx} = 174 + 2(553)$$
$$= 1,280 \text{ in.}^4$$

(Referring to structural tables it will be seen that the exact I_{xx} of an 18 in. × 8 in. × 80 lb B.S.B. is 1,292·07 in.^{4})

An alternative method of calculating the moment of inertia about X–X is to calculate the I_{xx} of rectangle $ABCD$ and subtract the I_{xx} of the two rectangles $EFGH$ (Fig. 11.15).

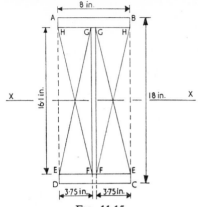

FIG. 11.15

Thus,

$$\text{total } I_{xx} = \frac{8 \times 18^3}{12} - \frac{2(3.75 \times 16.1^3)}{12}$$
$$= 3,888 - 2,608$$
$$= 1,280 \text{ in.}^4$$

Note. Particular care should be taken in using this method of the subtraction of moments of inertia to see that all the rectangles concerned have axis X–X as their common neutral axis.

The I_{yy} of the above mentioned joist may most easily be calculated by adding the I_{yy}s of the three rectangles of which the joist consists as shown in Fig. 11.16.

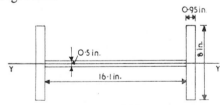

FIG. 11.16

$$I_{yy} = \frac{0.95 \times 8^3}{12} + \frac{0.95 \times 8^3}{12} + \frac{16.1 \times 0.5^3}{12}$$
$$= 40.5 + 40.5 + 0.17$$
$$= (81.17) \text{ in.}^4$$

Compare with the exact value for an 18 in. $\times$ 8 in. $\times$ 80 lb of

69·43 in.⁴ as given in Table 12.1B, where the tapering of the flanges, etc., is taken into account.

The method shown above is, however, accurate when sections are built up by welding together rectangular cross-section plates.

Miscellaneous Examples. Moments of Inertia

EXAMPLE 1

A steel tee section is 6 in. × 6 in. × 1 in. as shown in Fig. 11.17. Calculate the I_{xx}.

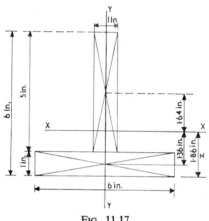

FIG. 11.17

Taking moments about the base to determine the position of the neutral axis X–X:

$$x \times 11 = (5 \times 3\tfrac{1}{2}) + (6 \times \tfrac{1}{2})$$

$$x = \frac{17 \cdot 5 + 3}{11}$$

$$= 1 \cdot 86 \text{ in.}$$

I_{xx} of vertical rectangle

$$= \frac{1 \times 5^3}{12} + (5 \times 1 \cdot 64^2) = 10 \cdot 41 + 13 \cdot 45$$

$$= 23 \cdot 86 \text{ in.}^4 \text{ units}$$

I_{xx} of horizontal table

$$= \frac{6 \times 1^3}{12} + (6 \times 1 \cdot 36^2) = 0 \cdot 5 + 11 \cdot 1$$

$$= 11 \cdot 6 \text{ in.}^4 \text{ units}$$

Total $I_{xx} = 23 \cdot 86 + 11 \cdot 6 = 35 \cdot 46 \text{ in.}^4 \text{ units}$

EXAMPLE 2

Calculate the I_{xx} and I_{yy} of the section shown in Fig. 11.18. Total area = $4 + 4 + 8 = 16$ sq in.

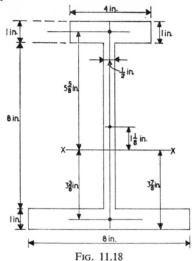

FIG. 11.18

Taking moments about the base to find the distance x to the neutral axis.

$$16 \times x = (8 \times 1 \times \tfrac{1}{2}) + (8 \times \tfrac{1}{2} \times 5) + (4 \times 1 \times 9\tfrac{1}{2})$$
$$= 4 + 20 + 38 = 62$$
$$x = 62/16 = 3\tfrac{7}{8} \text{ in.}$$

The figure is divided into three rectangles as shown, the areas are 8, 4 and 4 sq in. and the distances of the centroids of each from the centroid of the girder are shown in the sketch.

$$I_{xx} \text{ (top flange)} = \frac{4 \times 1^3}{12} + (4 \times 5\tfrac{5}{8}^2) = 0\cdot33 + 126\cdot5$$
$$= 126\cdot83 \text{ in.}^4 \text{ units}$$

$$I_{xx} \text{ (web)} = \frac{\tfrac{1}{2} \times 8^3}{12} + (4 \times 1\tfrac{1}{8}^2) = 21\cdot33 + 5\cdot06$$
$$= 26\cdot39 \text{ in.}^4 \text{ units}$$

$$I_{xx} \text{ (bottom flange)} = \frac{8 \times 1^3}{12} + (8 \times 3\tfrac{3}{8}^2) = 0\cdot67 + 91$$
$$= 91\cdot67 \text{ in.}^4 \text{ units}$$

Total I_{xx} of girder = $126\cdot83 + 26\cdot39 + 91\cdot67 = 244\cdot89$ in.^{4} units

$$I_{yy} = \frac{1 \times 4^3}{12} + \frac{1 \times 8^3}{12} + \frac{8 \times \tfrac{1}{2}^3}{12}$$
$$= 5\cdot33 + 42\cdot67 + 0\cdot08$$
$$= 48\cdot08 \text{ in.}^4 \text{ units}$$

EXAMPLE 3

Calculate the I_{xx} and I_{yy} of the steel channel shown in Fig. 11.19.

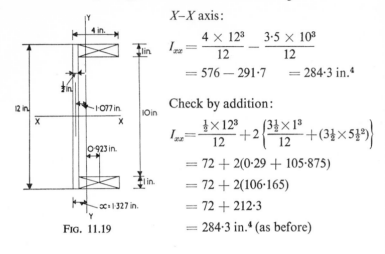

FIG. 11.19

X–X axis:

$$I_{xx} = \frac{4 \times 12^3}{12} - \frac{3 \cdot 5 \times 10^3}{12}$$

$$= 576 - 291 \cdot 7 \qquad = 284 \cdot 3 \text{ in.}^4$$

Check by addition:

$$I_{xx} = \frac{\frac{1}{2} \times 12^3}{12} + 2 \left\{ \frac{3\frac{1}{2} \times 1^3}{12} + (3\frac{1}{2} \times 5\frac{1}{2}^2) \right\}$$

$$= 72 + 2(0 \cdot 29 + 105 \cdot 875)$$

$$= 72 + 2(106 \cdot 165)$$

$$= 72 + 212 \cdot 3$$

$$= 284 \cdot 3 \text{ in.}^4 \text{ (as before)}$$

Y–Y axis:

Taking moments about back of channel—

$$\text{Distance } x \times \text{ area} = (6 \times \tfrac{1}{4}) + (3\tfrac{1}{2} \times 2\tfrac{1}{4}) + (3\tfrac{1}{2} \times 2\tfrac{1}{4})$$

$$= 1 \cdot 5 + 7 \cdot 875 + 7 \cdot 875 = 17 \cdot 25$$

$$\text{Distance } x = 17 \cdot 25/13 = 1 \cdot 327 \text{ in.}$$

$$I_{yy} = \frac{12 \times \tfrac{1}{2}^3}{12} + (6 \times 1 \cdot 077^2) + 2 \left\{ \frac{1 \times 3\tfrac{1}{2}^3}{12} + (3\tfrac{1}{2} \times 0 \cdot 923^2) \right\}$$

$$= 0 \cdot 125 + 6 \cdot 96 + 2(3 \cdot 575 + 2 \cdot 97)$$

$$= 7 \cdot 085 + 13 \cdot 09$$

$$= 20 \cdot 18 \text{ in.}^4$$

Check by subtraction:

$$I_{yy} = \left\{ \frac{12 \times 4^3}{12} + (48 \times 0 \cdot 673^2) \right\} - \left\{ \frac{10 \times 3\tfrac{1}{2}^3}{12} + (35 \times 0 \cdot 923^2) \right\}$$

$$= (64 + 21 \cdot 7) - (35 \cdot 8 + 29 \cdot 7)$$

$$= 85 \cdot 7 - 65 \cdot 5$$

$$= 20 \cdot 2 \text{ in.}^4$$

EXAMPLE 4

Calculate the I_{xx} and I_{yy} of the compound girder shown in Fig. 11.20. The properties of the R.S.J. alone are—

$$\text{Area} = 16.18 \text{ in.}^2$$
$$I_{xx} = 288 \cdot 7 \text{ in.}^4$$
$$I_{yy} = 54 \cdot 74 \text{ in.}^4$$

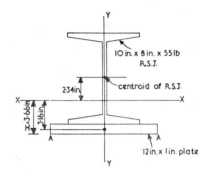

FIG. 11.20

Note. The moment of inertia given above for the R.S.J. (without the plate) is of course about the X–X axis of the R.S.J.

The addition of a single plate renders the compound section unsymmetrical about the X–X axis of the compound, and the Ah^2 of the R.S.J. must be added to its own I_{xx}.

Taking moments about the line A–A:

$$\text{Distance } x = \frac{(16 \cdot 18 \times 6) + (12 \times \frac{1}{2})}{16 \cdot 18 + 12}$$

$$= \frac{97 \cdot 08 + 6 \cdot 0}{28 \cdot 18} = 3 \cdot 66 \text{ in.}$$

$$I_{xx} = 288 \cdot 7 + (16 \cdot 18 \times 2 \cdot 34^2) + \frac{12 \times 1^3}{12} + (12 \times 3 \cdot 16^2)$$

$$= 288 \cdot 7 + 88 \cdot 6 + 1 \cdot 0 + 120$$

$$= 498 \cdot 3 \text{ in.}^4 \text{ units}$$

$$I_{yy} = 54 \cdot 74 + \frac{1 \times 12^3}{12}$$

$$= 54.74 + 144$$

$$= 198 \cdot 74 \text{ in.}^4 \text{ units}$$

EXAMPLE 5

Calculate the I_{xx} and I_{yy} of the compound girder shown in Fig. 11.21. The properties of the R.S.J. *alone* are—

$$I_{xx} = 288 \cdot 7 \text{ in.}^4$$
$$I_{yy} = 54 \cdot 74 \text{ in.}^4$$
$$A = 16 \cdot 18 \text{ in.}^2$$

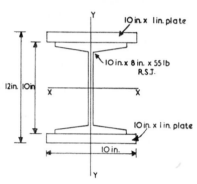

FIG. 11.21

Note. The addition of a 10 in. $\times$ 1 in. plate to each flange does not move the neutral axis of the R.S.J. from its original position, so that—

$$I_{xx} = 288 \cdot 7 + \left[\frac{10 \times 12^3}{12} - \frac{10 \times 10^3}{12} \right]$$

$$= 288 \cdot 7 + 1,440 - 833 \cdot 4$$

$$= 895 \cdot 3 \text{ in.}^4 \text{ units}$$

Check I_{xx} by addition of I_{xx}s of plates

$$I_{xx} = 288 \cdot 7 + 2 \left\{ \left(\frac{10 \times 1^3}{12} \right) + (10 \times 5 \cdot 5^2) \right\}$$

$$= 288 \cdot 7 + 2(0 \cdot 83 + 302 \cdot 5)$$

$$= 288 \cdot 7 + 606 \cdot 6$$

$$= 895 \cdot 3 \text{ in.}^4 \text{ units (as before)}$$

$$I_{yy} = 54 \cdot 74 + \frac{2 \times 10^3}{12}$$

$$= 54 \cdot 74 + 166 \cdot 7$$

$$= 221 \cdot 44 \text{ in.}^4 \text{ units}$$

SUMMARY

With respect to beam sections, the moment of inertia about an axis is the sum of the second moments of area about that axis, i.e.

$$I = \Sigma a y^2$$

This means that if a section is divided into an infinite number of strips parallel to the axis in question and the area of each strip is multiplied by the square of its distance from the axis and then all these quantities are added together, the result is the moment of inertia of the section.

For geometrical shapes, for the moments of inertia formulae can be obtained by the aid of the calculus. Examples are given on page 212.

Principle of Parallel Axes: To determine the moment of inertia of any shape about an axis Z–Z parallel to another axis X–X at a perpendicular distance of H, the amount AH^2 (i.e. area of shape multiplied by the square of the distance H) must be added to the moment of inertia about X–X.

$$I_{zz} = I_{xx} + AH^2$$

EXERCISE 11

Questions 1 to 8. Calculate the I_{xx} and I_{yy} of the shapes shown in Figs. 11.22 to 11.29.

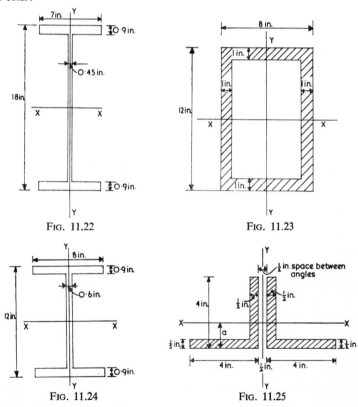

Fig. 11.22

Fig. 11.23

Fig. 11.24

Fig. 11.25

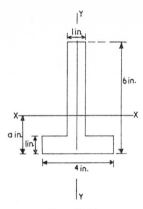

FIG. 11.26

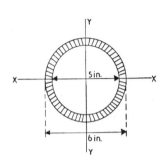

FIG. 11.27

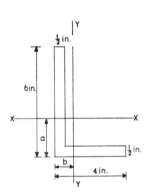

FIG. 11.28

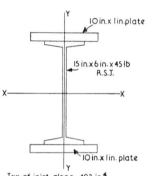

Ixx of joist alone = 492 in.⁴
Iyy of joist alone = 19·87 in.⁴

FIG. 11.29

9. A steel joist (12 in. × 5 in. × 30 lb R.S.J.) has an I_{xx} of 206·9 in.⁴ and I_{yy} of 8·77 in.⁴ The area of the joist is 8·82 sq in. A beam consists of one such joist with a 10 in. × 1 in. plate on the top flange only.

Calculate the value of I_{xx} and I_{yy} of the compound girder.

10. Two steel channels, 9 in. × 3 in. are to be arranged (at a distance a apart as shown) as a compound section, so that the I_{xx} and I_{yy} of the compound are equal (Fig. 11.30). The properties of one single channel are—

$$I_{xx} = 67·4 \text{ in.}^4$$
$$I_{yy} = 4·2 \text{ in.}^4 \text{ (about axis shown dotted)}$$
$$\text{distance } b = 0·76 \text{ in.}$$
$$\text{Area} = 5·8 \text{ sq in.}$$

What should be the distance a?

11. The properties of a single 16 in. × 6 in. × 50 lb R.S.J. are as follows—

$$I_{xx} = 618{\cdot}09 \text{ in.}^4$$
$$I_{yy} = 22{\cdot}47 \text{ in.}^4$$
$$A = 14{\cdot}71 \text{ sq in.}$$

Calculate the I_{xx} and I_{yy} of a built-up section consisting of two such joists at $12\frac{1}{2}$ in. centres as shown in Fig. 11.31.

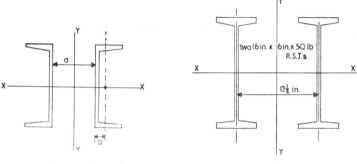

FIG. 11.30   FIG. 11.31

12. Calculate the dimensions x in. and y in. to the centroid of the figure shown (Fig. 11.32), and determine the values of I_{xx} and I_{yy}.

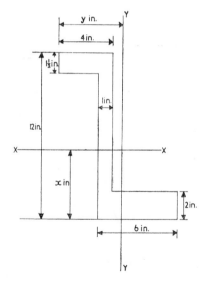

FIG. 11.32

13. Calculate the dimension x to the centroid of the figure shown in Fig. 11.33 and determine I_{xx}.

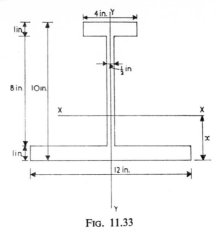

FIG. 11.33

14. Calculate the dimension x to the centroid (X–X axis) in Fig. 11.34 Determine I_{xx}.

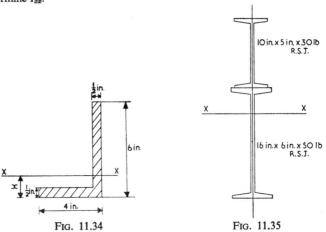

FIG. 11.34   FIG. 11.35

15. A 20 in. deep steel joist has an I_{xx} of 1,700 in.[4] net after having deducted two $1\frac{3}{16}$ in. diameter holes from each flange. What will be the net I_{xx} of a compound girder consisting of one such joist with one 12 in. × 1 in. plate on each flange, allowing for one $1\frac{3}{16}$ in. diameter hole from each plate?

16. A steel joist (which may be considered as consisting of three rectangles) is 18 in. deep × 8 in. wide overall. It has a $\frac{5}{8}$ in. web and two $\frac{1}{2}$ in. flanges. Determine I_{xx} and I_{yy}.

17. A tee section 6 in. × 6 in. × 1 in. overall may be considered as consisting of two rectangles. Calculate I_{xx} and I_{yy}.

18. A compound girder is formed by two R.S.J.s as shown in Fig. 11.35. The properties of the individual joists are—

10 in. × 5 in. R.S.J.	16 in. × 6 in. R.S.J.
$A = 8.85$ sq in.	$A = 14.71$ sq in.
$I_{xx} = 146.23$ in.[4]	$I_{xx} = 618.09$ in.[4]

Calculate the gross I_{xx} of the compound section.

19. Calculate the I_{xx} and I_{yy} of the square section as shown in Fig. 11.36.

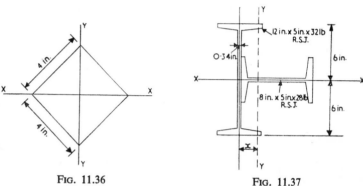

FIG. 11.36   FIG. 11.37

20. A hollow rectangular section is 12 in. deep overall, and each thickness is 1 in. The I_{xx} about the horizontal axis is 531 in.[4] units. What is the overall width of the section?

21. The I_{xx} of a 12 in. deep steel joist is 488 in.[4] The beam has to be increased in strength by the addition of a 10 in. wide plate to each flange so that the total I_{xx} of the compound girder is brought up to 1,098.3 in.[4] What thickness plate will be required to each flange? Ignore rivet holes.

22. The R.S.J. mentioned in Question 21 ($I_{xx} = 488$ in.[4]) is to be increased in strength by the addition of 1 in. thick plate to each flange so that the I_{xx} is increased to 1,503.9 in.[4] What width plates will be required? Rivet holes need not be deducted.

23. A hollow circular steel section has an external diameter of 8 in. The I_{xx} of the section is 137.5 in.[4] What is the thickness of the metal?

24. A special stanchion section is built up by using two steel joists together as shown in Fig. 11.37. The properties of the individual R.S.J.s are—

12 in. × 5 in. R.S.J.	8 in. × 5 in. R.S.J.
$A = 9.45$ sq in.	$A = 8.28$ sq in.
$I_{xx} = 221.1$ in.[4]	$I_{xx} = 89.7$ in.[4]
$I_{yy} = 9.69$ in.[4]	$I_{yy} = 10.2$ in.[4]

Calculate (a) the dimension x to the centroid of the compound section; (b) the I_{xx} and I_{yy} of the compound section.

25. The properties of a single 10 in. $\times$ 3½ in. steel channel are given as follows—

$$A = 8 \cdot 39 \text{ sq in.}$$
$$I_{xx} = 119 \cdot 5 \text{ in.}^4$$
$$I_{y_1 y_1} = 8 \cdot 5 \text{ in.}^4$$

A strut is made as shown in Fig. 11.38 by inserting a 10 in. $\times$ 1 in. steel plate between two such channels. Calculate the values of I_{xx} and I_{yy}.

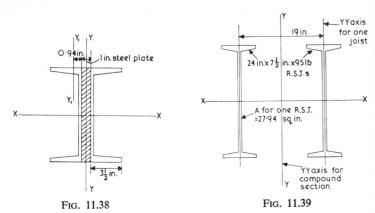

FIG. 11.38   FIG. 11.39

26. Calculate the I_{xx} and I_{yy} of the compound section shown in Fig. 11.39 if the I_{xx} and I_{yy} of one 24 in. $\times$ 7½ in. R.S.J. are 2,533 and 62·54 in.⁴ respectively. (Note that the Y–Y axis of the compound section is not the Y–Y axis of a single joist.)

27. Calculate the I_{xx} and I_{yy} of the compound section as Question 26 if the joists are at 10 in. centres instead of at 19 in. centres.

28. Calculate I_{xx} for the section shown in Fig. 11.40.

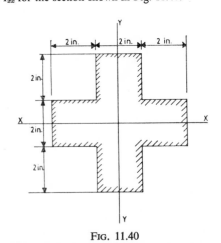

FIG. 11.40

29. Calculate the values of dimension x and I_{xx} for the tee section as shown in Fig. 11.41.

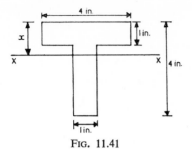

Fig. 11.41

CHAPTER 12

Simple Beam Design

THE previous two chapters have tried to show—

1. That when a beam is loaded, the beam has a bending tendency which is measured in pounds-inches or tons-inches, etc., and known as the *bending moment* on the beam. There is for every loaded beam a certain critical point at which this bending moment has a maximum value.

2. That the shape of the beam's cross-section has an effect upon its strength and this shape effect is measured in inch⁴ units and is called the *moment* of *inertia*.

3. That the material of which the beam is constructed also affects the beam's strength and that this factor is measured in terms of the material's safe allowable stress (in tension or compression) and is measured in pounds per square inch or tons per square inch, etc.

The first of these three factors (the maximum bending moment) depends on the length of the beam and on the nature and disposition of the applied loads.

The second factor, i.e. the factor measuring the strength of the section by virtue of its shape may be varied by the designer so that when the third factor, i.e. the strength of the material, is also taken into account, a beam may be designed of just sufficient strength to take the calculated bending moment.

Factor 1 may be thought of as the *punishment factor*.

A suitable combination of factors 2 and 3 may be described as the beam's *resistance factor* and indeed, this factor is termed the *moment of resistance* of the beam. The exact relationship is quite a simple one in use and may be expressed as—

$$MR = \frac{fI}{y}$$

MR is the moment of resistance of the beam and, when designing beams, the moment of resistance must be made equal to the bending moment, *M*. The design formula is therefore—

$$M = \frac{fI}{y}$$

(The proof of this relationship follows on page 238, but building and architectural students will be more interested in the use of the formula in practical design and this chapter will be devoted mainly to the solution of practical problems.)

In the above formula f is the permissible bending stress for the material of the beam, and for ordinary mild steel, f is taken as 10 to 10·5 tons/sq in., providing the compression flange of the beam is adequately restrained laterally to prevent sideways buckling. Beams which are not restrained laterally are not permitted such a high stress and examples of design of such beams will, it is hoped, be given in a companion volume to this work.

A steel beam may be considered to be laterally supported when it forms part of a reinforced concrete floor, the beam itself being encased in concrete. When a steel beam supports timber joists which are adequately fixed to the top flange of the beam, adequate lateral support may be assumed to be given. The student may assume that all the beams dealt with in this chapter are adequately supported laterally.

Permissible Stresses for Timber

The permissible bending stress f, for timber, varies according to the type of timber. The L.C.C. By-laws permit 1,000 lb/sq in. for Grade A timber and 800 lb/sq in. for Grade B timber. (Examples of

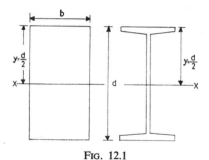

Fig. 12.1

Grade A timbers are Douglas fir, longleaf pitch pine and shortleaf pitch pine. Examples of Grade B timbers are Canadian spruce, European larch, red pine, western hemlock and whitewood.)

The formula $M = \dfrac{fI}{y}$ may be further simplified as follows—

I is the moment of inertia of the cross-section of the beam and y is the distance from the neutral axis (centroid) to the extreme fibre of the beam, in compression or tension. In the case of rectangular cross-section beams and rolled steel joists (British Standard Beams) y is equal to half the depth of the section (Fig. 12.1).

We know (page 212) that I_{xx} for a rectangular section is $\dfrac{bd^3}{12}$

therefore

$$\frac{I}{y} = \frac{bd^3}{12} \div \frac{d}{2}$$

$$= \frac{bd^2}{6}$$

This term, $\dfrac{bd^2}{6}$, is called the *modulus of section* and is denoted by the symbol Z.

Therefore $M = \dfrac{fI}{y}$ may also be expressed as $M = fZ$.

In the case of rolled steel joists (R.S.J.) the values of Z (i.e. I/y) are normally taken directly from tables similar to those on pages 253, and 255 but for examination purposes the student may be expected to calculate his own values of I and Z (assuming the shapes to be built up of simple rectangles), and the following examples will include both types of approach.

The values of Z for sections which are unsymmetrical about axis X–X will be discussed later.

EXAMPLE 1

A timber beam of rectangular cross-section is 6 in. wide and 12 in. deep. The maximum allowable bending stress in tension and compression must not exceed 1,000 lb/sq in. What maximum bending moment in lb-in. can the beam safely carry?

$$\text{Section modulus} = Z = \frac{bd^2}{6} = \frac{6 \times 12^2}{6} = 144 \text{ in.}^3 \text{ units}$$

$$\text{Safe allowable bending moment} = M = fZ = 1,000 \times 144$$
$$= 144,000 \text{ lb-in.}$$

EXAMPLE 2

A timber beam has to support loading which will cause a maximum bending moment of 180,000 lb-in. The safe bending stress must not exceed 1,000 lb/sq in. What section modulus will be required in choosing a suitable size section?

$$M = fZ \text{ and therefore the required } Z = \frac{M}{f}$$

$$Z = \frac{180,000}{1,000} = 180 \text{ in.}^3$$

EXAMPLE 3

A timber beam is required to span 12 ft carrying a total uniform load (inclusive of the beam's self-weight) of 4 tons. The safe allowable bending stress is 1,500 lb/sq in. Choose a suitable depth for the beam if the width is to be 5 in.

$$\text{Maximum B.M.} = \frac{WL}{8} = \frac{(4 \times 2,240) \times (12 \times 12)}{8} = 161,280 \text{ lb-in.}$$

Note. Units have been carefully chosen, weight being in *pounds*, and sizes (including span) in *inches*.

$$M = fZ$$

Therefore required $Z = \dfrac{M}{f} = \dfrac{161{,}280}{1{,}500} = 107\cdot5$ in.^{3}

The Z of the section is $\dfrac{bd^2}{6}$, where b is given as **5** in.

Therefore $\dfrac{5 \times d^2}{6} = 107\cdot5$ in^3

Thus $d^2 = \dfrac{107\cdot5 \times 6}{5} = 129$

The required depth $d = \sqrt{129} = 11\cdot4$ in. approximately. In practice, a 12 in. × 5 in. timber joist would be used.

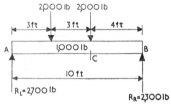

Fig. 12.2

EXAMPLE 4

A timber beam spanning 10 ft has to carry a uniform load inclusive of self-weight of 1,000 lb and two point loads of 2,000 lb each as shown in Fig. 12.2. If the maximum bending stress must not exceed 1,000 lb/sq in. and the breadth of the beam is to be 5 in., what depth of beam is required to resist the maximum bending moment?

Taking moments about A,

$$R_R = \frac{(2{,}000 \times 3) + (2{,}000 \times 6) + (1{,}000 \times 5)}{10}$$

$$= \frac{6{,}000 + 12{,}000 + 5{,}000}{10}$$

$$= 2{,}300 \text{ lb}$$

$$R_L = 5{,}000 - 2{,}300 = 2{,}700 \text{ lb}$$

Applying the rule for the position of maximum bending moment, it becomes obvious that this occurs at the right-hand point load at C.

The maximum bending moment in lb-ft

$$= (2,300 \times 4) - (400 \times 2)$$
$$= 8,400 \text{ lb-ft}$$
$$= 100,800 \text{ lb-in.}$$

$$M = fZ$$

Therefore required $Z = \dfrac{M}{f} = \dfrac{100,800}{1,000} = 100\cdot8 \text{ in.}^3$

$\dfrac{bd^2}{6}$ must $= 100\cdot8$ and b has been fixed as 5 in.

Therefore

$$\frac{5 \times d^2}{6} = 100\cdot8, \qquad d^2 = \frac{100\cdot8 \times 6}{5} = 120\cdot96 \text{ in.}$$

$$\text{Required depth } d = \sqrt{120\cdot96}$$
$$= \text{say } 11 \text{ in.}$$

A beam 11 in. $\times$ 5 in. would suffice.

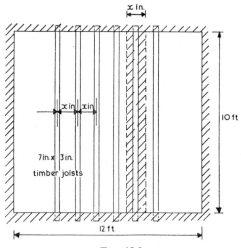

Fig. 12.3

EXAMPLE 5

The section of floor shown in Fig. 12.3 is to be carried by 7×3 timber joists spanning the 10 ft length. The bending stress must not exceed 1,000 lb/sq in. and the total load per sq ft of floor inclusive is estimated to be 105 lb. At what cross-centres x in inches must the timber beams be fixed?

The area of floor carried by *one* timber joist (in sq in.) will be $(10 \times 12) \times x$

$$= 120x \text{ sq in.}$$
$$= 0.834x \text{ sq ft}$$

Therefore total load carried by *one* timber joist

$$= 0.834x \times 105 \text{ lb}$$
$$= 87.5x \text{ lb}$$

$$Z \text{ of joist} = \frac{bd^2}{6} = \frac{3 \times 7^2}{6} = 24.5 \text{ in.}^3$$

Moment of resistance of one joist = bending moment on one joist

$$M = fZ = 1{,}000 \times 24.5$$
$$= 24{,}500 \text{ lb-in.}$$
$$= 2{,}042 \text{ lb-ft}$$

Thus
$$\text{B.M.} = \frac{WL}{8} = \frac{87.5x \times 10}{8} = 2{,}042 \text{ lb-ft}$$

and
$$x \text{ in inches} = \frac{2{,}042 \times 8}{87.5 \times 10} = 18.7 \text{ in.}$$

In practice, the 7 in. $\times$ 3 in. timber joists could be at 18 in. centres.

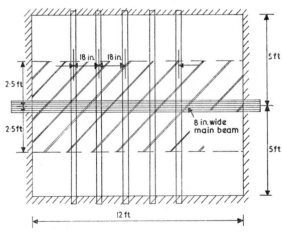

FIG. 12.4

EXAMPLE 6

If the floor mentioned in Example 5 has its 7 in. $\times$ 3 in. timber joists at 18 in. centres and the span of the timber joists is halved by the introduction of a main timber beam 8 in. wide, as shown in Fig. 12.4, (*a*) what load in lb/sq ft will the floor now safely carry? (b) what will be the required depth of the 8 in. wide main timber beam if $f = 1,000$ lb/sq in.?

Let w be safe load in lb/sq ft
Area carried by one secondary timber joist (in sq ft)

$$= 5 \times 1\tfrac{1}{2} = 7{\cdot}5 \text{ sq ft}$$

Load carried by one secondary timber joist $= 7{\cdot}5w$ lb.
Moment of resistance of one joist $=$ B.M. $=$ as before fZ

$$= 1,000 \times 24{\cdot}5$$

$$= 24,500 \text{ lb-in.}$$

$$= 2,042 \text{ lb-ft}$$

Therefore $$M = \frac{WL}{8} = \frac{7{\cdot}5w \times 5}{8} = 2,042 \text{ lb-ft}$$

And $$w = \frac{2,042 \times 8}{7{\cdot}5 \times 5} = 436 \text{ lb/sq ft}$$

Total load on the main beam:
It should be noted that each secondary timber joist transfers half of its load to the main beam in the form of an end reaction, and the other half to the wall.

Thus, the total area of floor load carried by the main beam is the area shown shaded in Fig. 12.4.

The total load carried by the main beam is thus $12 \times 5 \times 436 = 26,160$ lb and, although this in fact consists of a large number of small point loads from the secondary beams, it is normal practice to treat this in design as a uniformly distributed load.

$$\text{B.M. on main beam} = \frac{26,160 \times 12 \times 12}{8} = 470,880 \text{ lb-in.}$$

Therefore

$$Z \text{ required for beam} = \frac{M}{f} = \frac{470,880}{1,000} = 470{\cdot}88 \text{ in.}^3$$

$$\frac{bd^2}{6} = \frac{8 \times d^2}{6} \text{ and this must equal } 470{\cdot}88$$

So $$d = \sqrt{\left(\frac{470{\cdot}88 \times 6}{8}\right)} = 18{\cdot}8 \text{ in.}$$

Required size $= 19$ in. $\times$ 8 in. timber

EXAMPLE 7

A steel joist is 6 in. wide and 12 in. deep and has a web $\frac{1}{2}$ in. thick and two 1 in. thick flanges as shown in Fig. 12.5. What safe uniform load can a beam of this section carry on a simply supported span of 13 ft if the safe allowable bending stress is 10 tons/sq in.?

$$I_{xx} \text{ of section} = \frac{6 \times 12^3}{12} - \frac{5\frac{1}{2} \times 10^3}{12}$$

$$= 864 - 458 = 406 \text{ in.}^4$$

$$Z_{xx} \text{ of section} = \frac{I}{y} = \frac{406}{6} = 67 \cdot 6 \text{ in.}^3$$

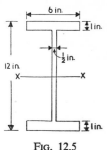

Safe moment of resistance

$$= fZ = 10 \times 67 \cdot 6 = 676 \text{ tons-in.}$$

$$= 56 \cdot 3 \text{ tons-ft}$$

FIG. 12.5

If $W =$ safe total uniform load in tons and $L =$ span in feet,

Then $\qquad \dfrac{WL}{8} = 56 \cdot 3 \text{ tons-ft}$

And $\qquad W = \dfrac{56 \cdot 3 \times 8}{L} = \dfrac{56 \cdot 3 \times 8}{13} = 34 \cdot 6 \text{ tons}$

EXAMPLE 8

A steel joist is required to span 20 ft between centres of simple supports carrying a 9 in. brick wall 10 ft high as in Fig. 12.6. The brickwork weighs 120 lb/cu ft. Choose from the tables of properties (p. 255) a suitable beam section if the safe stress in bending is 10 tons/sq in.

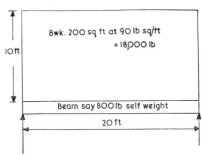

FIG. 12.6

As the wall is 9 in. ($\frac{3}{4}$ ft) thick, and 1 cu ft weighs 120 lb, the 9 in. wall will obviously weigh $\frac{3}{4} \times 120 = 90$ lb/sq ft of wall surface.

Therefore total weight of wall $= 20 \times 10 \times 90 = 18,000$ lb

$$= 8 \cdot 04 \text{ tons}$$

Estimated weight of beam itself $= 20$ ft at 40 lb $= 800$ lb

$$= 0.36 \text{ ton}$$

Therefore $\qquad$ total $W = 8.04 + 0.36 = 8.4$ tons

$$\text{B.M.} = \frac{WL}{8} = \frac{8.4 \times 20 \times 12}{8} = 252 \text{ tons-in.}$$

$$Z \text{ required} = \frac{M}{f} = \frac{252}{10} = 25.2 \text{ in.}^3$$

A suitable section would be the 10 in. $\times$ 5 in. $\times$ 30 lb B.S.B. (or R.S.J.) with an actual Z of 29·25 in.^{3}, slightly in excess of the required Z of 25·2.

Note. In choosing a suitable joist, the student will perhaps argue that the 8 in. $\times$ 6 in. R.S.J. (with a Z of 28·76 in.^{3}) is nearer to the 25·2 required.

This is so, but the 8 in. $\times$ 6 in. weighs 35 lb/ft, whereas the 10 in. $\times$ 5 in. R.S.J. chosen weighs only 30 lb/ft and, being deeper, is actually a better choice than the heavier but shallower 8 in. $\times$ 6 in. R.S.J.

EXAMPLE 9

A plan of a floor is shown in Fig. 12.7. The floor consists of a reinforced concrete slab spanning in the directions of the arrows and resting on two steel beams as shown. The R.C. slab itself weighs 50 lb/sq ft and is to carry a superimposed load of 112 lb/sq ft. Choose a suitable section for the beams, if the safe bending stress is not to exceed 10·5 tons/sq in.

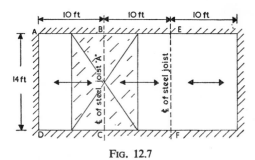

Fig. 12.7

Allow for design purposes 100 lb/ft for self weight of steel beam and concrete casing.

As shown in previous examples, half the load on portion *ABCD* and half of that on portion *BCEF* will be carried by beam *A*.

Load on beam $A = 10 \times 14 = 140$ sq ft of floor $+$ weight of beam

$$\text{Weight per sq ft from floor's weight} = 50 \text{ lb}$$
$$\text{Weight per sq ft from super load} = 112 \text{ lb}$$
$$\text{Total} = 162 \text{ lb}$$

Total weight on one beam $= (162 \times 140) + (14 \text{ ft} \times 100 \text{ lb})$
$$= 22{,}680 + 1{,}400 = 24{,}080 \text{ lb}$$
$$= 10 \cdot 75 \text{ tons}$$

$$\text{Maximum } M = \frac{WL}{8} = \frac{10 \cdot 75 \times 14 \times 12}{8} = 226 \text{ tons-in.}$$

$$Z \text{ required} = \frac{M}{f} = \frac{226}{10 \cdot 5} = 21 \cdot 6 \text{ in.}^3$$

From tables (page 253) choose 10 in. $\times$ 4½ in. $\times$ 25 lb R.S.J. ($Z = 24 \cdot 47$ in.^{3})

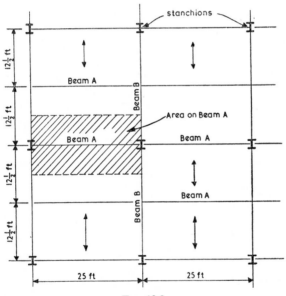

Fig. 12.8

EXAMPLE 10

Fig. 12.8 shows a small portion of floor of a steel-framed building. The floor slab, which weighs 60 lb/sq ft, spans in the direction of the arrows, carrying a super load of 100 lb/sq ft and transferring it to the secondary beams A. These in turn pass the load to the main beams B and to the stanchions.

Choose suitable sizes for beams A and B, using a safe stress of 10·5 tons/sq in

Secondary beam A:

$$\text{Weight per sq ft} = \text{super load} \quad 100$$
$$+ \text{ dead load} \quad 60$$
$$\overline{\qquad}$$
$$160 \text{ lb/sq ft}$$

Therefore W for beam $A = (12 \cdot 5 \times 25 \times 160) + \text{self weight (say 200 lb/ft)}$

$$= 50,000 + (25 \times 200)$$

$$= 50,000 + 5,000 = 55,000 \text{ lb} = 24 \cdot 6 \text{ tons}$$

$$\text{Maximum } M = \frac{WL}{8} = \frac{24 \cdot 6 \times 25 \times 12}{8} = 923 \text{ tons-in.}$$

$$Z \text{ required} = \frac{M}{f} = \frac{923}{10 \cdot 5} = 88 \text{ in.}^3$$

Use 18 in. $\times$ 6 in. $\times$ 55 lb. R.S.J. ($Z = 93 \cdot 53$ in.^{3})

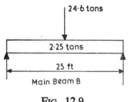

FIG. 12.9

Main beam B:

Each of the two beams A which connect to the centre of span of beam B transmits a reaction of $12 \cdot 3$ tons to beam B (Fig. 12.9).

Total point load at mid-span of beam $B = 24 \cdot 6$ tons

Estimated weight of beam $B = 25 \times 200 = 5,000$ lb say $2 \cdot 25$ tons

Loading to beam B is as in Fig. 12.9

$$\text{Maximum } M = \frac{24 \cdot 6 \times 25 \times 12}{4} + \frac{2 \cdot 25 \times 25 \times 12}{8}$$

$$= 1,840 + 84 \cdot 5 = 1,924 \cdot 5 \text{ tons-in.}$$

$$Z \text{ required} = \frac{1,924 \cdot 5}{10 \cdot 5} = 184 \text{ in.}^3$$

Use 24 in. $\times$ 7$\frac{1}{2}$ in. $\times$ 95 lb ($Z = 211 \cdot 09$ in.^{3})

Proof of the General Theory of Bending

It has been seen that, in general, most beams tend to bend in the form shown in Fig. 12.10, and if X–X is the neutral axis of such a beam, the fibres above *X–X* are stressed in compression and those below *X–X* in tension.

Furthermore, fibres far away from the neutral axis are stressed more heavily than those near to the neutral axis. Fibres lying on the neutral axis are neither in tension or compression, and are, in fact, quite unstressed.

The distribution of stress across a plane section such as *A–A* in

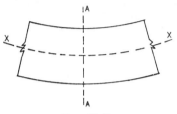

FIG. 12.10

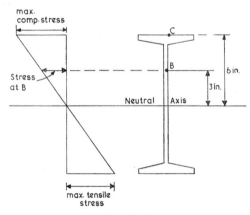

FIG. 12.11

Fig. 12.10 may thus be seen to vary from zero at the N.A. to maximum tension and maximum compression at the extreme fibres, as shown in the stress distribution diagram (Fig. 12.11).

The stress varies directly as the distance from the neutral axis, i.e. the stress per sq in. at *C* is twice that at *B*.

The student might appreciate now a statement made in earlier chapters—that material far away from the N.A. is more useful than material near to the N.A. He should also appreciate why the common rolled steel joist is such a popular beam section; the mass of its material (i.e. the two flanges) is positioned as far as possible from the centroid, that is, from the neutral axis.

A simple analogy will help the reader to see how the compression and tension generated within the beam combine to resist the external bending moment.

Consider, for example, the cantilever shown in Fig. 12.12, and let a load of *W* tons be suspended from the free end *B*, the self-weight of the beam being neglected. If the beam were to be sawn through at section *C–C*, then obviously, the portion to the right of the cut would fall, but the portion could be prevented from falling by an arrangement as shown in Fig. 12.13.

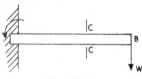

FIG. 12.12.

A weight of *W* is attached to a wire which, in turn, passes over a pulley *P* and is connected to the small portion of cantilever. (The weight of the cantilever itself is ignored for the purpose of this discussion.)

However, although this arrangement would prevent the small portion from falling, the portion would still not be in equilibrium, for it would now twist or rotate as shown by the broken lines. This

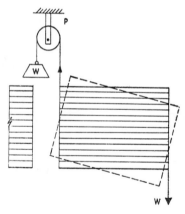

FIG. 12.13

rotation could also be prevented by a small length of chain *D–D* and a steel block at *S–S*, as shown in Fig. 12.14.

This is because the chain exerts a pull (tension) on the portion of cantilever to the right, and the steel block exerts a push (compression) on the portion.

These forces *T* and *C* are equal to each other, and they form an *internal couple* which is equal to and resists the bending moment

Wx. This couple is in fact the moment of resistance of the section and equals $T \times$ lever arm or $C \times$ lever arm. In a real beam these forces T and C are, of course, provided by the actual tension and compression in the many fibres of the cross-section.

Similarly, in a real beam, the force W which prevents the portion from falling is provided by the shear stress generated within the beam itself.

A cantilever has been chosen to illustrate the nature of these

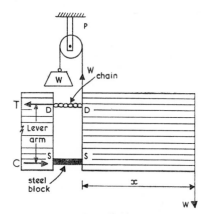

FIG. 12.14

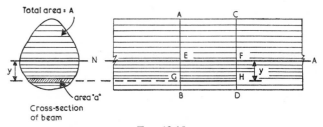

FIG. 12.15

internal forces and moments, but the principle remains the same in the case of the simply supported beam, except of course, that the tension will now occur in the layers below the N.A. and compression in those above the N.A.

Fig. 12.15 shows a short portion of beam (of any shape) before loading, with two plane sections A–B and C–D taken very close together. The layer E–F lies on the N.A. and layer G–H is one at a distance of y below the N.A. and having a small cross-sectional area of a.

Fig. 12.16 shows the same length of beam after bending. The sections A–B and C–D remain straight but are rotated to the positions shown, A_1–B_1 and C_1–D_1. The small portion has bent through an angle of ϕ radians, at a radius of curvature (measured to the N.A.) of R.

The fibre AC has decreased in length to A_1–C_1, whilst the fibre BD has increased in length to B_1–D_1. G–H has also increased to

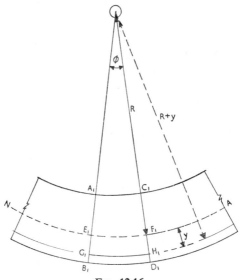

Fig. 12.16

G_1–H_1 but, obviously, the increase is less than in the case of the fibre B–D. The fibre E–F, being on the N.A. neither increases nor decreases, and E–$F = E_1$–F_1.

This straining (alteration in length) of the various fibres in the depth of the section is shown in Fig. 12.17(b), and as stress and strain are proportional to each other (stress/strain $= E$), a similar diagram, 12.17(c), shows the distribution of stress over the depth of the section.

Referring again to Fig. 12.16:

The fibre G–H increases in length to G_1–H_1.

Therefore   the strain in fibre G–$H = \dfrac{\text{increase in length}}{\text{original length}}$

$$= \frac{G_1\text{–}H_1 - (G\text{–}H)}{G\text{–}H}$$

But   length of arc = radius × angle in radians

Therefore G_1–$H_1 = (R + y)\phi$

Now E_1–F_1 remains the same length and thus E_1–$F_1 = GH$

Also $\qquad E_1$–$F_1 = R\phi$

Thus $\dfrac{G_1$–$H_1 - G$–$H}{G$–$H} =$ strain in fibres G–$H = \dfrac{(R + y)\phi - R\phi}{R\phi}$

$$= \frac{R\phi + y\phi - R\phi}{R\phi} = \frac{y}{R} \qquad . \qquad . \qquad . \quad (1)$$

$\dfrac{\text{stress}}{\text{strain}} = E$, and stress $=$ strain $\times E$

stress in fibres G–$H = f = \dfrac{y}{R} \times E = \dfrac{Ey}{R} \qquad . \qquad . \qquad . \quad (2)$

i.e. $\qquad\qquad\qquad\qquad \dfrac{f}{y} = \dfrac{E}{R} \qquad . \qquad . \qquad . \quad (3)$

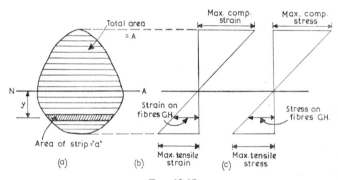

Fig. 12.17

The total load over the area $\quad a =$ stress on the area $\times$ the area

$$= \frac{Ey}{R} \times a = \frac{Eay}{R}$$

The first moment of the load about the N.A. $=$ load $\times y$

$$= \frac{Eay^2}{R}$$

The summation of all such moments over the total area A (i.e. the sum of the moments of all such areas as a), including areas above the neutral axis as well as below $= \sum \dfrac{Eay^2}{R}$ and this is the total moment of resistance of the section.

244 **Structural Mechanics**

But E and R are constants (i.e. only a and y^2 vary) and, since in design the moment of resistance is made equal to the bending moment, M—

$$MR = M = \frac{E}{R} \Sigma ay^2$$

i.e., the safe bending moment $= \frac{E}{R} \times$ the sum of all the ay^2.

But what we have already called the moment of inertia or the second moment of area of the shape is equal to Σay^2.

So we may now write
$$M = \frac{EI}{R} \qquad . \qquad . \qquad . \qquad . \quad (4)$$

Referring again to equation (3), $\frac{f}{y} = \frac{E}{R}$

Substituting $\frac{f}{y}$ for $\frac{E}{R}$ in equation (4),

$$M = \frac{fI}{y} = f\left(\frac{I}{y}\right)$$

Finally, the factor $\frac{I}{y}$ is the Z or section modulus.

Therefore
$$M = fZ$$

The main formulæ arising from this proof may be stated $\dfrac{M}{I} = \dfrac{f}{y} = \dfrac{E}{R}$, and the most important portion consists of the first two terms—

$$\frac{M}{I} = \frac{f}{y}, \text{ or } M = \left(\frac{I}{y}\right)f, \text{ or } M = fZ$$

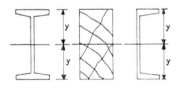

FIG. 12.18

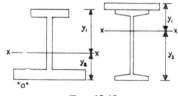

FIG. 12.19

Where a beam is symmetrical about its X–X axis, as in the case of those shown in Fig. 12.18, the distance y to the top flange is the same as that to the bottom flange and,

$$Z = \frac{I_{xx}}{y} = \frac{I_{xx}}{d/2}$$

But, where the beam sections are unsymmetrical about the X–X axis, (Fig. 12.19), the factor y has two values, y_1 and y_2, and there are thus *two* values of Z_{xx}—one obtained by dividing I_{xx} by the distance y_1, and the other obtained by dividing I_{xx} by the value of y_2.

If in these unsymmetrical shapes the safe stress is the same for both top and bottom flanges, as it is in the case of mild steel, then the safe bending moment $= f \times$ least Z.

If, as in the case of the now almost obsolete cast iron joist shown in Fig. 12.19, the safe stresses in tension and compression are not the same, then the safe B.M. is the least of the two factors—

$$M = \frac{I}{y_1} \times \text{compression stress}$$

or

$$M = \frac{I}{y_2} \times \text{tension stress}$$

It is perhaps of interest to note that as cast iron is much stronger in compression than in tension then these two expressions give least $Z \times$ greatest stress and large $Z \times$ least stress, and, in a well designed cast iron joist, these two expressions gave similar numerical results, thus justifying the unsymmetrical shape.

Examples of Unsymmetrical Beams

EXAMPLE 11

A 14 in. $\times$ 6 in. $\times$ 46 lb R.S.J. has one 10 in. $\times$ 1 in. steel plate welded to the top flange only, as shown in Fig. 12.20. The area of the steel joist alone is 13·59 in.^{2} and the I_{xx} is 443 in.^{4} What safe uniform load can such a beam carry on an 18 ft simply supported span if $f = 10$ tons/sq in. in tension or compression?

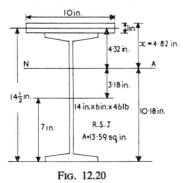

FIG. 12.20

Taking moments about the top of the plate to find the neutral axis which passes through the centroid of the section:

$$23 \cdot 59x = (10 \times \tfrac{1}{2}) + (13 \cdot 59 \times 8) = 5 + 108 \cdot 7 = 113 \cdot 7$$

Therefore $x = \dfrac{113 \cdot 7}{23 \cdot 59} = 4 \cdot 82$ in.

(The distance from the bottom of the section is therefore 10·18 in.)

$$I_{xx} = 443 + (13\cdot59 \times 3\cdot18^2) + \frac{(10 \times 1^3)}{12} + (10 \times 4\cdot32^2)$$

$$= 443 + 137\cdot3 + 0\cdot83 + 186\cdot8 = 767\cdot9 \text{ in.}^4$$

$$\text{The least } Z = \frac{I_{xx}}{10\cdot18} = \frac{767\cdot9}{10\cdot18} = 75\cdot5 \text{ in.}^3$$

Thus safe $M = f \times \text{least } Z = 10 \times 75\cdot5 = 755$ tons-in.

Since the load is uniform, the maximum bending moment is $\dfrac{WL}{8}$

$$\frac{WL}{8} = 755, \quad \frac{W \times 18 \times 12}{8} = 755$$

$$W = \frac{755 \times 8}{18 \times 12}$$

$$W = 28 \text{ tons}$$

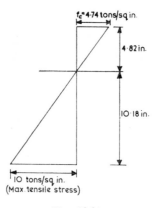

FIG. 12.21

Note. The maximum compressive stress f_c will be much less than 10 tons/sq in. and by similar triangles (Fig. 12.21)

$$\frac{f_c}{4\cdot82} = \frac{10}{10\cdot18} \quad \text{so} \quad f_c = \frac{10 \times 4\cdot82}{10\cdot18}$$

$$= 4\cdot74 \text{ tons/sq in.}$$

EXAMPLE 12

Fig. 12.22 shows an old type cast iron joist, with a tension flange of 16 sq in. and a compressive flange of 5 sq in.

The safe stress in compression is 3 tons/sq in., and in tension $1\frac{1}{2}$ tons/sq in. (*a*) What is the safe bending moment for the section? (*b*) What safe uniform load will the beam carry on a 16 ft span?

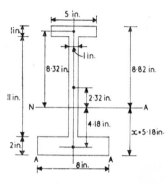

FIG. 12.22

Taking moments about the lower edge *A–A* to find the neutral axis,

$$x \times (5 + 16 + 11) = (16 \times 1) + (11 \times 7\cdot5) + (5 \times 13\cdot5)$$

$$x = \frac{16 + 82\cdot5 + 67\cdot5}{32} = \frac{166}{32} = 5\cdot18 \text{ in.}$$

$$\text{Total } I_{xx} = \frac{5 \times 1^3}{12} + (5 \times 8\cdot32^2) + \left(\frac{1 \times 11^3}{12}\right) + (11 \times 2\cdot32^2)$$

$$+ \left(\frac{8 \times 2^3}{12}\right) + (16 \times 4\cdot18^2)$$

$$= 0\cdot42 + 346 + 110\cdot9 + 59\cdot2 + 5\cdot34 + 280 = 801\cdot9 \text{ in.}^4$$

The safe bending moment in tension = tension f × tension Z

$$= 1\frac{1}{2} \times \frac{801\cdot9}{5\cdot18} = 232 \text{ tons-in.}$$

The safe bending moment in compression = compression f × compression Z

$$= 3 \times \frac{801\cdot9}{8\cdot82} = 273 \text{ tons-in.}$$

(*a*) Thus tension is the critical stress, and the safe bending moment = 232 tons-in.

(*b*) $\quad \dfrac{WL}{8} = 232, \quad W = \dfrac{232 \times 8}{L} = \dfrac{232 \times 8}{16 \times 12} = 9 \cdot 7$ tons

Miscellaneous Beam Problems

EXAMPLE 13

A rolled steel joist 12 in. deep and 7 in. wide, as shown in Fig. 12.23, spans 20 ft. It carries a load of 20 tons uniformly distributed, with an additional load of 3 tons at the centre of the span. Determine the maximum stress due to bending.

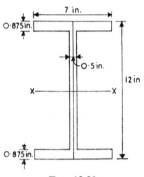

FIG. 12.23

M due to uniform load $= \dfrac{WL}{8} = \dfrac{20 \times 20 \times 12}{8} = 600$ tons-in.

M due to central load $= \dfrac{WL}{4} = \dfrac{3 \times 20 \times 12}{4} = 180$ tons-in.

$\qquad$ Total maximum $M = 780$ tons-in.

I_{xx} of section $= \dfrac{7 \times 12^3}{12} - \dfrac{6\frac{1}{2} \times 10\frac{1}{4}^3}{12} = 1{,}008 - 583$

$\qquad\qquad\qquad\qquad = 425$ in.^{4}

Z_{xx} of section $= \dfrac{I_{xx}}{6} = \dfrac{425}{6} = 70 \cdot 8$ in.^{3}

But $M = fZ$. So stress due to bending $(f) = \dfrac{M}{Z}$

$\qquad\qquad = \dfrac{780}{70 \cdot 8} = 11$ tons/sq in.

EXAMPLE 14

A timber joist has a 1 in. thick flange of the same timber fixed to it as shown below in Fig. 12.24, so that the resulting section may be considered to act as a tee beam.

Calculate the safe distributed load on a span of 12 ft with an extreme fibre stress of 1,000 lb/sq in.

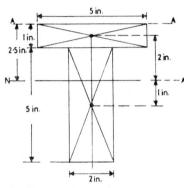

FIG. 12.24

Taking moments about line *A–A* to find the neutral axis,

$$x \times 15 = (5 \times 1 \times \tfrac{1}{2}) + (5 \times 2 \times 3\tfrac{1}{2}) = 2\cdot5 + 35 = 37\cdot5$$

$$x = \frac{37\cdot5}{15} = 2\cdot5 \text{ in.}$$

$$I_{xx} = \frac{5 \times 1^3}{12} + (5 \times 2^2) + \frac{2 \times 5^3}{12} + (10 \times 1^2)$$

$$= 0\cdot42 + 20 + 20\cdot8 + 10 = 51\cdot22 \text{ in.}^4$$

The least $Z_{xx} = \dfrac{I_{xx}}{y} = \dfrac{51\cdot22}{3\cdot5} = 14\cdot63 \text{ in.}^3$

Therefore $M = fZ = 14\cdot62 \times 1,000 = 14,620 \text{ lb-in.}$

$$= 1,218 \text{ lb-ft}$$

If $W =$ safe distributed load in pounds, $\dfrac{WL}{8} = 1,218$

$$W = \frac{1,218 \times 8}{12} = 812 \text{ lb}$$

EXAMPLE 15

A timber cantilever beam projects 6 ft and carries a 12 cwt point load at the free end. The beam is 6 in. wide throughout, but varies in depth from 6 in. to 10 in., as shown in Fig. 12.25. Calculate the stress in the extreme fibres (*a*) at the support (*b*) at a point 3 ft from the support. Ignore the weight of the beam.

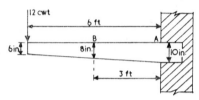

FIG. 12.25

(*a*) To find stress at the support:

$$M = 12 \times 112 \times 6 \times 12 = 96{,}768 \text{ lb-in.}$$

$$Z \text{ at point } A = \frac{bd^2}{6} = \frac{6 \times 10^2}{6} = 100 \text{ in.}^3$$

$$\text{Stress } f \text{ at } A = \frac{M}{Z} = \frac{96{,}768}{100} = 967 \cdot 68 \text{ lb/sq in.}$$

(*b*) To find stress at point *B*

$$\text{B.M.} = 12 \times 112 \times 3 \times 12 = 48{,}384 \text{ lb-in.}$$

$$Z \text{ at point } B = \frac{bd^2}{6} = \frac{6 \times 8^2}{6} = 64 \text{ in.}^3$$

$$\text{Stress } f \text{ at } B = \frac{M}{Z} = \frac{48{,}384}{64} = 756 \text{ lb/sq in.}$$

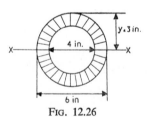

FIG. 12.26

EXAMPLE 16

A hollow steel pipe of 6 in. external and 4 in. internal diameter, as shown in Fig. 12.26, is to span between two buildings. What is the greatest permissible span in feet if the stresses in tension and compression must not exceed 10 tons/sq in.?

Note: The steel weighs 490 lb/cu ft.

$$\text{Area} = \frac{\pi}{4} (6^2 - 4^2) = 0 \cdot 7854 (36 - 16) = 15 \cdot 71 \text{ sq in.}$$

If $L = $ length of span in inches, then

$$\text{Total volume of pipe} \quad = L \times 15 \cdot 71 \text{ cu in.}$$

$$\text{Total volume in cubic feet} = \frac{L \times 15 \cdot 71}{1,728}$$

$$\text{Total weight of pipe} = \frac{L \times 15 \cdot 71 \times 490}{1,728} = 4 \cdot 45\ L \text{ lb}$$

$$\text{But } I_{xx} \text{ of pipe} = \frac{\pi}{64}\ (6^4 - 4^4) = \frac{\pi \times 1,040}{64} = 51 \text{ in.}^4$$

$$\text{Therefore } Z_{xx} \text{ of pipe} = \frac{I}{y} = \frac{51}{3} = 17 \text{ in.}^3$$

$$\text{Permissible } M = MR = \frac{WL}{8} = Zf = 17 \text{ in.}^3 \times 10 \text{ tons/sq in.}$$
$$= 170 \text{ tons-in.}$$
$$= 380,800 \text{ lb-in.}$$

$$\text{Therefore } \quad \frac{4 \cdot 45L \times L}{8} = 380,800 \quad \text{and} \quad L^2 = \frac{380,800 \times 8}{4 \cdot 45}$$
$$= 685,000$$

$$L = \sqrt{685,000} = 828 \text{ in.}$$
$$= 69 \text{ ft}$$

SUMMARY

Design of Timber and Steel Beams

$$M = f\left(\frac{I}{y}\right) = fZ$$

$M = $ maximum bending moment in tons-inches or pounds-inches.

$f = $ maximum permissible bending stress in tons per square inch or pounds per square inch.

$I = $ moment of inertia of the section about the axis of bending (inches⁴).

$y = $ the distance from the neutral axis to the extreme beam fibre.

$Z = $ section modulus (inches³) $= \dfrac{I}{y}$.

For rectangular cross-section beams, $Z = \dfrac{bd^2}{6}$.

For circular cross-section beams, $Z = \dfrac{\pi D^3}{32}$.

For rolled steel sections, values of Z can be found from tables (pp. 253, 255).
For sections built up with rectangular plates, values of Z can be calculated from first principles, having first obtained the moments of inertia (see Chapter 11).

TABLE 12.1A

Joists: Dimensions and Properties

(Reproduced by permission of the British Constructional Steelwork Association and the British Steel Makers)

Size $D \times B$	Weight per foot	Thickness		Radius		Depth between Fillets d	Ratio $\dfrac{D}{T}$	Area of Section
		Web t	Flange T	Root r_1	Toe r_2			
in.	lb	in.	in.	in.	in.	in.		in.^{2}
$24 \times 7\frac{1}{2}$	95	0·57	1·011	0·73	0·36	20·22	23·7	27·94
22×7	75	0·50	0·834	0·69	0·34	18·68	26·4	22·06
$20 \times 6\frac{1}{2}$	65	0·45	0·820	0·65	0·32	16·81	24·4	19·12
18×6	55	0·42	0·757	0·61	0·30	15·03	23·8	16·18
16×6	50	0·40	0·726	0·61	0·30	13·09	22·0	14·71
15×6	45	0·38	0·655	0·61	0·30	12·23	22·9	13·24
14×6	46	0·40	0·698	0·61	0·30	11·14	20·1	13·59
$14 \times 5\frac{1}{2}$	40	0·37	0·627	0·57	0·28	11·39	22·3	11·77
13×5	35	0·35	0·604	0·53	0·26	10·54	21·5	10·30
12×8	65	0·43	0·904	0·77	0·38	8·32	13·3	19·12
12×6	44	0·40	0·717	0·61	0·30	9·12	16·7	13·00
12×5	32	0·35	0·550	0·53	0·26	9·66	21·8	9·45
10×8	55	0·40	0·783	0·77	0·38	6·56	12·8	16·18
10×6	40	0·36	0·709	0·61	0·30	7·13	14·1	11·77
10×5	30	0·36	0·552	0·53	0·26	7·64	18·1	8·85
$10 \times 4\frac{1}{2}$	25	0·30	0·505	0·49	0·24	7·84	19·8	7·35
9×4	21	0·30	0·457	0·45	0·22	7·04	19·7	6·18
8×6	35	0·35	0·648	0·61	0·30	5·25	12·3	10·30
8×4	18	0·28	0·398	0·45	0·22	6·16	20·1	5·30
7×4	16	0·25	0·387	0·45	0·22	5·18	18·1	4·75
6×5	25	0·41	0·520	0·53	0·26	3·72	11·5	7·37
6×3	12	0·23	0·377	0·37	0·18	4·41	15·9	3·53
$5 \times 4\frac{1}{2}$	20	0·29	0·513	0·49	0·24	2·83	9·7	5·88
4×3	10	0·24	0·347	0·37	0·18	2·47	11·5	2·94

TABLE 12.1B

JOISTS: DIMENSIONS AND PROPERTIES

(Reproduced by permission of the British Constructional Steelwork Association and the British Steel Makers)

Size $D \times B$	Moment of Inertia			Radius of Gyration		Section Modulus	
	Axis x-x		Axis y-y	Axis x-x	Axis y-y	Axis x-x	Axis y-y
	Gross	Net					
in.	in.⁴	in.⁴	in.⁴	in.	in.	in.³	in.³
24 × 7½	2533·04	2289·84	62·54	9·52	1·50	211·09	16·68
22 × 7	1676·80	1504·98	41·07	8·72	1·36	152·44	11·73
20 × 6½	1226·17	1087·74	32·56	8·01	1·31	122·62	10·02
18 × 6	841·76	752·52	23·64	7·21	1·21	93·53	7·83
16 × 6	618·09	551·05	22·47	6·43	1·24	77·26	7·49
15 × 6	491·91	438·78	19·87	6·10	1·23	65·59	6·62
14 × 6	442·57	393·71	21·45	5·71	1·26	63·22	7·15
14 × 5½	377·06	331·47	14·79	5·66	1·12	53·87	5·38
13 × 5	283·51	246·07	10·82	5·25	1·03	43·62	4·33
12 × 8	487·77	437·33	65·18	5·05	1·85	81·30	16·30
12 × 6	316·76	280·59	22·12	4·94	1·30	52·79	7·37
12 × 5	221·07	192·01	9·69	4·84	1·01	36·84	3·88
10 × 8	288·69	258·74	54·74	4·22	1·84	57·74	13·69
10 × 6	204·80	180·56	21·76	4·17	1·36	40·96	7·25
10 × 5	146·23	126·35	9·73	4·06	1·05	29·25	3·89
10 × 4½	122·34	104·06	6·49	4·08	0·94	24·47	2·88
9 × 4	81·13	69·81	4·15	3·62	0·82	18·03	2·07
8 × 6	115·06	101·21	19·54	3·34	1·38	28·76	6·51
8 × 4	55·63	47·85	3·51	3·24	0·81	13·91	1·75
7 × 4	39·51	33·80	3·37	2·89	0·84	11·29	1·69
6 × 5	43·69	37·36	9·10	2·44	1·11	14·56	3·64
6 × 3	20·99	17·57	1·46	2·44	0·64	7·00	0·97
5 × 4½	25·03	20·86	6·59	2·06	1·06	10·01	2·93
4 × 3	7·79	6·46	1·33	1·63	0·67	3·89	0·88

NOTE: One hole is deducted from each flange in calculating the Net Moment of Inertia about x-x.

TABLE 12.1C

Joists: Safe Loads

Based on B.S. 449:1959

(Reproduced by permission of the British Constructional Steelwork Association and the British Steel Makers)

Size D × B inches	Weight per foot in pounds	Safe Distributed Loads in Tons for Spans in Feet													
		10	12	14	16	18	20	22	24	26	28	30	32	36	4
24×7½	95	148	123	106	92·4	82·1	73·9	67·2	61·6	56·8	52·8	49·3	46·2	41·0	3
22×7	75	107	88·9	76·2	66·7	59·3	53·4	48·5	44·5	41·0	38·1	35·6	33·3	27·6	2
20×6½	65	85·8	71·5	61·3	53·6	47·7	42·9	39·0	35·8	33·0	30·7	28·6	25·5	20·2	1
18×6	55	65·5	54·6	46·8	40·9	36·4	32·7	29·8	27·3	25·2	22·9	20·0	17·5	13·9	
16×6	50	54·1	45·1	38·6	33·8	30·0	27·0	24·6	22·5	19·5	16·8	14·7	12·9		
15×6	45	45·9	38·3	32·8	28·7	25·5	23·0	20·9	18·2	15·5	13·4	11·7			
14×6	46	44·3	36·9	31·6	27·7	24·6	22·1	19·5	16·4	14·0	12·0				
14×5½	40	37·7	31·4	26·9	23·6	20·9	18·9	16·6	14·0	11·9	10·3				
13×5	35	30·5	25·4	21·8	19·1	17·0	15·1	12·5	10·5	8·9					
12×8	65	56·9	47·4	40·7	35·6	31·6	26·0	21·5	18·1	15·4					
12×6	44	37·0	30·8	26·4	23·1	20·5	16·9	14·0	11·7	10·0					
12×5	32	25·8	21·5	18·4	16·1	14·3	11·8	9·7	8·2	6·9					

Generally, tabular loads are based on a flexural stress of 10·5 tons/in.², assuming adequ
lateral support.

Tabular loads to left of dotted zigzag line exceed the load buckling capacity of
unstiffened web without allowance for actual length of bearing. In addition, the l
bearing capacity should be checked.

TABLE 12.1D

Joists: Safe Loads

Based on B.S.449:1959

(Reproduced by permission of the British Constructional Steelwork Association and the British Steel Makers)

Size × B inches	Weight per foot in pounds	\multicolumn{14}{c}{Safe Distributed Loads in Tons for Spans in Feet}													
		3	4	5	6	7	8	9	10	11	12	14	16	18	20
×8	55							44·9	40·4	36·7	33·7	28·9	24·1	19·0	15·4
×6	40					41·0	35·8	31·9	28·7	26·1	23·9	20·5	17·1	13·5	10·9
×5	30		43·2 †	41·0	34·1	29·3	25·6	22·8	20·5	18·6	17·1	14·6	12·2	9·6	7·8
×4½	25			34·3	28·5	24·5	21·4	19·0	17·1	15·6	14·3	12·2	10·2	8·0	6·5
×4	21	32·4 †	31·6	25·2	21·0	18·0	15·8	14·0	12·6	11·5	10·5	8·8	6·7	5·3	4·3
×6	35			33·6 †	33·5	28·8	25·2	22·4	20·1	18·3	16·8	12·5	9·5	7·5	6·1
×4	18	26·9 †	24·3	19·5	16·2	13·9	12·2	10·8	9·7	8·8	8·1	6·0	4·6	3·6	2·9
×4	16	21·0 †	19·8	15·8	13·2	11·3	9·8	8·7	7·9	6·9	5·8	4·3	3·3		
×5	25	29·5 †	25·5	20·4	17·0	14·6	12·7	11·3	9·3	7·7	6·4	4·7			
×3	12	16·3	12·3	9·8	8·1	7·0	6·1	5·4	4·4	3·7	3·1	2·2			
×4½	20		17·4 †	14·0	11·7	10·0	8·3	6·5	5·3	4·4					
×3	10	9·0	6·8	5·4	4·5	3·3	2·5	2·0	1·6						

Tabular loads to right of full zigzag line are reduced so that deflexion will equal 1/325th the span.

Tabular loads marked thus † are based on the maximum shear value of the web and are [less] than the permissible flexural load.

EXERCISE 12

1. A 10 in × 3 in. timber beam with its longer edge vertical spans 6 ft between simple supports. What safe uniformly distributed load W can the beam carry if the permissible bending stress is 1,200 lb/sq in.?

2. A timber joist 3 in. wide has to carry a uniform load of 4,000 lb on a span of 12 ft. The bending stress is to be 1,000 lb/sq in. What depth should the joist be?

3. A steel joist, as shown in Fig. 12.27 spans 12 ft carrying a uniform load over the entire span. The bending stress is to be 10 tons/sq in. What may be the value of the uniform load?

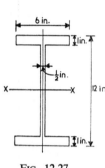

FIG. 12.27

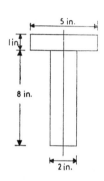

FIG. 12.28

4. The properties of a 15 in. × 6 in. × 45 lb B.S.B. are as follows:

$$I_{xx} = 491 \cdot 91 \text{ in.}^4 \qquad I_{yy} = 19 \cdot 87 \text{ in.}^4$$

What safe uniform load will the beam carry on a span of 12 ft, if the stress is to be 8 tons/sq in.?

5. A 15 in. × 6 in. steel joist, as in Question 4, spans 14 ft carrying a uniform load of 17 tons. What is the maximum bending stress in tons per sq in.?

6. Two 10 in. × 3½ in. steel channels, arranged back to back with 1 in. space between them, act as a beam on a span of 16 ft. Each channel has a section modulus (Z) about axis x–x of 23·9 in.³ Calculate the maximum point load that the beam can carry at mid-span if the safe stress is 8 tons/sq in. and the beam's self weight is ignored.

7. A timber tee-beam is formed by rigidly fixing together two joists, as shown in Fig. 12.28. The resulting section is used (with the 8 in. rectangle placed vertically) as a beam spanning 12 ft between simple supports. Calculate the safe uniformly distributed load if the extreme fibre stress is 800 lb/sq in.

8. A 6 in. × 6 in. × 1 in. steel tee section, as shown in Fig. 12.29, may be stressed to not more than 10 tons/sq in. What safe inclusive uniform load can the section carry as a beam spanning 8 ft between simple supports?

9. Timber floor joists 8 in. × 3 in. at 12 in. centres span 10 ft between centres of simple supports (Fig. 12.30). What safe inclusive load per sq ft may the floor carry if the timber stress is not to exceed 1,200 lb/sq in.?

10. A small floor 16 ft × 14 ft is to be supported by one main beam and

6 in. × 2 in. timbers spanning between the wall and the beam, as shown in Fig. 12.31. (a) Calculate the safe inclusive floor load if the stress in the timber has a maximum value of 1,000 lb/sq in. (b) Choose a suitable section modulus for the main steel beam if the stress is not to exceed 10·5 tons/sq in. Ignore the weights of the beams.

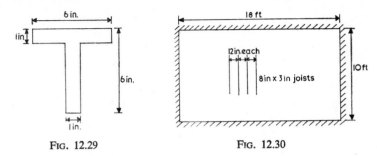

FIG. 12.29   FIG. 12.30

11. (a) Calculate the dimension x to the centroid of the section shown in Fig. 12.32; (b) Determine I_{xx} and the two values of Z_{xx} for the section; (c) What safe inclusive uniformly distributed load can a beam of this section carry on a span of 12 ft if the tension stress must not exceed $1\frac{1}{2}$ tons/sq in. and the compression stress 6 tons/sq in.?

12. How deep would a 6 in. wide timber beam need to be to carry the same load as the beam investigated in Question 11 if the maximum flexural stress equals 1,000 lb/sq in.?

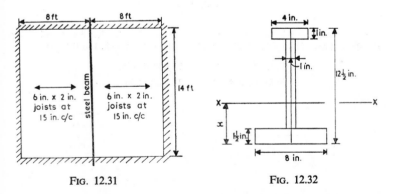

FIG. 12.31   FIG. 12.32

13. Choose suitable section moduli and select R.S.J.s (i.e. B.S.B.s) for the conditions shown in Fig. 12.33 (a) to (f). $f = 10$ tons/sq. in.

14. A steel joist 24 in. deep has a section modulus (Z_{xx}) of 211 in.[3] The joist spans 36 ft, carrying an inclusive uniform load of 10 tons and a central point load of 5 tons; (a) calculate the maximum stress due to bending; (b) what is the intensity of flexural stress at a point 6 in. above the neutral axis and 10 ft from L.H. reaction?

15. A steel tank 6 ft × 5 ft × 4 ft weighs $1\frac{1}{2}$ tons empty and is supported, as

shown, by two steel joists weighing 1 ton each (Fig. 12.34). Choose a suitable section for the steel joists if the tank may be filled with water weighing 62·5 lb/cu ft. The permissible bending stress on the section is 10 tons/sq in.

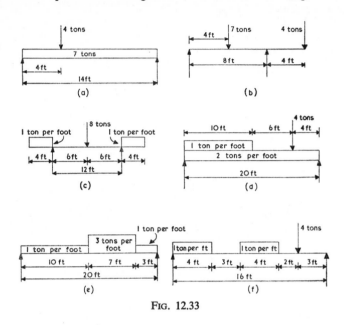

Fig. 12.33

16. Choose suitable timber joists and calculate sizes for R.S.J.s *A* and *B* for the floor shown in Fig. 12.35 if the inclusive floor loading is 180 lb/sq ft.

> Safe timber stress = 1,000 lb/sq in.
> Safe steel stress = 10 tons/sq in.

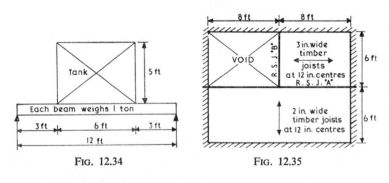

Fig. 12.34   Fig. 12.35

17. A steel base slab 3 ft wide transmits an axial load of 80 tons to a single tier grillage consisting of four R.S.J.s, as shown in Fig. 12.36. Choose a suitable

section for the R.S.J.s, assuming the maximum bending moment to be at the centre of the length of the R.S.J.s ($f = 12$ tons/sq in.).

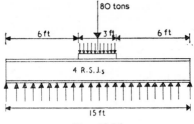

FIG. 12.36

18. The symmetrically loaded beam, shown in Fig. 12.37, carries three loads, and the internal span L has to be such that the negative bending moment at each support equals the positive bending moment at C. What is the span L? If each load W is 10 tons, choose a suitable B.S.B. ($f = 10$ tons/sq in.).

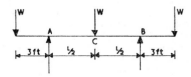

FIG. 12.37

19. A steel joist, 24 in. deep and with an I_{xx} of 2,532 in.⁴ units is simply supported on a span of L ft. The beam weights 95 lb/ft run. What will be the maximum permissible span if the stress in the beam under its own weight reaches $1\frac{1}{2}$ tons/sq in.?

20. The plan of a floor of a steel-frame building is as shown in Fig. 12.38.

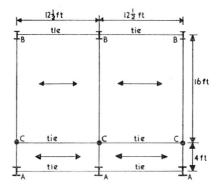

FIG. 12.38

Reinforced concrete slabs spanning as indicated ($\leftrightarrow$) are supported by steel beams AB. Each beam AB carries a stanchion at C, and the point load from each stanchion is 9½ tons. The total inclusive loading will be 186 lb/sq ft of area, which may be assumed to include the weight of the beams. Calculate and select a suitable beam *AB* for the floor, using a safe bending stress of 10 tons/sq in.

21. A steel beam carries loads, as shown in Fig. 12.39. Calculate the position and amount of the maximum bending moment and draw the shearing force and bending moment diagrams. Choose a suitable steel joist for the beam, using a safe bending stress of 9 tons/sq in.

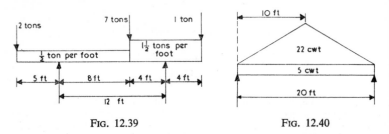

Fig. 12.39   Fig. 12.40

22. Two 12 in × 3½ in. steel channels, arranged back to back with a ½ in. space between them, act as a simply supported beam on a span of 14 ft. Each has a Z_{xx} of 26·62 in.[3] and a web thickness of 0·38 in. The safe stress is 10 tons/sq in. (*a*) Ignoring the self weight of the steel channels, calculate the maximum safe central point load which can be suspended from the channels. (*b*) If this load is suspended by a short steel flat member ½ in. thick, fitted and rivetted between the channels, calculate the necessary width for the flat member assuming two rows of rivets at ¾ in. diameter. The safe stress in tension = 10 tons/sq in.

23. A rectangular timber beam 12 in. deep and 10 in. wide, freely supported on a span of 20 ft carries a uniform load of 5 cwt and a triangular load of 22 cwt as shown in Fig. 12.40.

What is the greatest central point load that can be added to this beam if the maximum bending stress is 1,200 lb/sq in.?

CHAPTER 13

Beams of Two Materials

THERE are two common cases of beams composed of more than one material. The most usual is, that of the reinforced concrete beam, where steel and concrete combine with each other in taking stress.

Similarly, a beam may consist of timber and steel acting together, as in the case of the composite beam in Fig. 13.1, where a timber joist is strengthened by the addition of a steel plate on the top and bottom, the three members being securely bolted together at intervals.

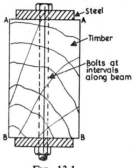

FIG. 13.1

The bolting together ensures that there is no slip between the steel and the timber at the sections A–A and B–B, and thus the steel and timber at these sections alter in length by the same amount. That is to say, the strain in the steel at A–A = strain in timber at A–A.

But, as was shown in Chapter 9,

$$E = \frac{\text{stress}}{\text{strain}}, \text{ and stress} = \text{strain} \times E$$

Stress in steel at A–A = E steel × strain
Stress in timber at A–A = E timber × (same strain)

Thus the $\dfrac{\text{stress in steel}}{\text{stress in timber}} = \dfrac{E\text{ steel}}{E\text{ timber}} = m$ . . . . (1)

The value $\dfrac{E\text{ steel}}{E\text{ timber}}$ is called the modular ratio of the two materials and is usually expressed by the letter m. Therefore, from (1)

Stress in steel = m × stress in timber . . (2)

If, for example, E for steel is 30,000,000 lb/sq in. and E for timber is 1,500,000 lb/sq in. then

$$m = \frac{30,000,000 \text{ lb/sq in.}}{1,500,000 \text{ lb/sq in.}} = 20$$

and, in effect, the steel plate can thus carry the same load as a timber member of equal thickness but m times the width of the steel.

The beam of the two materials can therefore be considered as an *all-timber beam* or *equivalent timber beam* as shown in Fig. 13.2.

Similarly, an imaginary *equivalent steel beam* could be formed by

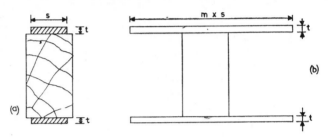

FIG. 13.2. (*a*) COMPOSITE BEAM OF TIMBER AND STEEL;
(*b*) "EQUIVALENT BEAM OF TIMBER"

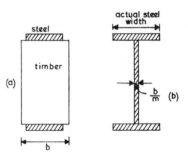

FIG. 13.3. (*a*) COMPOSITE BEAM OF TIMBER AND STEEL;
(*b*) "EQUIVALENT BEAM OF STEEL"

substituting for the timber a steel plate having the same depth but only $1/m$th the thickness of the timber, as in Fig. 13.3.

It should be noted, that in forming these equivalent beams, the width only has been altered. Any alteration in the vertical dimensions of the timber or steel would affect the value of the strain and therefore only horizontal dimensions may be altered in forming the equivalent sections.

The strength of the *real* beam may now be calculated by determining the strength of the equivalent timber beam or the equivalent steel beam in the usual manner—treating the section as a normal homogeneous one, but making certain that neither of the maximum permissible stresses (timber and steel) is exceeded.

EXAMPLE 1

A composite beam consists of a 12 in. × 8 in. timber joist strengthened by the addition of two steel plates 7 in. × $\frac{1}{2}$ in., as in Fig. 13.4. The safe stress in the timber = 1,000 lb/sq in., the safe stress in the steel is 20,000 lb/sq in. and $m = 20$. Calculate the moment of resistance in lb-in.

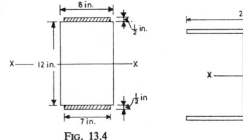

FIG. 13.4

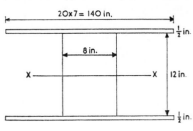

FIG. 13.5

The equivalent timber beam would be as shown in Fig. 13.5.

$$I_{xx} \text{ of eq. timber} = \frac{8 \times 12^3}{12} + 2\left(\frac{140 \times \frac{1}{2}^3}{12}\right) + 2\,(70 \times 6\tfrac{1}{4}^2)$$

$$= 1{,}152 + 2(1\cdot458 + 2{,}734\cdot4)$$

$$= 1{,}152 + 5{,}472 = 6{,}624 \text{ in.}^4$$

$$Z_{xx} = \frac{6{,}624}{6\cdot5} = 1{,}019 \text{ in.}^3$$

Stress in timber = 1,000 lb/sq in.

Therefore $MR = 1{,}019 \times 1{,}000$

$$= 1{,}019{,}000 \text{ lb-in.}$$

The equivalent steel beam would be as in Fig. 13.6.

I_{xx} of equivalent steel beam

$$= \frac{0\cdot4 \times 12^3}{12} + \frac{7}{12}\,(13^3 - 12^3)$$

$$= 57\cdot6 + 273\cdot6 = 331\cdot2 \text{ in.}^4$$

$$Z_{xx} = \frac{331\cdot2}{6\cdot5} = 50\cdot953 \text{ in.}^3$$

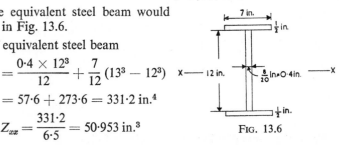

FIG. 13.6

Stress in steel = 20 × stress in timber

$$= 20{,}000 \text{ lb/sq in.}$$

Therefore $MR = Zf = 50\cdot953 \times 20{,}000$

$$= 1{,}019{,}000 \text{ lb-in.}$$

Note. In this example, the ratio of the permissible stresses is equal to the modular ratio.

EXAMPLE 2

A composite beam as shown in Fig. 13.7 consists of a 12 in. × 6 in. timber joist strengthened by the addition of two steel plates each 1 in. thick. The stress in the steel must not exceed 18,000 lb/sq in.; the stress in the timber must not exceed 1,200 lb/sq in.; the modular ratio for the materials is 20. Calculate (a) the safe moment of resistance of the section in lb-in.; (b) the safe uniform load in pounds on a span of 12 ft.

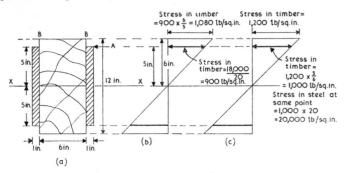

FIG. 13.7. (a) COMPOSITE BEAM; (b) STEEL STRESSED TO 18,000 lb/sq in.; (c) TIMBER STRESSED TO 1,200 lb/sq in.

This case has one additional complication which was not present in Example 1. The stresses in steel and timber are not to exceed 18,000 and 1,200 lb/sq in. respectively, but it may be that stressing the steel to 18,000 lb/sq in. would result in a stress of more than 1,200 lb/sq in. in the timber. Alternatively, a stress of 1,200 lb/sq in. in the timber may result in causing more than 18,000 lb/sq in. in the steel.

The critical case may be reasoned as follows: If the steel at *A* is stressed to 18,000 lb/sq in., then

$$\text{The stress in the timber at } A = \frac{18,000}{20}$$

$$= 900 \text{ lb/sq in.}$$

From the stress distribution triangles it follows that—

$$\text{The stress in the timber at } B = \frac{900 \times 6}{5}$$

$$= 1,080 \text{ lb/sq in.}$$

Both these stresses (18,000 and 1,080 lb/sq in.) are permissible.

If the timber at B is stressed to 1,200 lb/sq in., then from the triangles of stress distribution—

$$\text{the stress in the timber at } A = \frac{1,200 \times 5}{6}$$

$$= 1,000 \text{ lb/sq in.}$$

and the stress in the steel at A would $= 1,000 \times m$

$$= 20,000 \text{ lb/sq in.}$$

This stress would be exceeding the safe allowable stress in the steel.

Thus it follows that the stress in the steel must be kept to 18,000 lb/sq in. and that in the timber to 1,080 lb/sq in., and in calculating the strength of the composite beam, the maximum permissible stress in the equivalent timber section is 1,080 lb/sq in.

Fig. 13.8 shows the equivalent timber section.

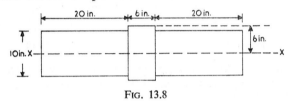

Fig. 13.8

$$I_{xx} \text{ of equivalent section} = 2\left(\frac{20 \times 10^3}{12}\right) + \frac{6 \times 12^3}{12}$$

$$= 3,333 + 864$$

$$= 4,197 \text{ in.}^4$$

$$Z_{xx} = \frac{4,197}{6} = 699\cdot5$$

(b) $\qquad M = fZ = 1,080 \times 699\cdot5 = 755,460 \text{ lb-in.}$

Then $\qquad \dfrac{W \times 144}{8} = 755,460$

$$W = \frac{755,460 \times 8}{144} = 41,970 \text{ lb}$$

Reinforced Concrete Beams

A further example of design in two materials is provided by reinforced concrete. Concrete is a material strong in its resistance to compression, but very weak indeed in tension. A good concrete will safely take a stress of 1,000 lb/sq in. in compression, but the safe stress in tension is no more than 100 lb/sq in. ($\frac{1}{10}$ of its compression stress). It will be remembered that in a homogeneous beam the stress distribution is as shown in Fig. 13.9, and in the case of a section symmetrical about the X–X axis, the actual stress in tension equals the actual stress in compression. If such a beam was of ordinary un-reinforced concrete, then the stresses in tension and in compression would of necessity have to be limited to 100 lb/sq in. to avoid over-stressing in the tension face, whilst the compressive

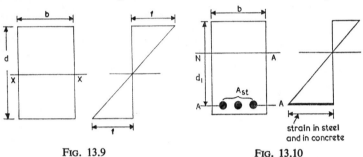

FIG. 13.9   FIG. 13.10

fibres would be taking only $\frac{1}{10}$th of their safe allowable stress. The result would be most uneconomical as the compressive concrete would be under-stressed.

In order to increase the safe load carrying capacity of the beam and allow the compression concrete to use to the full its compressive resistance, steel bars are introduced in the tension zone of the beam to carry the whole of the tensile forces.

This may, at first, seem to the student to be a little unreasonable—for the concrete is capable of carrying some tension, even though its safe tensile stress is as low as 100/lb sq in. In fact it will be seen from Fig. 13.10 that the strain in the steel and in the concrete at A–A are the same, and therefore if the stress in steel $= 18,000$ lb/sq in. the concrete would be apparently stressed to $1/m$th (i.e. $\frac{1}{15}$th) of this, i.e. to 1,200 lb/sq in. m, which is the ratio of the elastic moduli of steel and concrete is usually taken as 15.

At a stress very much lower than this, however, the concrete would crack through failure in tension, and thus the assumption that the steel takes all the tension is in fact well justified.

Assumptions made in reinforced concrete beam design are—

1. Plane sections through the beam before bending remain plane after bending.

2. The concrete above the neutral axis carries *all* the compression.

3. The tensile steel carries *all* the tension.

4. Concrete is an elastic material, and that therefore stress is proportional to strain.

5. The concrete in setting shrinks and thus grips the steel bars firmly so that there is no slip between the steel and the surrounding concrete.

Basis of Design

As the concrete below the N.A. is ignored from the point of view of its tensile strength, the actual beam shown in Fig. 13.11(*a*) is, in fact, represented by an area of concrete above the neutral axis carrying compression, and a relatively small area of steel taking

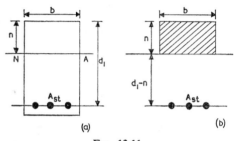

Fig. 13.11

tension as in Fig. 13.11(*b*). Thus the position of the neutral axis (N.A.) will not normally be at $d_1/2$ from the top of the beam, but will vary in position according to the relation between the amount of concrete above the N.A. and the area of steel.

The distance from the top face of the beam to the neutral axis is normally shown as *n* as in the sketch.

Critical Area of Steel

It is obvious that in a beam of a given size, say 8 in. broad and 12 in. effective depth, the area of steel could be varied—it could be 1 sq in. in area, or 2 sq in., etc., and each addition of steel would make for a stronger beam, but not necessarily for an economical one.

TOO LITTLE STEEL. If, for example, only a very small steel area is included, as in Fig. 13.12, and this small steel content is stressed up to its safe allowable value, then the concrete will probably still be very much under-stressed, so that the concrete is not used to its full advantage. From this point of view, an uneconomical beam results.

TOO MUCH STEEL. If, on the other hand, an over-generous amount of steel is included, as in Fig. 13.13, then, stressing this steel to its safe allowable value will probably result in over-stressing the concrete. Thus, to keep the concrete stress to its safe amount, the stress

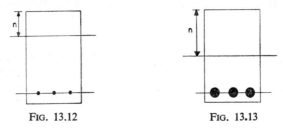

FIG. 13.12   FIG. 13.13

in the steel will have to be reduced, and again the result is an uneconomical section.

Only one critical area of steel for a given size of beam will allow the stress in the concrete to reach its permissible value, say 750 lb/sq in., at the same time as the stress in the steel reaches its maximum allowable stress of, say 18,000 lb/sq in. ($m = 15$). In reinforced concrete beam calculation the designer is nearly always seeking to choose a depth of beam and an area of steel which will allow these stresses to be attained together. The breadth of the beam is normally chosen from practical considerations.

Design Constants

If the two given safe stresses are reached together, then the required area of steel will always remain a constant fraction of the

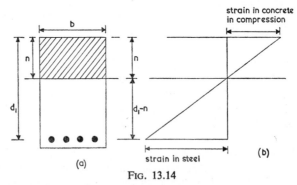

FIG. 13.14

beam's area (bd_1) and the factor $\dfrac{n}{d_1}$ will also have a constant value.

The following pages show how the various constants may be calculated for any given safe stresses.

Fig. 13.14(*a*) shows a normal R.C. beam and (*b*) the strain diagram for the beam.

From similar triangles it will be seen that

$$\frac{\text{strain in concrete}}{\text{strain in steel}} = \frac{n}{d_1 - n} \quad . \quad . \quad . \quad (1)$$

But $\dfrac{\text{stress}}{\text{strain}}$ for any material $= E$ (Young's modulus) for the material

Therefore
$$\text{strain} = \frac{\text{stress}}{E}$$

Let p_{cb} represent the permissible compressive stress in bending in lb/sq in. and let p_{st} represent the permissible tensile stress in the steel in lb/sq in.

Thus from equation (1) $\dfrac{n}{d_1 - n} = \dfrac{\text{stress in concrete}}{E_c} \div \dfrac{\text{stress in steel}}{E_s}$

$$\frac{n}{d_1 - n} = \frac{p_{cb}}{E_c} \div \frac{p_{st}}{E_s} = \frac{p_{cb}}{E_c} \times \frac{E_s}{p_{st}}$$

But $\dfrac{E_s}{E_c} =$ the modular ratio m,

therefore
$$\frac{n}{d_1 - n} = \frac{m p_{cb}}{p_{st}} \quad . \quad . \quad . \quad (2)$$

This latter equation (2) shows that n and d_1 will always be proportional to each other when m, p_{cb}, and p_{st} are constant.

From equation (2) $d_1 - n = \dfrac{n p_{st}}{m p_{cb}}$ and $d_1 = n + \dfrac{n p_{st}}{m p_{cb}}$

$$d_1 = n\left(1 + \frac{p_{st}}{m p_{cb}}\right)$$

So
$$n = \frac{d_1}{1 + (p_{st}/m p_{cb})} \quad . \quad . \quad . \quad (3)$$

Note. n is the distance down to the N.A. from the compression face of the beam, and is expressed in inches.

As n is, however, seen to be a constant ratio of d_1 for fixed values of m, p_{cb} and p_{st}, it is frequently useful to know the value of the constant n/d_1, and this constant n/d_1 is usually termed n_1.

As n has been seen to be $\dfrac{d_1}{1 + p_{st}/m p_{cb}}$

then
$$n_1 = \frac{n}{d_1} = \frac{1}{1 + (p_{st}/m p_{cb})} \quad . \quad . \quad . \quad (4)$$

For the values $m = 15$, $p_{cb} = 750$ lb/sq in., $p_{st} = 18,000$ lb/sq in.

$$n_1 = \frac{1}{1 + \dfrac{18,000}{15 \times 750}} = 0.384$$

and

$$n = 0.384 d_1$$

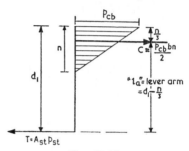

Fig. 13.15

Fig .13.15 shows that the stress in the concrete from the top of the section to the N.A. follows the normal distribution for ordinary homogeneous sections, and the total compression force C then $= p_{cb} bn/2$, i.e. an area $b \cdot n$ of concrete, taking stress at an average rate of $p_{cb}/2$ lb/sq in.

The tension, however, will now all be taken by the steel and will be $T = A_{st} \times p_{st}$, i.e. an area of steel A_{st} taking stress at p_{st} lb/sq in. These two internal forces T and C are equal to each other and opposite in their direction and they form an internal couple acting at $d_1 - (n/3)$ apart.

This internal couple or moment of resistance may thus be written as—

In terms of concrete $\qquad \dfrac{p_{cb} bn}{2}\left(d_1 - \dfrac{n}{3}\right) = \text{M.R.} \qquad . \qquad . \quad (5)$

$$= \text{B.M.}$$

or in terms of steel $A_{st} \times p_{st} \times \left(d_1 - \dfrac{n}{3}\right) = \text{M.R.} \qquad . \qquad . \quad (6)$

Depth of beam:
From the M.R. in terms of concrete

$$M = \frac{p_{cb} bn}{2}\left(d_1 - \frac{n}{3}\right) \qquad . \qquad . \qquad . \qquad . \quad (5)$$

But just as $\dfrac{n}{d_1}$ is a "constant n_1," similarly $\dfrac{d_1 - (n/3)}{d_1}$ is also a constant j

Therefore $\qquad \dfrac{d_1 - (n/3)}{d_1} = j$ or $d_1 - \dfrac{n}{3} = jd_1$

The lever arm, which is here expressed as jd_1, is also frequently expressed by l_a.

For the values $m = 15$, $p_{cb} = 750$, $p_{st} = 18{,}000$

$$\dfrac{d_1 - \dfrac{n}{3}}{d_1} = \dfrac{1 - \dfrac{0\cdot384}{3}}{1} = 0\cdot872 = j$$

$(l_a = 0\cdot872d_1)$

Substituting the constants n_1 and j in (5),

$$\text{M.R.} = \dfrac{p_{cb}bn}{2}\left(d_1 - \dfrac{n}{3}\right) = \dfrac{p_{cb}}{2} \times b \times n_1d_1 \times jd_1$$

$$= \dfrac{p_{cb}}{2} \times n_1 \times j(bd_1{}^2)$$

As $\dfrac{p_{cb}}{2}$, n_1 and j are all constants, then $\dfrac{p_{cb}}{2} \times n_1 \times j$ has a constant value which is usually called R, and we may write

$$\text{B.M.} = Rbd_1{}^2 \qquad . \qquad . \qquad . \qquad . \qquad (7)$$

Using again the values $m = 15$, $p_{cb} = 750$ lb/sq in., $p_{st} = 18{,}000$ lb/sq in.

$$R = \dfrac{p_{cb}}{2} \times n_1 \times j = 375 \times 0\cdot384 \times 0\cdot872 = 126$$

and $\qquad M = 126bd_1{}^2$

So $\qquad\qquad d_1{}^2 = \dfrac{M}{126b}$ and $d_1 = \sqrt{\dfrac{M}{126b}} \qquad . \qquad . \qquad . \qquad (8)$

Area of steel:

As the M.R. (or M) in terms of steel $= A_{st} \times p_{st} \times jd_1$ then the

$$\text{required area of steel} = \dfrac{M}{p_{st} \times jd_1} = \dfrac{M}{p_{st}l_a}$$

$$= \dfrac{\text{bending moment}}{\text{safe stress in steel} \times \text{lever arm}}$$

Therefore $\qquad A_{st} = \dfrac{\text{B.M.}}{p_{st} \times jd_1} = \dfrac{M}{p_{st}l_a} . \qquad . \qquad . \qquad (9)$

Note. As the area of steel is a constant fraction of the area $b \times d_1$

(i.e. $A_{st} = bd_1 \times$ a constant), it is usual to describe this relationship by specifying the percentage area of steel as p,

where $$p\% = \frac{A_{st}}{bd_1} \times 100 \quad \text{or} \quad A_{st} = bd_1 \times \frac{p}{100}$$

Calculation of p for any given value of p_{cb}, p_{st} and m:

From equation (9) $$A_{st} = \frac{M}{p_{st}jd_1}$$

But $$M = Rbd_1^2 = \frac{p_{cb}}{2} \times n_1 \times j \times bd_1^2$$

Therefore $$A_{st} = \frac{p_{cb} \times n_1 \times j \times bd_1^2}{2 \times p_{st} \times jd_1} = \frac{p_{cb} \times n_1 \times bd_1}{2 \times p_{st}}$$

and $$\frac{A_{st}}{bd_1} = \frac{p_{cb}n_1}{2p_{st}}$$

So $p =$ percentage of steel $= \dfrac{A_{st}}{bd_1} \times 100 = \dfrac{p_{cb} \times n_1 \times 100}{2p_{st}}$

$$p\% = \frac{50 \times p_{cb} \times n_1}{p_{st}} \qquad . \qquad . \qquad . \quad (10)$$

Using the values $p_{cb} = 750$, $p_{st} = 18{,}000$ lb/sq in., $m = 15$,

$$p = \frac{50 \times 750 \times 0{\cdot}384}{18{,}000} = 0{\cdot}80 \text{ per cent}$$

So $$A_{st} = bd_1 \times \left(\frac{0{\cdot}8}{100}\right) = 0{\cdot}008bd_1$$

From all the above it will be seen that in designing simple R.C. beams for $m = 15$, $p_{cb} = 750$ lb/sq in., $p_{st} = 18{,}000$ lb/sq in., the procedure is as follows—

1. Calculate maximum B.M. in lb-in.

2. Choose a suitable breadth of beam (b).

3. Calculate effective depth to centre of steel $d_1 = \sqrt{\dfrac{M}{126b}}$.

4. Determine area of steel required from

$$A_{st} = \frac{M}{18{,}000 \times 0{\cdot}872d_1} \quad \text{or} \quad A_{st} = 0{\cdot}008bd_1$$

Should the allowable stresses used be different (e.g. $m = 15$, $p_{cb} = 900$, $p_{st} = 20,000$), then the procedure remains the same, but, of course, different values of R and $p\%$ will be needed, and these may be derived from

$$n_1 = \frac{1}{1 + (p_{st}/mp_{cb})}, \qquad j = 1 - \frac{n_1}{3}$$

$$R = \frac{p_{cb}}{2} \times n_1 \times j, \qquad p\% = \frac{50 \times p_{cb} \times n_1}{p_{st}}$$

Permissible Stresses

CONCRETE: C.P. 114, 1957, give permissible stresses for concrete in compression due to bending as shown in Table 13.1.

TABLE 13.1

Nominal Mix	Permissible Compressive Stress due to Bending
1 : 1 : 2	1,500 lb/sq in.
1 : 1½ : 3	1,250 lb/sq in.
1 : 2 : 4	1,000 lb/sq in.

Note that these stresses assume that the concrete has cube crushing strengths as specified in the code. When difficulty is found in reaching the requisite cube strengths, figures 25 per cent lower than those given may be accepted, providing that the permissible stresses are reduced in the same ratio.

This means that for, say, 1 : 2 : 4 mix, the permissible compressive stress due to bending may be reduced in some cases to 750 lb/sq in., 25 per cent less than 1,000 lb/sq in. Note also that a "nominal 1 : 2 : 4 mix" means 1 cwt of cement to 2½ cu ft of fine aggregate and 5 cu ft of coarse aggregate. The other mixes are in similar proportions.

STEEL. The permissible tension stress for ordinary mild steel is 18,000 lb/sq in. to 20,000 lb/sq. in. Steels with certain guaranteed yield points, and special steels, are permitted higher stresses.

Examples of Reinforced Concrete Beam Design

$$m = 15, \quad p_{cb} = 750, \quad p_{st} = 18,000 \text{ lb/sq in.}$$

EXAMPLE 3

Design a simple reinforced concrete beam 6 in. wide to withstand a maximum bending moment of 98,000 lb-in.

$$M = 98,000 \text{ lb-in.} \quad \text{Required } d_1 = \sqrt{\left(\frac{98,000}{126 \times b} \right)}$$

$$= \sqrt{\left(\frac{98,000}{126 \times 6} \right)}$$

$$d_1 = \sqrt{129 \cdot 6} = 11 \cdot 4 \text{ in.}$$

$$A_{st} = 0 \cdot 008 \times 6 \times 11 \cdot 4 = 0 \cdot 547 \text{ sq in.}$$

Three $\frac{1}{2}$ in. diameter bars (area $3 \times 0 \cdot 196 = 0 \cdot 588$ sq in.) would be suitable. See Table 13.2 on page 277.

Note. The effective depth d_1 is, of course, from the top face to the centre of the steel bars. The bars themselves need an effective

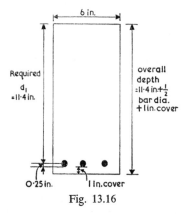

Fig. 13.16

cover of at least 1 in., so to determine the overall depth it is necessary to add (half the bar diameter + 1 in.) to the effective depth d_1 (see Fig. 13.16).

In this case overall depth = $11 \cdot 4 + \frac{1}{4}$ in. + 1 in. = $12 \cdot 65$ in. Say 6 in. × 13 in. overall with three $\frac{1}{2}$ in. diameter bars.

EXAMPLE 4

A simple reinforced concrete beam is to span 18 ft carrying a total uniform load of 6 tons inclusive of self weight, and a point load of 8 tons from a secondary beam as shown in Fig. 13.17. The beam is to be 12 in. wide. Choose a suitable overall depth and area of tensile steel reinforcement for the maximum bending moment.

$$R_R = 3 + \frac{8 \times 4}{18} = 3 + 1{\cdot}78 = 4{\cdot}78 \text{ tons}$$

$$R_L = 14 - 4{\cdot}78 = 9{\cdot}22 \text{ tons}$$

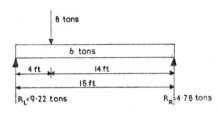

FIG. 13.17

Maximum bending moment occurs at the 8 tons load and equals

$$(9{\cdot}22 \times 4) - \left(\frac{6}{18} \times 4 \times 2\right)$$

$$= 34{\cdot}21 \text{ tons-ft}$$

$$= 921{,}000 \text{ lb-in}$$

(1) $$d_1 = \sqrt{\left(\frac{921{,}000}{126 \times 12}\right)} = 24{\cdot}6 \text{ in.}$$

(2) $$A_{st} = \frac{921{,}000}{18{,}000 \times 0{\cdot}872 \times 24{\cdot}6} = 2{\cdot}38 \text{ sq in.}$$

Use four $\frac{7}{8}$ in. diameter bars ($A = 2{\cdot}4$ sq in)

(3) Overall depth $= 24{\cdot}6 \ (d_1) + 0{\cdot}44$ (half diameter bar) $+ 1{\cdot}0$ (cover)—say, $26\frac{1}{2}$ in. deep.

Examples of Reinforced Concrete Beams using Values other than 15/750/18,000

EXAMPLE 5

A simply supported beam is to span 12 ft carrying a uniform load of 6 tons inclusive of self weight. The beam is to be 6 in. wide, and the stresses in steel and concrete respectively are to be 20,000 and 1,000 lb/sq in. ($m = 15$).

Determine the constants n_1, j, R and $p\%$, and choose a suitable effective depth, overall depth and area of steel for the beam.

Constants:

$$n_1 = \frac{n}{d_1} = \frac{1}{1 + \dfrac{p_{st}}{mp_{cb}}} = \frac{1}{1 + \dfrac{20,000}{15 \times 1,000}} = 0.428$$

$$j = 1 - \frac{n_1}{3} = 1 - \frac{0.428}{3} = 1 - 0.143 = 0.857$$

$$R = \frac{p_{cb}}{2} \times n_1 \times j = 500 \times 0.428 \times 0.857 = 183$$

$$p\% = \frac{50 \times p_{cb} \times n_1}{p_{st}} = \frac{50 \times 1,000 \times 0.428}{20,000} = 1.07 \text{ per cent}$$

Maximum bending moment $= \dfrac{WL}{8} = \dfrac{6 \times 12}{8} = 9$ tons-ft

$$= 241,920 \text{ lb-in.}$$

$$d_1 = \sqrt{\left(\frac{241,920}{183 \times 6}\right)} = \sqrt{220} = 14.83 \text{ in. effective depth}$$

$$A_{st} = \frac{1.07}{100} \times 6 \times 14.83 = 0.953 \text{ sq in. of steel}$$

This could be obtained by using two $\frac{3}{4}$ in. diameter bars and one $\frac{1}{2}$ in. diameter bar ($A = 1.078$ sq in.)

Total depth $= 14.83 + 0.375 + 1 = 16.205$ in., say $16\frac{1}{2}$ in. $\times$ 6 in.

SUMMARY

Timber and Steel Composite Beam

Replace the steel by its equivalent area of timber by multiplying the width of the steel (parallel to the axis of bending) by the modular ratio E_s/E_t). Calculate the value of Z for the equivalent timber section. Determine the maximum permissible stress (f) in the extreme fibres of the beam such that neither the maximum permissible steel stress nor the maximum permissible timber stress is exceeded.

Then $\qquad\qquad$ M.R. $= fZ$

Reinforced Concrete Beams

$$750 - 18,000 - 15 \text{ concrete}$$

$$M = 126bd_1^2$$

$$\text{Area of Steel} = A_{st} = \frac{M}{18,000 \times 0.87d_1}$$

$$1000 - 18,000 - 15 \text{ concrete}$$

$$M = 193bd_1^2$$

$$A_{st} = \frac{M}{18,000 \times 0.848d_1}$$

For other given stresses, design formulae may be obtained as described on page 273.

Note: A reinforced concrete beam cannot be considered as being fully designed until shear stresses are investigated. Usually, for rectangular cross-section beams, the shear stresses are low.

TABLE 13.2

Areas of Steel Bars

Diameter (in.)	$\frac{1}{4}$	$\frac{3}{8}$	$\frac{1}{2}$	$\frac{5}{8}$	$\frac{3}{4}$	$\frac{7}{8}$	1
Area (sq in.)	0·049	0·110	0·196	0·307	0·442	0·601	0·785

EXERCISE 13

1. A composite beam is formed using a 14 in. × 8 in. timber beam with a 12 in. × ½ in. steel plate securely fixed to each side as shown in Fig. 13.18. The maximum stresses in the steel and timber respectively must not exceed 20,000 and 1400 lb/sq in. respectively, and the modular ratio is 20.
What will be the actual stresses used for, (*a*) the steel, and (*b*) the timber ?

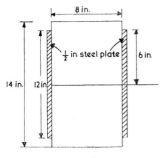

FIG. 13.18

2. What is the safe moment of resistance in pound-inches for the beam section shown in Question 1?

3. A timber flitch beam is composed of two 12 in. × 6 in. timber beams and one 10 in. × ¾ in. steel plate placed between the timbers so that when properly bolted together the centre lines of all three members coincide. Calculate the maximum safe uniformly distributed load in pounds that this beam could carry over a span of 15 ft if the stress in the steel is not to exceed 18,000 lb/sq in. and that in the timber 1,000 lb/sq in., and given that the modular ratio $E_s/E_t = 20$.

4. A timber beam 6 in. wide and 12 in. deep has two steel plates, each 5 in. × ½ in. bolted to it as shown in Fig. 13.19. Assuming the safe steel stress is 20,000 lb/sq in., the safe timber stress is 1,000 lb/sq in., E for steel is 30,000,000 lb/sq in. and E for timber is 1,200,000 lb/sq in., calculate the moment of resistance of the beam. (Ignore bolt holes.)

5. A timber beam in an existing building is 8 in. wide and 15 in. deep and is 20 ft span simply supported at its ends. (*a*) Calculate the maximum safe uniformly distributed load for the timber alone if the bending stress must not exceed 1,000 lb/ sq in. (*b*) It is proposed to strengthen the beam to enable it to carry a uniformly distributed load of 33,040 lb by bolting two steel plates to the beam as indicated in Fig. 13.20. Calculate the required thickness *t* of the plates if the maximum permissible stress for the steel is 20,000 lb/sq in. and the modular ratio is 24.

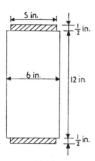

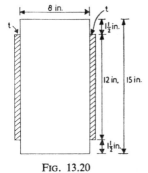

FIG. 13.19   FIG. 13.20

6. A short concrete beam is required to be constructed without any steel reinforcement to span 10 ft, carrying a total inclusive uniform load of 2 tons. If the concrete has a safe tensile stress of only 100 lb/sq in., state what depth would be needed for a suitable beam 8 in. wide.

7. Design a reinforced concrete section for the loading conditions as in Question 6 if the beam remains 8 in. wide.

$$p_{cb} = 750 \text{ lb/sq in.,} \qquad p_{st} = 18,000 \text{ lb/sq in.,} \qquad m = 15.$$

8. A simply supported reinforced concrete beam, 10 in. wide, carries inclusive loads as shown in Fig. 13.21. Determine (*a*) the effective depth d_1 in inches (*b*) the required steel area if $p_{cb} = 750$ lb/sq in., $p_{st} = 18,000$ lb/sq in., $m = 15$. The weight of the beam may be assumed to be included in the given loads.

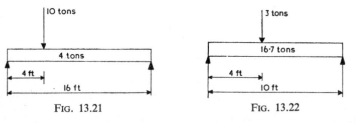

FIG. 13.21   FIG. 13.22

9. A reinforced concrete beam is simply supported on a span of 10 ft and carries loads as shown in Fig. 13.22. Calculate the required effective depth from the top of the beam to the centre of the tensile reinforcement if the beam width is (*a*) 6 in. (*b*) 8 in. (*c*) 10 in. (*d*) 16 in. The weight of the beam may be assumed to be included in the given loads. (750–18,000–15 concrete.)

10. Referring to Example 6 on page 233, design a reinforced concrete beam (750–18,000–15 concrete) as an alternative to the 19 in. × 8 in. timber beam.

Assume that the floor load is 436 lb/sq ft and allow 2,600 lb for the weight of the reinforced concrete beam. Take the breadth of the beam as 10 in.

11. Referring to Example 8 on page 235, for loading conditions but substituting 4,000 lb for the weight of the beam instead of 800 lb, design a reinforced concrete beam (1,000–18,0000–15 concrete) 9 in. wide. When the design is complete, check the assumed weight of beam, taking the weight of reinforced concrete as 150 lb/cu ft.

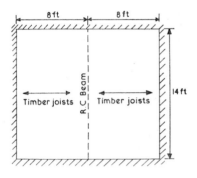

Fig. 13.23

12. A small floor 16 ft × 14 ft is to be supported by one main beam and timber joists spanning between the walls and the beam, as shown in Fig. 13.23. The total floor load is 120 lb/sq ft and 2,500 lb can be assumed as the weight of the beam. Design the beam assuming a breadth of 10 in. and 750–18,000–15 concrete.

13. Referring to Example 15 on page 257, but taking 1,800 lb as the weight of each beam instead of the value given, design reinforced concrete beams assuming a breadth of 9 in. (1,000–20,000–15 concrete).

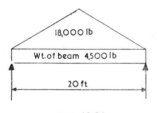

Fig. 13.24

14. Referring to Example 16 on page 258, design beams *A* and *B* in reinforced concrete (750–18,000–15 mix). Take the weight of beam *B* as 400 lb and the weight of beam *A* as 3,500 lb (in addition to the floor load given).

15. A reinforced concrete beam 12 in. wide freely supported on a span of 20 ft carries a triangular load of 18,000 lb in addition to its own weight, which may be assumed to be 4,500 lb (Fig. 13.24). Design the beam in 1,000–18,000–15 concrete.

CHAPTER 14

Deflexion of Beams

A BEAM may be strong enough to resist safely the bending moments due to the applied loading and yet not be structurally suitable because its deflexion is too great. Excessive deflexion might give rise to minor troubles such as cracking of plaster ceilings, cracking of partitions, and cracking of supporting brickwork. In some cases, deflexion might be such as to affect the stability of the structure.

B.S.449: 1959 states: "The maximum deflexion of any beam shall not exceed 1/325 of the span. However, in cases where greater deflexion would not impair the strength and efficiency of the structure, lead to damage of finishings or be unsightly, it is possible to exceed this limit." Referring to Fig. 14.1, the span of the beam is 27 ft, i.e. 324 in. The maximum permitted deflexion (exaggerated in

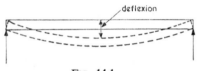

FIG. 14.1

diagram) is 1/325 of 324 inches or 1 inch approximately. The deflexion would probably be allowed to exceed this value to some extent if there were no finishings, etc., likely to be damaged.

Calculation of Deflexion

For many beams in most types of buildings, e.g. flats, offices, warehouses, it will usually be found that if the beams are made big enough to resist the bending stresses the deflexions will not exceed the permitted values. In beams of long spans, however, it may be necessary to calculate deflexions to ensure that the bending of the beams is not excessive. The derivation of formulae for calculating deflexions usually involves the calculus. In this chapter, therefore, only a general treatment will be attempted (with one exception, page 283) and deflexion formulae for a few common cases of beam loadings will be given without proof. General methods of calculation of deflexions are given in standard books on theory of structures or strength of materials.

Effect of Load on Deflexion

AB (Fig. 14.2) represents a beam of span *L* inches supported simply at its ends and carrying a point load of *W* tons at mid-span. Let us assume that the deflexion due to the load is $\frac{1}{4}$ in. It is obvious that if the load is increased the deflexion will increase and it can be

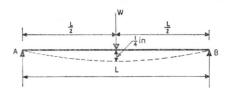

FIG. 14.2

proved that the deflexion is directly proportional to the load, i.e. a load of 2*W* will cause a deflexion of $\frac{1}{2}$ in., 3*W* will produce a deflexion of $\frac{3}{4}$ in. and so on. *W* must be therefore a term in any formula for calculating deflexion.

Effect of Span on Deflexion

In Fig. 14.3(*a*) and (*b*) the loads *W* are equal and the weights of the beams, which are assumed to be equal in cross-section, are ignored

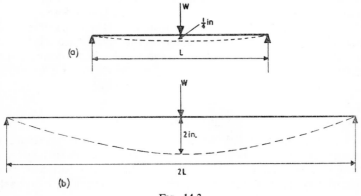

FIG. 14.3

for purposes of this discussion. The span of beam (*b*) is twice that of beam (*a*). It is obvious that the deflexion of beam (*b*) will be greater than that of beam (*a*) but the interesting fact (which can be demonstrated experimentally or proved by mathematics) is that instead of the deflexion of (*b*) being twice that of (*a*) it is 8 times (e.g. 2 in. in this example). If the span of beam (b) were 3L its deflexion would be 27 times that of beam (a). In other words, the deflexion of a beam is proportional to the cube of the span, therefore L^3 is a term in the deflexion formula.

Effect of Size and Shape of Beam on Deflexion

Fig. 14.4(a) and (b) represents two beams (their weights being ignored) of equal spans and loading but the moment of inertia of beam (b) is twice that of beam (a). Obviously, the greater the size

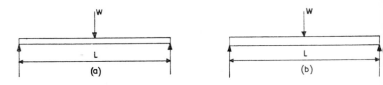

FIG. 14.4. (a) MOMENT OF INERTIA OF BEAM = 1 UNIT;
(b) MOMENT OF INERTIA OF BEAM = 2 UNITS

of the beam, the less will be the deflexion (other conditions being equal) and it can be proved that the deflexion is inversely proportional to the moment of inertia, e.g. the deflexion of beam (b) will be one half of that of beam (a). Moment of inertia I is therefore a term in the denominator of the deflexion formula. (It may be noted that the moment of inertia of a rectangular cross-section beam is $bd^3/12$, therefore doubling the breadth of a rectangular beam decreases the deflexion by one half, whereas doubling the depth of a beam decreases the deflexion to one-eighth of the previous value.)

Effect of "Stiffness" of Material on Deflexion

The stiffer the material of a beam, i.e. the greater its resistance to bending, the less will be the deflexion, other conditions such as span, load, etc., remaining constant. The measure of the "stiffness" of a material is its modulus of elasticity E and deflexion is inversely proportional to the value of E.

A formula for calculating deflexion must therefore contain: the load W, the cube of the span L^3, the moment of inertia I and the modulus of elasticity E, and will be of the form CWL^3/EI. W and L^3 are in the numerator of the formula because increase in their values means increase of deflexion, whereas E and I are in the denominator because increase in their values means decrease of deflexion. At least one other factor *C* has to be considered and that is the disposition of the load or loads on the beam.

Referring to Fig. 14.5 it should be obvious (neglecting the weights of the beams) that although the beams are equally loaded, the deflexion of beam *b* will be less than that of beam *a*. In fact, the maximum deflexion of beam *a*

$$= \frac{1}{48} \frac{WL^3}{EI} = \frac{8}{384} \frac{WL^3}{EI}$$

and the maximum deflexion of beam *b*

$$= \frac{5}{384} \frac{WL^3}{EI}$$

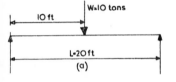
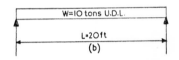

Fig. 14.5

For standard cases of loading the deflexion formula can be expressed in the form $C\,WL^3/EI$ where *C* is a numerical coefficient depending on the disposition of the load and also on the manner in which the beam is supported, that is, whether the ends of the beam are simply supported or fixed, etc. For Fig. 14.5 the values of *C* are respectively $1/48$ and $5/384$.

Table 14.1 gives the values of *C* for some common types of loading, etc. When the load system is complicated, e.g. several point loads of different magnitudes, or various combinations of point loads and uniformly distributed loads, the deflexions must be calculated from first principles.

Simple Example of Derivation of Deflexion Formulae

In certain simple cases it is possible to derive deflexion formulae mathematically without using the calculus, and the following example is given for the more mathematically minded student. Neglecting the weight of the beam, shear force and bending moment diagrams are given in Fig. 14.6 for the beam loaded as shown. The maximum bending moment is $Wa/2$ and this moment is constant along the length *AB*, the shear force being zero. Since the moment is constant,

TABLE 14.1

Condition of Loading	Values of C (Maximum deflexion, which occurs at $A = C\dfrac{WL^3}{EI}$)
Simply supported beam, central point load W, spans $\frac{L}{2}$, $\frac{L}{2}$, deflexion at A	$\dfrac{1}{48}$
Simply supported beam, two loads $\frac{W}{2}$ at third points, spans $\frac{L}{3}$, $\frac{L}{3}$, $\frac{L}{3}$, deflexion at A	$\dfrac{23}{1296}$
Simply supported beam, two loads $\frac{W}{2}$, spans $\frac{L}{4}$, $\frac{L}{2}$, $\frac{L}{4}$, deflexion at A	$\dfrac{11}{768}$
U.D.L. W over span L, deflexion at A	$\dfrac{5}{384}$
W central point load, spans $\frac{L}{2}$, $\frac{L}{2}$, deflexion at A — Fixed Beam	$\dfrac{1}{192}$
Span L, U.D.L. W, deflexion at A — Fixed Beam	$\dfrac{1}{384}$
Span L, point load W at free end, deflexion at A — Cantilever	$\dfrac{1}{3}$
Span t, U.D.L. W, deflexion at A — Cantilever	$\dfrac{1}{8}$

Further examples can be found in handbooks issued by structural steel firms.

the portion AB of the beam bends into the arc of a circle with a radius of curvature R. In triangle OBC,

$$R^2 = (R - \delta)^2 + \left(\frac{L}{2}\right)^2$$

$$= R^2 - 2R\delta + \delta^2 + \frac{L^2}{4}$$

$$R^2 - R^2 + 2R\delta - \delta^2 = \frac{L^2}{4}$$

$$2R\delta - \delta^2 = \frac{L^2}{4} \qquad . \qquad . \qquad . \qquad . \quad (1)$$

δ^2 is the square of a small quantity and can be ignored.

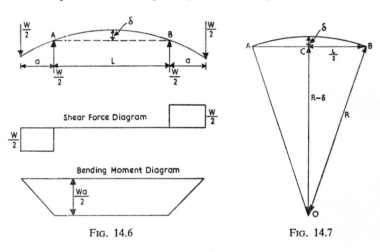

Fig. 14.6   Fig. 14.7

Therefore

$$2R\delta = \frac{L^2}{4}$$

For example, if $L = 10$ ft $= 120$ in. and $\delta = 1$ in., which is a big deflexion for such a small span, then from equation (1)

$$2R \times 1 - 1^2 = \frac{120^2}{4}$$

$$2R - 1 = 3{,}600$$

$$2R = 3{,}599$$

$$R = 1{,}799\cdot 5$$

If we ignore the term δ^2, $R = 1{,}800$, so the inaccuracy is very small, even with such a large comparative deflexion.

Therefore
$$2R\delta = \frac{L^2}{4} \qquad . \qquad . \qquad . \qquad . \qquad . \qquad (2)$$

It was shown in Chapter 12, page 244, that

$$\frac{M}{I} = \frac{E}{R}, \qquad \text{or} \qquad R = \frac{EI}{M}$$

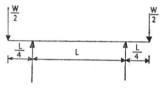

Fig. 14.8

Substituting this value of R in equation (2)

$$2 \times \frac{EI}{M} \times \delta = \frac{L^2}{4}$$

$$\delta = \frac{ML^2}{8EI}$$

M is the bending moment and equals $\dfrac{Wa}{2}$

Therefore
$$\delta = \frac{WaL^2}{16EI} \qquad . \qquad . \qquad . \qquad . \qquad (3)$$

a can be expressed in terms of the span L. If for example the overhanging portion a is a quarter $\left(\dfrac{L}{4}\right)$ of the interior span (Fig. 14.8) then, substituting in equation (3)

$$\delta = \frac{W \times L/4 \times L^2}{16EI} = \frac{1}{64} \frac{WL^3}{EI}$$

EXAMPLE 1

A 16 in. × 6 in. × 50 lb B.S.B. is simply supported at the ends of a span of 16 ft and carries a uniformly distributed load of 2 tons per foot run. Calculate the maximum deflexion ($E = 13,000$ tons/sq in.). The formula for the maximum deflexion is

$$\delta = \frac{5}{384} \frac{WL^3}{EI} \qquad \text{(Table 14.1)}$$

$$W = 32 \text{ tons}$$
$$L = 16 \text{ ft} = 192 \text{ in.}$$
$$E = 13,000 \text{ tons/sq in.}$$
$$I = 618 \cdot 09 \text{ in.}^4 \quad \text{(Table 12.1B)}$$

$\dfrac{1}{360} \times \text{Span}$

Therefore
$$\delta = \frac{5}{384} \times \frac{32 \times 192 \times 192 \times 192}{13,000 \times 618 \cdot 09}$$
$$= 0 \cdot 368 \text{ in.}$$

EXAMPLE 2

Calculate the safe inclusive uniformly distributed load for an 18 in. × 6 in. B.S.B. simply supported at its ends if, (*a*) the span is 20 ft (*b*) the span is 40 ft. The maximum permissible bending stress is 10 tons/sq in. and the maximum permissible deflexion is 1/325 of the span. *E* is 13,000 tons/sq in.

(*a*) From Table 12.1B, $Z = 93 \cdot 53$ in.^{3}
$$M = fZ = 10 \times 93 \cdot 53 = 935 \cdot 3 \text{ tons-in.}$$

Maximum bending moment is $\dfrac{WL}{8}$

Therefore
$$\frac{W \times 20 \times 12}{8} = 935 \cdot 3$$
$$W = 31 \cdot 1 \text{ tons}$$

Maximum deflexion, $\delta = \dfrac{5}{384} \dfrac{WL^3}{EI}$

$W = 31 \cdot 1$ tons, $L = 20$ ft $= 240$ in.,
$E = 13,000$ tons/sq in., I (Table 12.1B) $= 841 \cdot 76$ in.^{4}

Therefore
$$\delta = \frac{5}{384} \times \frac{31 \cdot 1 \times 240 \times 240 \times 240}{13,000 \times 841 \cdot 76}$$
$$= 0 \cdot 51 \text{ in. (slide rule)}$$

Maximum permissible deflexion $= \dfrac{240}{325} = 0 \cdot 74$ in.

Safe load therefore $= 31 \cdot 1$ tons

(*b*) $M = 935 \cdot 3$ tons-in.

$$\frac{W \times 40}{8} \times 12 = 935 \cdot 3$$
$$W = 15 \cdot 5 \text{ tons}$$

Maximum deflexion due to this load

$$= \frac{5}{384} \times \frac{15 \cdot 5 \times 480 \times 480 \times 480}{13,000 \times 841 \cdot 76}$$
$$= 2 \cdot 04 \text{ in.}$$

Maximum permissible deflexion $= \dfrac{480}{325} = 1 \cdot 48$ in.

This means that although the beam is quite satisfactory from the strength point of view the deflexion is too great, therefore the load must be reduced.

Now
$$\delta = \frac{5}{384} \frac{WL^3}{EI}$$

Therefore
$$1 \cdot 48 = \frac{5}{384} \times \frac{W \times 480^3}{13,000 \times 841 \cdot 76}$$

$$W = 11 \cdot 2 \text{ tons}$$

and this is the maximum permitted load for the beam. (Instead of using the deflexion formula, W can be obtained from $W = \dfrac{1 \cdot 48}{2 \cdot 04} \times 15 \cdot 5 = 11 \cdot 2$ tons.)

EXAMPLE 3

Calculate the safe inclusive uniformly distributed load for an 8 in. × 2 in. timber joist of Class B timber, simply supported at its ends, if (a) the span is 12 ft, (b) the span is 24 ft. The maximum permissible bending stress is 800 lb/sq in. and the maximum permissible deflexion is 1/333 of the span (L.C.C. By-laws). E is 1,200,000 lb/sq in. (Table 14.2).

(a)
$$M = \frac{fbd^2}{6}$$

Therefore
$$\frac{W \times 12 \times 12}{8} = \frac{800 \times 2 \times 8 \times 8}{6}$$

$$W = 948 \text{ lb (slide rule)}$$

$$\text{Maximum deflexion} = \frac{5}{384} \frac{WL^3}{EI}$$

$$W = 948 \text{ lb}, \qquad L = 12 \text{ ft} = 144 \text{ in.},$$

$$E = 1,200,000 \text{ lb/sq in.} \qquad I = \frac{2 \times 8^3}{12} = 85\tfrac{1}{3} \text{ in.}^4$$

$$\delta = \frac{5}{384} \times \frac{948 \times 144 \times 144 \times 144}{1,200,000 \times 85\tfrac{1}{3}}$$

$$= 0 \cdot 36 \text{ in.}$$

$$\text{Maximum permissible deflexion} = \frac{144}{333} = 0 \cdot 43 \text{ in.}$$

$$\text{Safe load} = 948 \text{ lb}$$

(b)
$$\frac{W \times 24 \times 12}{8} = \frac{800 \times 2 \times 8 \times 8}{6}$$

$$W = 474 \text{ lb}$$

Maximum deflexion due to this load

$$= \frac{5}{384} \times \frac{474 \times 288 \times 288 \times 288}{1,200,000 \times 85\frac{1}{3}}$$

$$= 1.44 \text{ in.}$$

Maximum permissible deflexion $= \dfrac{288}{333} = 0.865$ in.

The load must be reduced to W where $0.865 = \dfrac{WL^3}{EI}$ or the answer

can be obtained by multiplying the load of $474 \times \dfrac{0.865}{1.44}$.

Therefore $\qquad\qquad$ Safe load = 284 lb

It appears from the two examples given above that before a beam can be passed as suitable, deflexion calculations must be made in addition to bending calculations. Fortunately, it is possible to derive simple rules which obviate deflexion calculations in the majority of cases. For example, if having designed a B.S.B. simply supported at its ends and carrying a U.D.L. ($f = 10$ tons/sq in.) it is found that the span of the beam does not exceed 19·2 times its depth, the beam will be suitable from the deflexion point of view. This rule is derived as follows:

The maximum deflexion for a simply supported beam with a U.D.L. is

$$\frac{5}{384} \times \frac{WL^3}{EI}$$

This formula can be re-arranged as follows,

$$\delta = \frac{5}{48} \times \frac{WL}{8} \times \frac{L^2}{EI}$$

Now $\dfrac{WL}{8}$ is the maximum bending moment $= M$

Thus $\qquad\qquad \delta = \dfrac{5}{48} \times \dfrac{M}{I} \times \dfrac{L^2}{E}$

But $\qquad\qquad \dfrac{M}{I} = \dfrac{f}{y}$ (see page 244)

$$\delta = \frac{5}{48} \times \frac{f}{y} \times \frac{L^2}{E}$$

But $f = 10$ tons/sq in.; $y = $ half the depth of the beam $= \dfrac{d}{2}$ (see page 244); and E is 13,000 tons/sq in.

Therefore
$$\delta = \frac{5}{48} \times \frac{10}{d/2} \times \frac{L^2}{13,000}$$
$$= \frac{100L^2}{624,000d} = \frac{L^2}{6,240d}$$

But δ must not exceed $\dfrac{L}{325}$

Therefore
$$\frac{L}{325} = \frac{L^2}{6,240d}$$
$$325L = 6,240d$$
$$L = \frac{6,240d}{325} = 19 \cdot 2d$$

TABLE 14.2

Beam	Maximum span-depth relationship unless load is reduced so that deflexion does not exceed $\frac{1}{325}$ span (steel) and $\frac{1}{333}$ span (timber)
STEEL f = 10 tons/sq in. E = 13,000 tons/sq in.	L = 19·2 d (L = 18·3 d when F = 10·5 tons/sq in.)
Grade A Timber f = 1,000 lb/sq in. E = 1,600,000 lb/sq in.	L = 23 d
Grade A Timber f = 1,000 lb/sq in. E = 1,000,000 lb/sq in.	L = 14·5 d
Grade B Timber f = 800 lb/sq in. E = 1,200,000 lb/sq in.	L = 21·6 d
Grade B Timber f = 800 lb/sq in. E = 750,000 lb/sq in.	L = 13·5 d

Similar rules can be derived in the same manner for rectangular timber sections, and Table 14.2 gives values for the stresses and values of E given in the L.C.C. By-laws. These rules are only applicable to beams simply supported at each end and carrying a U.D.L., but they err on the side of safety in the case of beams carrying a point load at mid-span.

Note that for each of the grades of timber mentioned in Table 14.2 two values of the elastic modulus are given. L.C.C. By-laws state that the mean value of the modulus of elasticity (1,600,000 lb/sq in. for Grade A timber and 1,200,000 lb/sq in. for Grade B timber) shall only be used for rafters and floor and ceiling joists and, in all other cases, the minimum value of the modulus of elasticity (1,000,000 and 750,000 lb/sq in. respectively) shall be used.

Deflexion of R.C. Beams

C.P.114 (Clause 309) states: "Reinforced concrete should possess adequate stiffness to prevent such deflexion or deformation as might impair the strength or efficiency of the structure or produce cracks in finishes or in partitions."

The moments of inertia of reinforced beams are not so easily obtainable as those of timber beams and rolled steel sections. Timber beams are usually rectangular in cross-section and moment of inertia $= bd^3/12$. Moment of inertia of rolled steel sections can be obtained from handbooks issued by structural steel firms (see Table 12.1).

Rectangular cross-section R.C. beams can be considered to be suitable from the deflexion point of view if the span does not exceed 20 times the depth of the beam. For normal conditions of loading and spans, if the reinforced concrete beam is designed to resist the bending stresses, the depth of the beam will be greater than $1/20$ of the span.

The safe values of deflexions for reinforced concrete slabs are given in Table 14.3.

TABLE 14.3

Description of slab	Minimum value of overall depth
Slabs simply supported and spanning in one direction only	$\dfrac{\text{span}}{30}$
Slabs as above but continuous	$\dfrac{\text{span}}{35}$
Cantilever slabs	$\dfrac{\text{span}}{12}$

SUMMARY

For standard examples of loading, the maximum beam deflexion $= C\,WL^3/EI$ where C is a numerical coefficient depending on the load system and the manner in which the beam is supported (fixed ends or simply supported ends). Values of C are given in Table 14.1, page 284. In general, the maximum deflexion must not exceed 1/325 of the span (steel) or 1/333 span (timber). This condition is satisfied for B.S.B.s when the span does not exceed 19·2 times the depth of the beam ($f = 10$ tons/sq in.). Span-depth ratios for timber beams are given in Table 14.2, page 290, and for reinforced concrete beams and slabs on page 291.

EXERCISE 14

1. A 22 in. × 7 in. × 75 lb B.S.B. is simply supported at the ends of a span of 24 ft. The beam carries (including its own weight) a uniformly distributed load (U.D.L.) of 40 tons. Calculate the maximum deflexion ($E = 13,000$ tons/sq in.).

2. A 15 in. × 5 in. × 42 lb B.S.B. is simply supported at the ends of a span of 20 ft. The beam carries a point load of 9 tons at mid-span. Calculate the deflexion due to this load (i.e. ignoring the weight of the beam). $E = 13,000$ tons/sq in.

3. A 24 in. × 7½ in. × 95 lb B.S.B. is simply supported at the ends of a span of 32 ft. It carries an inclusive U.D.L. of ½ ton/ft run and a point load of 12 tons at mid-span. Calculate the maximum deflexion. $E = 13,000$ tons/sq in.

4. Calculate the safe inclusive U.D.L. for a 14 in. × 8 in. × 70 lb B.S.B. simply supported at the ends of a span of 30 ft. The maximum permissible bending stress is 10 tons/sq in. and the maximum permissible deflexion is 1/325 of the span. E is 13,000 tons/sq in. $I_{xx} = 705{\cdot}6$ in.[4]

5. Calculate the maximum deflexion of a cantilever beam (15 in. × 5 in. × 42 lb B.S.B.) of 10 ft span, fixed at one end and carrying an inclusive U.D.L. of 9 tons. $E = 13,000$ tons/sq in. $I_{xx} = 428{\cdot}5$ in.[4]

6. A 7 in. × 4 in. × 16 lb B.S.B. is fixed at one end and cantilevers for a distance of 4 ft. The beam supports a point load of 1½ tons at its free end. Calculate the maximum deflexion, ignoring the weight of the beam. $E = 13,000$ tons/sq in.

7. A 9 in. × 4 in. × 21 lb B.S.B. is fixed at one end and cantilevers for a distance of 6 ft. The beam supports an inclusive U.D.L. of ½ ton per foot run and a point load of 1 ton at the free end. Calculate the maximum deflexion. $E = 13,000$ tons/sq in.

8. A timber beam 3 in. wide and 6 in. deep is simply supported at the ends of a span of 6 ft. The beam carries a U.D.L. (including its own weight) of 2,000 lb. Calculate the maximum deflexion. $E = 1,000,000$ lb/sq in.

9. A timber beam 3 in. wide and 9 in. deep is simply supported at the ends of a span of 10 ft. The beam carries a point load of 1,080 lb at mid-span. Calculate the deflexion due to this load (i.e. ignoring the weight of the beam). $E = 750,000$ lb/sq in.

10. A timber beam 4 in. wide and 12 in. deep is simply supported at the ends of a span of 14 ft. It carries an inclusive U.D.L. of 2,000 lb and a point load of 1,000 lb at mid-span. Calculate the maximum deflexion. $E = 750,000$ lb/sq in.

11. A timber beam 3 in. wide and 9 in. deep is simply supported at the ends of a span of 15 ft. Calculate (*a*) the value of the safe U.D.L. if the maximum bending stress is not to exceed 800 lb/sq in., and the amount the beam deflects

is not important; (b) the value of the safe U.D.L. if the maximum deflexion must not exceed $\frac{1}{333}$ of the span. $E = 750,000$ lb/sq in.

12. A timber beam is simply supported at the ends of a span of 16 ft and has to support a U.D.L. of 1,680 lb. (a) Assuming the breadth of the beam is 3 in., and the permissible bending stress is 1,000 lb/sq in., and that deflexion is not important, calculate the required depth of the beam. (b) If the deflexion must not exceed $\frac{1}{333}$ of the span, calculate the depth of the beam. ($E = 1,000,000$ lb/sq in.)

13. Calculate the maximum deflexion of a cantilever beam of timber 3 in. wide and 9 in. deep. The beam is 6 ft 9 in. span fixed at one end and carries an inclusive U.D.L. of 1,000 lb. $E = 1,600,000$ lb/sq in.

14. A timber beam 3 in. wide and 6 in. deep is fixed at one end and cantilevers for a distance of 4 ft 6 in. It carries a U.D.L. of 200 lb and a point load of 160 lb at the free end of the cantilever. Calculate the maximum deflexion. $E = 1,200,000$ lb/sq in.

15. A cantilever beam of 8 ft span is 3 in. wide and 12 in. deep. Calculate the value of the safe U.D.L. if the permissible bending stress is 800 lb/sq in., and deflexion need not be considered. Calculate the permissible uniformly distributed load if the maximum deflexion must not exceed $\frac{1}{333}$ of the span.

16. Prove the rules given in Table 14.2, page 290.

17. Calculate the maximum span-depth relationship for a cantilever beam of steel supporting a U.D.L. so that the deflexion does not exceed $\frac{1}{325}$ of the span. Permissible bending stress is 10 tons/sq in. and Young's modulus (E) is 13,000 tons/sq in.

18. Calculate the maximum span-depth relationship for a cantilever beam of timber supporting a U.D.L. so that the deflexion does not exceed $\frac{1}{333}$ of the span. Permissible stresses and values of E are:—

(a) $f = 1,000$ lb/sq in., $E = 1,600,000$ lb/sq in.

(b) $f = 1,000$ lb/sq in., $E = 1,000,000$ lb/sq in.

(c) $f = 800$ lb/sq in., $E = 1,200,000$ lb/sq in.

(d) $f = 800$ lb/sq in., $E = 750,000$ lb/sq in.

19. Calculate the maximum span-depth relationship for a steel beam simply supported at its ends and carrying a point load at mid-span if the deflexion must not exceed $\frac{1}{325}$ of the span. Ignore the weight of the beam. $f = 10$ tons/sq in. $E = 13,000$ tons/sq in.

20. A timber beam 3 in. wide and 6 in. deep simply supported at the ends of a span of 6 ft deflects 0·18 in. under a U.D.L. of 2,000 lb. Without calculating the modulus of elasticity, calculate the maximum deflexion of a beam of similar timber 6 in. wide and 12 in. deep due to a U.D.L. of 8,000 lb, the simply supported span being 12 ft.

21. A block of timber 3 in. × 3 in. × 12 in. shortened by 0·015 in. (gauge length = 12 in.) due to a load of 9,000 lb applied by a compression machine. Calculate the maximum deflexion in a beam of similar material 3 in. wide 9 in. deep due to a U.D.L. of 2,400 lb on a simply supported span of 9 ft.

CHAPTER 15

Solution of Problems by Application of Deflexion Principles

IF two beams A and B of the same material are placed side by side over the same span and they support the load in such a manner that their maximum deflexions are equal, then the loads carried by the two beams are in the same ratio as their moments of inertia.

e.g.   If I_A = moment of inertia of beam A

and I_B = moment of inertia of beam B

W_A = load carried by beam A

W_B = load carried by beam B

Where $W_A + W_B$ = total load W on the two beams

Then
$$\frac{I_A}{I_B} = \frac{W_A}{W_B}$$

Or
$$W_A = \frac{I_A}{I_A + I_B} \times W$$

EXAMPLE 1

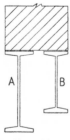

In Fig. 15.1, beam A is a 16 in. × 6 in. × 50 lb B.S.B. and beam B is a 12 in. × 6 in. × 44 lb B.S.B. Both beams span the same distance of 20 ft and are simply supported at their ends. The total load uniformly distributed over the whole span is 38 tons. Calculate the maximum fibre stresses in the beams.

Let W_A = load carried by beam A

W_B = load carried by beam B

Then, since the maximum deflexions are equal,

$$\frac{5}{384} \cdot \frac{W_A l^3}{EI_A} = \frac{5}{384} \cdot \frac{W_B l^3}{EI_B}$$

A   B

FIG. 15.1

294

Since the spans and the values of E are the same for both of the beams,

$$\frac{W_A}{I_A} = \frac{W_B}{I_B}$$

$$\frac{W_A}{W_B} = \frac{I_A}{I_B}$$

or $W_A I_B = W_B I_A$ . . . . (1)

But $\qquad\qquad W_A + W_B = W$ (i.e. total load)

Therefore $\qquad\qquad W_B = W - W_A$

Substituting this value of W_B in equation (1)

$$W_A I_B = (W - W_A) I_A$$

$$= W I_A - W_A I_A$$

$$W_A I_B + W_A I_A = W I_A$$

$$W_A(I_A + I_B) = W I_A$$

Therefore $\qquad\qquad W_A = \frac{I_A}{I_A + I_B} \times W$

Similarly, $\qquad\qquad W_B = \frac{I_B}{I_A + I_B} \times W$

From Table 12.1B, page 253, $I_A = 618 \cdot 09$ and $I_B = 316 \cdot 76$, Therefore

$$W_A = \frac{618 \cdot 09 W}{618 \cdot 09 + 316 \cdot 76}$$

$$= \frac{618 \cdot 09}{934 \cdot 85} \times 38$$

$$= 0 \cdot 66 \times 38 = 25 \cdot 08 \text{ tons}$$

$$W_B = 38 - 25 \cdot 08 = 12 \cdot 92 \text{ tons}$$

Considering beam A,

$$M = \frac{WL}{8} = \frac{25 \cdot 08 \times 20}{8} \times 12 \text{ tons-in.}$$

$$= 752 \cdot 4 \text{ tons-in.}$$

$$f = \frac{M}{Z} = \frac{752 \cdot 4}{77 \cdot 26} = 9 \cdot 75 \text{ tons/sq in.}$$

$$\left(Z \text{ is obtained from Table 12.1B, page 253, or it can be obtained from} \right.$$

$$\left. \frac{I}{y}, \text{ i.e. } \frac{618 \cdot 09}{8} \right)$$

Considering beam B,

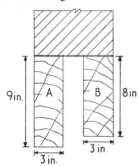

$$M = \frac{12 \cdot 92 \times 20}{8} \times 12 \text{ tons-in.}$$

$$= 387 \cdot 6 \text{ tons-in.}$$

$$f = \frac{M}{Z} = \frac{387 \cdot 6}{52 \cdot 79} = 7 \cdot 35 \text{ tons/sq in.}$$

FIG. 15.2

EXAMPLE 2

Two timber beams as shown in Fig. 15.2 are 15 ft span simply supported at their ends. Calculate the value of the inclusive U.D.L. these two beams can support if the maximum fibre stresses must not exceed 800 lb/sq in.

Let W_A and W_B be the loads carried by beams A and B respectively and W be the total load.

$$I_A = \frac{3 \times 9 \times 9 \times 9}{12} = 182 \cdot 25 \text{ in.}^4$$

$$I_B = \frac{3 \times 8 \times 8 \times 8}{12} = 128 \text{ in.}^4$$

$$W_A = \frac{182 \cdot 25}{182 \cdot 25 + 128} \times W = \frac{182 \cdot 25 W}{310 \cdot 25} = 0 \cdot 59 W$$

Therefore $$W_B = 0 \cdot 41 W$$

Considering beam A

$$M = f \frac{bd^2}{6}$$

Therefore $$\frac{0 \cdot 59 W \times 15}{8} \times 12 = 800 \times \frac{3 \times 9 \times 9}{6}$$

Whence $$W = 2,440 \text{ lb}$$

Considering beam B

$$\frac{0 \cdot 41 W \times 15}{8} \times 12 = 800 \times \frac{3 \times 8 \times 8}{6}$$

Whence $$W = 2,780 \text{ lb}$$

The maximum safe load is, therefore, 2,440 lb.

(*Note.* Two different beams side by side do not work at the same maximum stress.)

"Crossed Beams" Problem

In Fig. 15.3 beams A and B are in contact at mid-span of each beam, beam A being supported at a slightly lower level than beam B. The beams carry a vertical load W at mid-span as shown. What proportion of the total load W does each beam support?

Let W_A represent the load supported by beam A

and W_B represent the load supported by beam B

$$(W_A + W_B = W)$$

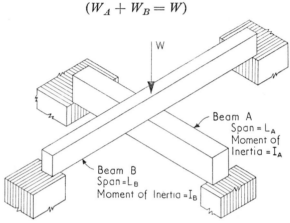

Fig. 15.3

The deflexion of beam A is equal to that of beam B at the point where they cross,

$$\frac{1}{48}\frac{W_A L^3{}_A}{EI_A} = \frac{1}{48}\frac{W_B L^3{}_B}{EI_B}$$

Assuming the material of the two beams is similar, then $1/48E$ can be cancelled from both sides of the equation, so that

$$\frac{W_A L^3{}_A}{I_A} = \frac{W_B L^3{}_B}{I_B} \qquad \cdot \qquad \cdot \qquad \cdot \quad (1)$$

or

$$\frac{W_A}{W_B} = \frac{L^3{}_B I_A}{L^3{}_A I_B}$$

If the beams are of equal dimensions so that $I_A = I_B$, then

$$\frac{W_A}{W_B} = \frac{L^3{}_B}{L^3{}_A} \qquad \cdot \qquad \cdot \qquad \cdot \quad (2)$$

$$= \left(\frac{L_B}{L_A}\right)^3$$

For example, if $L_B = 20$ ft and $L_A = 10$ ft, then

$$\frac{W_A}{W_B} = \left(\frac{20}{10}\right)^3 = \left(\frac{2}{1}\right)^3 = \frac{8}{1}$$

W_A supports $\frac{8}{9}$ of the total load W

and $\qquad\qquad W_B$ supports $\frac{1}{9}$ of the total load W

The load relationship can be expressed also in the following manner (assuming $I_A = I_B$).

From equation (1) or (2), $W_A L^3{}_A = W_B L^3{}_B$ . . . (3)

Now $\qquad\qquad W_A + W_B = $ the total load W

Substituting in equation (3)

$$W_A L^3{}_A = (W - W_A) L^3{}_B$$

$$W_A L^3{}_A = W L^3{}_B - W_A L^3{}_B$$

$$W_A L^3{}_A + W_A L^3{}_B = W L^3{}_B$$

$$W_A(L^3{}_A + L^3{}_B) = W L^3{}_B$$

$$W_A = \frac{L^3{}_B}{L^3{}_A + L^3{}_B} \times W$$

Similarly, $\qquad W_B = \frac{L^3{}_A}{L^3{}_A + L^3{}_B} \times W$

Note that (assuming equal moments of inertia) the shorter beam carries a higher proportion of the total load than the longer beam. A little reflection should show that this must be so, because the maximum deflexions of the beams are equal and more load is required to produce a given deflexion in a short beam than in a long beam. The formulae given above only apply when the beams cross at mid-span. When the beams do not cross at mid-span it is necessary to calculate the actual deflexion formulae from first principles before proceeding with the problem.

EXAMPLE 3

Two beams cross at mid-span as indicated in Fig. 15.3. Beam A is a 12 in. × 8 in. × 65 lb B.S.B. of 8 ft span and beam B is a 10 in. × 8 in. × 55 lb B.S.B. of 12 ft span. Calculate the value of the greatest point load which can be placed where the two beams cross if the permissible bending stress is 10 tons/sq in.

From Table 12.1. $\quad I_A = 487\cdot8; \qquad I_B = 288\cdot7$

Also $\qquad\qquad L_A = 8$ ft; $\qquad L_B = 12$ ft

The deflexions of the two beams where they cross at mid-span are equal,

Let $$W_A = \text{load carried by beam } A$$

$$W_B = \text{load carried by beam } B$$

Where $$W_A + W_B = \text{the total load, } W$$

Therefore $$\frac{1}{48} \frac{W_A \times 8^3}{E \times 487 \cdot 8} = \frac{1}{48} \frac{W_B \times 12^3}{E \times 288 \cdot 7}$$

$$\frac{W_A \times 8^3}{487 \cdot 8} = \frac{W_B \times 12^3}{288 \cdot 7}$$

(Note that, normally, the spans in deflexion formulae must be expressed in inches, but in this case, since only the ratio between W_A and W_B is required, it is in order to express the spans in feet.)

Therefore $$\frac{W_A}{W_B} = \frac{12^3 \times 487 \cdot 8}{8^3 \times 288 \cdot 7} = \frac{5 \cdot 7}{1}$$

i.e. $$W_A = 5 \cdot 7 W_B$$

Therefore $$W_A = \frac{5 \cdot 7}{6 \cdot 7} W = 0 \cdot 85 W$$

$$W_B = 0 \cdot 15 W$$

Beam A will decide the total load that may be carried, but calculations can be made for both beams if the student has any doubts. Considering beam A:

$$M = \frac{0 \cdot 85 W \times 8}{4} \times 12 \text{ tons-in.}$$

$$= 20 \cdot 4 W \text{ tons-in.}$$

Now $$M = fZ$$

Where $f = 10$ tons/sq in. and $Z = 81 \cdot 3$ in.^{3}

$$20 \cdot 4 W = 10 \times 81 \cdot 3$$

$$W = \frac{813}{20 \cdot 4} = 39 \cdot 8 \text{ tons}$$

Considering beam B:

$$M = \frac{0 \cdot 15 W \times 12}{4} \times 12 \text{ tons-in.} = 5 \cdot 4 W \text{ tons-in.}$$

$$M = fZ$$

Where $f = 10$ tons/sq in. and $Z = 57 \cdot 74$

$$5 \cdot 4W = 577 \cdot 4$$
$$W = 107 \text{ tons}$$

The safe point load is therefore 39·8 tons (assuming beam is safe in shear).

Propped Cantilever

Before proceeding to a discussion of the type of beam known as a propped cantilever, let us consider the difference between a beam simply supported at its two ends and a beam with its two ends rigidly fixed.

In Fig. 15.4(*a*), the ends of the beam are free to turn and there is

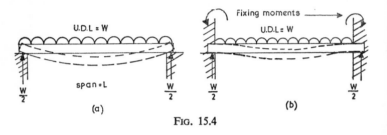

Fig. 15.4

therefore no bending moment at these points. The maximum bending moment is at mid-span and equals $WL/8$.

In Fig. 15.4(*b*), the ends of the beam are restrained from turning and therefore the middle of the beam does not deflect so much as in Fig. 15.4(*a*). The bending moment at mid-span is positive and can be proved to be equal to $WL/24$. Since the ends of the beam cannot turn, there are negative bending moments due to the restraining action of the supports, and the value of the bending moment at each end is $WL/12$.

Note that the beam of Fig. 15.4(*a*) could be converted into a beam of the type shown in Fig. 15.4(*b*) by applying moments at each end.

Propped cantilever: It is, in fact, wrong to call the type of beam shown in Fig. 15.5 a cantilever, since the beam is supported at both ends, but it will be seen later why the beam has been so named.

Referring to Fig. 15.5, the reactions at A and B are not equal. If each end, A and B, were simply supported, each reaction would be $W/2$, but the effect of the moment applied at A is to relieve the pressure on the support at B and to increase the pressure on the support at A. The reactions at the supports of the beam cannot be calculated by the methods described in Chapter 5. This type of beam is an example of redundant or statically indeterminate structures. The reactions and moments in a propped cantilever carrying a U.D.L. can, however, be calculated from a consideration of deflexions.

Fig. 15.6 is a cantilever fixed at A and the deflexion at the free end is given by $WL^3/8EI$. (Note that the deflexions shown in the diagrams are grossly exaggerated.)

Fig. 15.7 is an unloaded cantilever beam (the weight of which is

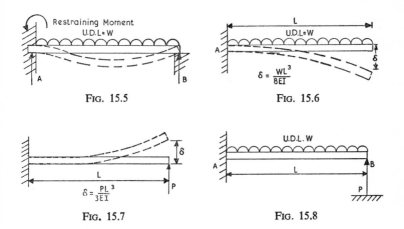

FIG. 15.5   FIG. 15.6

FIG. 15.7   FIG. 15.8

neglected) with an upward pressure of P lb or tons at its free end. The deflexion at the free end is $PL^3/3EI$.

Now consider Fig. 15.8, which can be called a propped cantilever. It is assumed that the prop is rigid and that end B of the beam is in the same horizontal line as A. If the prop were to be removed, B would deflect by $WL^3/8EI$. The upward deflexion due to the force P (i.e. $PL^3/3EI$) counteracts the downward deflexion due to the load (i.e. $WL^3/8EI$).

Therefore
$$\frac{PL^3}{3EI} = \frac{WL^3}{8EI}$$

Since L, E and I are the same values on both sides of the equation,

$$\frac{P}{3} = \frac{W}{8}, \text{ therefore } P = \frac{3}{8}W$$

Once the reaction at the prop is known, the shear force and bending moment diagrams can be drawn.

The shear force and bending moment diagrams are shown in

Fig. 15.9. Note that the maximum positive bending moment (considering the loads to the right of X) is (3 tons × 3 ft) — (3 tons × $1\frac{1}{2}$ ft) = $4\frac{1}{2}$ tons-ft. In general terms,

$$M = \left(\frac{3}{8}\,W \times \frac{3}{8}\,L\right) - \left(\frac{3}{8}\,W \times \frac{3}{16}\,L\right)$$

$$= \frac{9}{64}\,WL - \frac{9}{128}\,WL = \frac{9}{128}\,WL$$

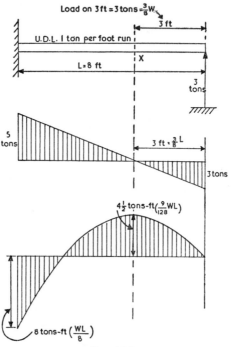

FIG. 15.9

The negative bending moment at the support is

(3 tons × 8 ft) — (8 tons × 4 ft) = —8 tons-ft

In general terms

$$M = \left(\frac{3}{8}\,W \times L\right) - \frac{W \times L}{2}$$

$$= \frac{3}{8}\,WL - \frac{WL}{2}$$

$$= \frac{3}{8}\,WL - \frac{4}{8}\,WL = -\frac{WL}{8}$$

Propped cantilevers which support point loads or a combination of point loads and uniformly distributed loads cannot be dealt with by the deflexion principle so easily as the beam described above. Books on theory of structures and strength of materials describe better methods of dealing with such cases.

The above method also does not apply if the shortening of the prop has to be taken into account.

Continuous Beam of Two Equal Spans carrying a Uniformly Distributed Load

The reactions and bending moments for the beam shown in Fig. 15.10 can be obtained in a similar manner to that employed for the propped cantilever.

The load on each span is W, so that the total load is $2W$. If the

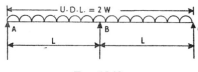

FIG. 15.10

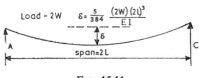

FIG. 15.11

middle support B were to be removed, the beam would deflect as shown in Fig. 15.11.

Let P (lb or tons) be the reaction supplied by the middle prop, and this reaction can be considered as a point load at the mid-span of a beam $2L$ units long. The deflexion due to this point load would be

$$\frac{(P)(2L)^3}{48EI}$$

Since the deflexion of the beam at the prop is zero,

$$\frac{(P)(2L)^3}{48EI} = \frac{5}{384} \cdot \frac{(2W)(2L)^3}{EI}$$

Cancelling equals from both sides

$$\frac{P}{48} = \frac{5}{384} \times 2W$$

$$P = \frac{10}{8} W = 1\tfrac{1}{4}W$$

Since the total load is $2W$, $R_A + R_C$ must equal $2W - 1\tfrac{1}{4}W$, i.e. $\tfrac{3}{4}W$; so that, from symmetry, $R_A = R_C = \tfrac{3}{8}W$.

Shear force and bending moment diagrams can be constructed as shown in Fig. 15.12.

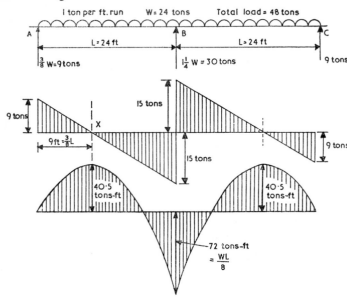

Fig. 15.12

Bending moment at $X = (9 \text{ tons} \times 9 \text{ ft}) - (9 \text{ tons} \times 4\tfrac{1}{2} \text{ ft})$
$$= 40\cdot5 \text{ tons-ft}$$

In general terms, $M = (\tfrac{3}{8}W \times \tfrac{3}{8}L) - (\tfrac{3}{8}W \times \tfrac{3}{16}L)$
$$= \frac{9}{128} WL = \frac{WL}{14\cdot2}$$

Bending moment at $B = (9 \text{ tons} \times 24 \text{ ft}) - (24 \text{ tons} \times 12 \text{ ft})$
$$= 216 - 288$$
$$= -72 \text{ tons-ft}$$

In general terms, $M = \tfrac{3}{8}W \times L - \dfrac{W \times L}{2}$
$$= -\frac{WL}{8}$$

SUMMARY

1. Two beams A and B, side by side and of equal spans

$$W = \text{total load}$$
$$W_A = \text{load carried by beam } A$$
$$W_B = \text{load carried by beam } B$$
$$I_A = \text{moment of inertia of beam } A$$
$$I_B = \text{moment of inertia of beam } B$$
$$\frac{W_A}{W_B} = \frac{I_A}{I_B} \quad \text{or} \quad W_A = \frac{I_A}{I_A + I_B} \times W$$

2. "Crossed beams" with point load at meeting point of the beams (mid-span)

$$L_A = \text{span of beam } A$$
$$L_B = \text{span of beam } B$$

Other symbols have same significance as in section (1) above.

$$\frac{W_A}{W_B} = \frac{L^3_B I_A}{L^3_A I_B}$$

If $I_A = I_B$ then $W_A = \dfrac{L^3_B}{L^3_A + L^3_B} \times W$

3. Propped cantilever of span L with U.D.L. of W

$$\text{Reaction at prop} = \frac{3}{8} W$$

$$\text{Maximum positive bending moment} = \frac{9}{128} WL$$

$$\text{Maximum negative bending moment} = \frac{WL}{8}$$

4. Continuous beam of two equal spans of L (total length $= 2L$) with U.D.L. of W on each span (total load $= 2W$).

$$\text{Reaction at centre support} = 1\tfrac{1}{4}W$$

$$\text{Reaction at each of two ends} = \frac{3}{8} W$$

$$\text{Maximum positive bending moment} = \frac{9}{128} WL$$

$$\text{Maximum negative bending moment} = \frac{WL}{8}$$

EXERCISE 15

1. Two steel beams A and B of 24 ft span, simply supported at their ends, are side by side as indicated in Fig. 15.1, page 294. The total load (inclusive of the weight of the beams) uniformly distributed over the whole span is 39 tons. Beam A is an 18 in. $\times$ 6 in. $\times$ 55 lb B.S.B. and beam B is a 15 in. $\times$ 5 in. $\times$ 42 lb B.S.B. ($I_{xx} = 428\cdot5$ in.⁴). Calculate the maximum fibre stresses in the beam.

2. Two timber beams A and B of 16 ft span, simply supported at their ends are side by side as indicated in Fig. 15.2, page 296. The total inclusive uniformly distributed load is 4,000 lb. Beam A is 3 in. wide and 12 in. deep and beam B is 4 in. wide and 8 in. deep. Calculate the maximum fibre stresses in the beams.

3. Two steel beams A and B of 20 ft span are side by side. Beam A is a 24 in. × 7½ in. × 95 lb B.S.B. and beam B is an 18 in. × 6 in. × 55 lb B.S.B. Calculate the maximum inclusive uniformly distributed load (U.D.L.) for the beams, the permissible bending stress being 10 tons/sq in.

4. Two timber beams A and B of 6 ft span simply supported at their ends are side by side. Beam A is 3 in. wide and 6 in. deep, while beam B is 2 in. wide and 8 in. deep. Calculate the maximum point load which may be placed at mid-span. The permissible bending stress for the timber is 800 lb/sq in.

5. A uniformly distributed load (which includes an allowance for the weights of the beams) of 14 tons has to be carried on a simply supported span of 12 ft. A 9 in. × 4 in. × 21 lb B.S.B. is to be used, together with another B.S.B. alongside it. Choose a suitable section for the second B.S.B., assuming a maximum fibre stress of 10 tons/sq in.

6. A uniformly distributed load (which includes an allowance for the weights of the beams) of 4,800 lb has to be carried on a simply supported span of 12 ft. A timber beam 3 in. wide by 12 in. deep is to be used alongside another timber beam also 3 in. wide. Calculate the required depth of the second beam, assuming a maximum fibre stress of 800 lb/sq in.

7. In an old building, a floor beam of timber is 8 in. wide and 12 in. deep and simply supported each end of a span of 16 ft. Calculate the safe U.D.L. for the beam, assuming a permissible bending stress of 1,000 lb/sq in. It is proposed to strengthen the floor by placing a 12 in. × 6 in. × 54 lb B.S.B. ($I_{xx} = 375 \cdot 8$ in.⁴) alongside the timber beam. Calculate the safe U.D.L. for the combined beams, assuming a steel stress of 20,000 lb/sq in. Calculate the maximum stress in the timber under the new arrangement. Young's modulus for steel is 30,000,000 lb/sq in. and Young's modulus for timber is 1,000,000 lb/sq in.

8. Two steel beams cross at mid-span in the manner indicated in Fig. 15.3, page 297. Each beam is a 12 in. × 5 in. × 32 lb B.S.B., one beam being 18 ft span and the other beam 16 ft span. The beams support a point load of 11½ tons at their point of intersection. Calculate the maximum stresses in the two beams, neglecting the weights of the beams.

9. Two "crossed beams" simply supported at their ends have dimensions as follows—

Lower beam—15 in. × 6 in. × 45 lb B.S.B. of 14 ft span

Upper beam—10 in. × 6 in. × 40 lb B.S.B. of 20 ft span

The beams support a point load of 22 tons at mid-span. Calculate the maximum stresses in the two beams.

10. Two "crossed beams" are simply supported at their ends and carry a load of 17 tons at mid-span. The lower beam is a 14 in. × 6 in. × 46 lb of 15 ft span, and the upper beam is 20 ft span. Assuming the lower beam to be stressed to 10 tons/sq in., choose a suitable B.S.B. for the upper beam, and calculate the maximum stress in it.

11. Two timber beams cross at mid-span as indicated in Fig. 15.3, page 297. Each beam is 3 in. wide and 6 in. deep and their spans are 8 ft and 12 ft respectively. The beams support a point load of 1,200 lb at the point where they cross. Calculate the maximum stresses in the two beams.

12. Two "crossed beams" of timber simply supported at their ends and crossing at mid-span have dimensions as follows—

Lower beam—3 in. wide, 9 in. deep, 9 ft span

Upper beam—3 in. wide, 6 in. deep, 12 ft span

Calculate the value of the maximum point load that may be placed at mid-span if the bending stress must not exceed 800 lb/sq in.

13. Two "crossed beams" of timber are simply supported at their ends and carry a load of 2,250 lb at the mid-span intersection point of the two beams. The lower beam is 3 in. wide and 8 in. deep of 8 ft span, and the upper beam is 3 in. wide and 12 ft span. Assuming the lower beam to be stressed to 1,000 lb/sq in., calculate the depth of the upper beam and the maximum stress in it.

14. A floor beam supporting a uniformly distributed load is a 15 in. × 5 in. × 42 lb B.S.B. of 20 ft span ($I_{xx} = 428 \cdot 5$ in.⁴). It is proposed to strengthen the floor by placing a cross beam symmetrically under the mid-span point of the 15 in. × 5in. × 42 lb B.S.B. This cross beam will be an 18 in. × 6 in. × 55 lb B.S.B. of 18 ft span. Calculate the safe uniformly distributed load for the system, the maximum bending stress being 10 tons/sq in. (Note that the load on the upper beam is uniformly distributed and the load on the lower beam is a point load at mid-span.)

15. Two cantilever steel beams are connected together as indicated in the plan of Fig. 15.13. Each beam is a 9 in. × 4 in. × 21 lb B.S.B. Calculate the maximum value of the load which can be suspended from A, the permissible bending stress being 10 tons/sq in.

16. A beam is 32 ft long and is continuous for two spans. There is a support at each end of the beam and another support at the same level 16 ft from each end support. The beam carries an inclusive U.D.L. of 1 ton per foot run. Calculate the reaction at the middle support and calculate the maximum positive and negative bending moments.

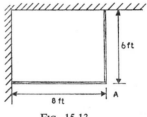

6 ft

8 ft

A

Fig. 15.13

17. A cantilever AB 10 ft long, fixed at A is originally horizontal (its own weight may be ignored). It is loaded with a U.D.L. of 8 tons. The deflected end B is then brought back to its original level by a stout strut at B. Determine the load on the strut. Calculate the value of the maximum bending moment in the beam.

18. A cantilever beam AB, 8 ft long, fixed at A, is a 10 in. × 6 in. × 40 lb B.S.B. and it supports a uniformly distributed load of 1 ton per foot run which includes the weight of the beam. (*a*) Calculate the maximum bending stress due to the load. (*b*) It is proposed to enable the beam to carry more load by propping up the end B to the same level as A by means of a column. Calculate the value of the extra U.D.L. that may be placed on the beam if the maximum permissible bending stress is 10 tons/sq in.

19. A steel beam AB is 40 ft long, simply supported at A and B, and at a point midway between A and B, so that the beam is continuous for two equal spans. The beam carries two point loads of 16 tons, one load being 10 ft from A and the other load 10 ft from B. Neglecting the weight of the beam, calculate the reactions and the maximum positive and negative bending moments.

20. Repeat Question 19, substituting $2L$ for 40 ft (i.e. each span is L ft) and W for each load of 16 tons.

CHAPTER 16

Axially Loaded Columns

WHEN the line of action of the resultant load is coincident with the centre of gravity axis of the column (Fig. 16.1), the column is said to be axially loaded and the stress produced in the material is said to be a *direct compressive stress*. This stress is uniform over the cross-section of the column. The term *concentric loading* is sometimes used instead of *axial loading*.

When the load is not axial, it is said to be eccentric (i.e. off-centre)

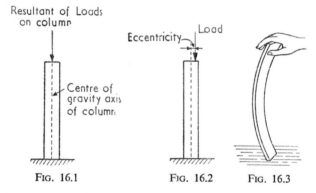

Resultant of Loads
on column

Centre of
gravity axis
of column

Eccentricity

Load

FIG. 16.1   FIG. 16.2   FIG. 16.3

and bending stress is induced in the column as well as a direct compressive stress (Fig. 16.2). Eccentric loading is dealt with in Chapter 18.

Other words used to describe members which are subjected to compressive stress are *pillar, post, stanchion, strut*. There are no definite rules as to when any one of these words should be used, but the following convention is fairly general:

Column and pillar can usually be applied to any material, e.g. timber, stone, concrete, reinforced concrete, steel. The word "post" is usually confined to timber. Stanchion is often used for rolled steel I sections and channel sections. Strut has a more general significance than stanchion or post but normally it is not applied to a main supporting member of a building. The word is often used for compression members of roof trusses whether the material is timber or steel.

Design Factors

The maximum axial load a column can be allowed to support depends on—

1. The material of which the column is made.

2. The slenderness of the column, which involves not only the length or height of the column but also the size and shape of its cross-section and the manner in which the two ends of the column are supported or fixed.

The majority of columns are designed by reference to tables of permissible stresses contained in British Standard Specifications and Building By-laws such as those of the London County Council. These tables of permissible stresses (which are reproduced on pages 311 and 319) have been constructed from complex formulae which have been derived as the result of a great deal of research, mathematical and experimental, into the behaviour of columns under load. It is not possible in this book to deal with the mathematical theories of column design but an attempt will be made to give an explanation of the general principles.

Timber Posts

Slenderness of Columns. A very short column will fail due to crushing of the material, but long columns are likely to fail by

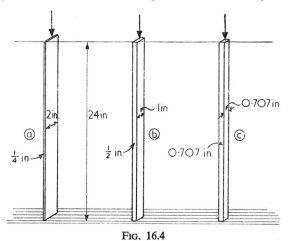

Fig. 16.4

"buckling," the failing load being much less than that which would cause failure in a short column of identical cross-sectional dimensions.

Consider Fig. 16.3, which represents a strip of pliable wood, say

$\frac{1}{4}$ in. $\times$ 2 in. in cross-section and 2 ft long. A small vertical force applied as shown will cause buckling. It should be obvious (but can be confirmed by experiment if necessary) that a larger force would be required to cause failure if the member were only 1 ft high. In other words, the 2 ft high member is more slender than the 1 ft high member of equal cross-sectional dimensions.

Now consider Fig. 16.4. All three members are of equal cross-sectional area (0·5 sq in.) and of equal height, yet member (b) will require more load to cause buckling than member (a) and member (c) is the strongest column.

Slenderness Ratio

By reference to Fig. 16.4 it should be obvious that the smaller cross-sectional dimension of the column is very important from the point of view of buckling and it appears that the slenderness ratio of a column can be defined as—

$$\frac{\text{height of column (in inches)}}{\text{least width of column (in inches)}}$$

e.g. slenderness ratio of columns $(a) = \dfrac{24}{0 \cdot 25} = 96$

$$(b) = \frac{24}{0 \cdot 5} = 48$$

$$(c) = \frac{24}{0 \cdot 707} = 34 \text{ approximately}$$

Since most timber posts and struts are rectangular in cross-section, it is reasonable to express the slenderness ratio in terms of the height and least width (i.e. least lateral dimension). This method is, in fact, adopted by the L.C.C. (Table 16.1) but note that there is an alternative slenderness ratio given, i.e.

$$\frac{\text{effective length}}{\text{least radius of gyration}}$$

and it is this slenderness ratio which must be used when the post is not of rectangular (solid) cross-section.

The properties of a column known as its effective height and least radius of gyration will be discussed later.

EXAMPLE 1

Calculate the permissible axial load for the following timber posts of Class B timber, all the posts being 10 ft effective height—

(a) 6 in. $\times$ 6 in.   (b) 9 in. $\times$ 4 in.   (c) 12 in. $\times$ 3 in.

(Note that these posts have equal cross-sectional areas.)

$$(a) \quad \text{Slenderness ratio} = \frac{120 \text{ in.}}{6 \text{ in.}} = 20$$

From Table 16.1 permissible stress $= 620 \text{ lb/sq in.}$

Area of cross-section $= 36 \text{ sq in.}$

Permissible axial load $= 620 \times 36$

$$= 22,320 \text{ lb}$$

$$(b) \quad \text{Slenderness ratio} = \frac{120}{4} = 30$$

The permissible stress for a slenderness ratio of 30 is not given directly in the table so the value must be found by interpolation.

Stress for $\frac{l}{b}$ of 29 $= 420 \text{ lb/sq in.}$

Stress for $\frac{l}{b}$ of 35 $= 320 \text{ lb/sq in.}$

TABLE 16.1

Maximum permissible compressive stress in posts and struts in lb/sq in.

Ratio of effective length to		Class of timber		Ratio of effective length to		Class of timber	
Least radius of gyration l/r	Least lateral dimension l/b	A	B	Least radius of gyration l/r	Least lateral dimension l/b	A	B
0	0	1,000	800	80	23	700	560
10	3	980	785	90	26	610	490
20	6	960	770	100	29	530	420
30	9	940	750	120	35	400	320
40	11	910	730	140	40	310	250
50	14	870	700	160	46	240	190
60	17	830	660	180	52	200	160
70	20	770	620	200	58	160	130

The maximum permissible compressive stress for intermediate values of l/r or l/b shall be obtained by interpolation between the two nearest stresses for the class of timber used.

(Examples of Class A timbers are Douglas fir, longleaf pitch pine and shortleaf pitch pine. Examples of Class B timbers are Canadian spruce, European larch, red pine, western hemlock and whitewood.)

Difference for $\dfrac{l}{b}$ of 6 = 100 lb/sq in.

Difference $\dfrac{l}{b}$ of 1 = 16·7 lb/sq in. approximately

Permissible stress for $\dfrac{l}{b}$ of 30 = 420 − 16·7

$$= 403·3 \text{ lb/sq in.}$$

Permissible axial load = 403·3 × 36

$$= 14,519 \text{ lb}$$

(c) Slenderness ratio $= \dfrac{120}{3} = 40$

Permissible stress = 250 lb/sq in.

Permissible axial load = 250 × 36

$$= 9,000 \text{ lb}$$

It is interesting to note that the 6 in. × 6 in. post can carry more than twice the load permitted for the 12 in. × 3 in. post.

EXAMPLE 2

A timber post of Class B timber of 10 ft effective height is required to support an axial load of 13,200 lb. Determine suitable dimensions for the cross-section of the post.

Dimensions must be assumed because it is not possible to determine the permissible stress until the slenderness ratio is known. For example, let the first trial be a post 6 in. square (area of cross-section = 36 sq in.).

Actual stress due to the load $= \dfrac{13,200}{36}$

$$= 366·7 \text{ lb/sq in.}$$

Slenderness ratio $= \dfrac{l}{b} = \dfrac{120}{6} = 20$

The permissible stress for a slenderness ratio of 20 is 620 lb/sq in., therefore the assumed size of 6 in. square is too large. As a second trial, assume a post 5 in. square.

Actual Stress $= \dfrac{13,200}{25} = 528 \text{ lb/sq in.}$

Slenderness ratio $= \dfrac{l}{b} = \dfrac{120}{5} = 24$

Permissible stress for $\frac{l}{b}$ of 23 = 560 lb/sq in.

$$26 = 490 \text{ lb/sq in.}$$
$$3 = 70 \text{ lb/sq in.}$$
$$1 = 23 \cdot 3 \text{ lb/sq in. (nearly)}$$

Permissible stress for $\frac{l}{b}$ of 24 = 560 − 23·3

$$= 536 \cdot 7 \text{ lb/sq. in.}$$

Since the permissible stress is slightly more than the actual stress due to the load, a 5 in. square post is suitable.

Steel Columns

Radius of Gyration

It has already been stated that the shape of the cross-section has an important bearing on the load carrying capacity of a column.

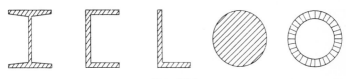

FIG. 16.5

A square timber post can support more load than a post of rectangular cross-section of equal area and equal height. It has been shown also that in the case of rectangular cross-section columns it is reasonable to base permissible stresses on a slenderness ratio obtained by dividing the height of the column by its least width. It is not possible, however, to use the dimension of least width when designing steel columns, one reason being the variety of steel sections which can be used. Some of these sections are shown in Fig. 16.5.

If one table of permissible stresses is to suffice for all steel columns, some method of calculating slenderness ratios must be adopted which can be applied to any shape of cross-section. A property which takes into account not only the size of the section (i.e. area) but also its shape (i.e. the arrangement of the material in the cross-section) is the *radius of gyration* which is obtained by dividing the moment of inertia I of the section by its area A and then extracting the square root. The symbol r is commonly used to denote radius of gyration but k and g are sometimes used.

Therefore $$r = \sqrt{\left(\frac{I}{A}\right)}$$

The use of the word "gyration" when applied to stationary columns in buildings may appear strange until it is realized that the word is also used in dynamics, which is the branch of mechanics dealing with bodies in motion. For example, consider Fig. 16.6 which

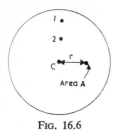

FIG. 16.6

represents a thin disc (such as a flywheel) rotating about its centre C. In dynamics, it is usually the mass (weight) of the wheel which enters into calculations but in this instance we shall consider the area A of the disc. Different particles of the disc travel at different velocities. For example, particle 1, in one revolution of the wheel, travels a greater distance than particle 2. In estimating the total energy of the disc the term Σay^2 enters into the calculations, Σay^2 being the sum of the second moments of all the particles of area about the centre C of the disc (Σay^2 is the moment of inertia, I).

Let it be imagined that all the area A of the disc is concentrated into *one* imaginary particle at a distance r from the centre of the disc. The moment of inertia about C of this particle is Ar^2 and if the total energy of the disc is to remain unaltered Ar^2 must equal the total moment of inertia I of the disc.

Therefore $$Ar^2 = I$$

and $$r = \sqrt{\left(\frac{I}{A}\right)}$$

The radius of gyration is, in this connexion, the distance from the centre at which the whole area of the wheel can be assumed to be concentrated so that the total energy remains unaltered.

In structural work, it is convenient to use the property $\sqrt{\left(\frac{I}{A}\right)}$ in conjunction with the height of the column for estimating slenderness ratios, and since this mathematical property of a cross-section is similar to the one used in dynamics for which the descriptive term "radius of gyration" exists, the same term is used in column calculations.

Least Radius of Gyration

In structural work we are not concerned with moment of inertia about a point as in the disc discussed above, but with moment of inertia with reference to a given axis. If a column of **I** section buckles under its load, the bending will be about the weaker axis

(axis $Y-Y$), as indicated in Fig. 16.7, therefore the radius of gyration must be calculated from I_{yy} which is the least moment of inertia.

Least radius of gyration

$$= \sqrt{\left(\frac{\text{least moment of inertia}}{\text{area of cross-section}}\right)}$$

i.e. $r = \sqrt{\left(\frac{I_{yy}}{A}\right)}$

Slenderness ratio

$$= \frac{\text{effective height of column (inches)}}{\text{least radius of gyration (inches)}}$$

$$= \frac{l}{r}$$

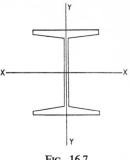

Fig. 16.7

Effective height will be defined later.

Further Discussion on Slenderness Ratio

A Swiss mathematician named Leonhard Euler (1707–1783) showed that a long thin homogeneous column, axially loaded, suffers no

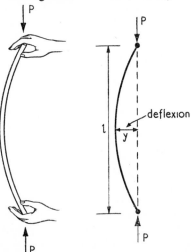

Fig. 16.8

deflexion as the load is gradually applied until a critical load (the collapsing or buckling load P) is reached. At this load, instability occurs and the column buckles into a curve, the column being in equilibrium under the action of the load P and its own elastic resisting forces (Fig. 16.8). The bending moment at mid-length of the column is Py.

It was shown in Chapter 14 that, in the case of uniform bending, a beam bends into the arc of a circle and the maximum deflexion y, is given by $y = Ml^2/8EI$ where M is the bending moment causing the deflexion. If, therefore, the curve of Fig. 16.8 is the arc of a circle, the same formula will apply, where Py is the bending moment, M.

$$y = \frac{Pyl^2}{8EI}$$

$$P = \frac{8EIy}{yl^2} = \frac{8EI}{l^2}$$

In fact, the curve of Fig. 16.8 is not the arc of a circle, and Euler found (with the aid of the calculus) that the buckling load P for a column such as that of Fig. 16.8 (two ends hinged or pinned) is

$$P = \frac{\pi^2 EI}{l^2} \text{, i.e. } \frac{9 \cdot 87 EI}{l^2}$$

Now $I = Ar^2$

$$P = \frac{\pi^2 EAr^2}{l^2}$$

Writing the formula in a different manner

$$\frac{P}{A} = \frac{\pi^2 E}{\left(\dfrac{l}{r}\right)^2}$$

P/A is the stress per unit area of cross-section at the critical or buckling load. As the term l/r becomes greater, the fraction $\pi^2 E/(l/r)^2$ becomes smaller, therefore the collapsing stress P/A gets less as the slenderness of the column increases.

Euler's formula is not used for design, since (except for very long columns) it gives a value of the collapsing load which is much higher than the actual collapsing load of practical columns, but it still forms part of modern column formulae. The object of the above discussion has been principally to give a reasonable explanation for the use of the radius of gyration in estimating the slenderness ratio of a column of any shape of cross-section.

EXAMPLE 3

Calculate the least radius of gyration of a 10 in. × 8 in. × 55 lb rolled steel joist section and its slenderness ratio, given that the effective height of the column is 10 ft.

From Table 12.1B $\quad I_{yy} = 54\cdot74$ in⁴.

$$A = 16\cdot18 \text{ sq. in.}$$

$$r = \sqrt{\left(\frac{54\cdot74}{16\cdot18}\right)} = 1\cdot84 \text{ in.}$$

Slenderness ratio $= \dfrac{l}{r} = \dfrac{120 \text{ in.}}{1\cdot84 \text{ in.}} = 65$ (approximately)

For most steel sections there is no need to calculate the radius of gyration since the values are tabulated in handbooks, etc. (see Table 12.1B).

Radius of Gyration of a Rectangular Cross-section Column

In Fig. 12.1B $\qquad$ least $I = I_{yy} = \dfrac{db^3}{12}$

$$A = db$$

Therefore least r

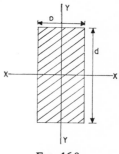

$$= \sqrt{\left(\frac{I}{A}\right)}$$

$$= \sqrt{\left(\frac{db^3}{12} \times \frac{1}{db}\right)}$$

$$= \sqrt{\left(\frac{b^2}{12}\right)} = \frac{b}{\sqrt{(12)}} = 0\cdot289b$$

$r_{yy} = 0\cdot289b$

Fig. 16.9

(Note that $r_{xx} = 0\cdot289d$)

EXAMPLE 4

A timber post is 4 in. × 3 in. in cross-section and has an effective height of 7 ft 3 in. Calculate its least radius of gyration and the slenderness ratio.

$$\text{Least } r = 0\cdot289b = 0\cdot289 \times 3 = 0\cdot867 \text{ in.}$$

$$\text{Effective height} = 7\text{ft } 3 \text{ in.} = 87 \text{ in.}$$

$$\text{Slenderness ratio} = \frac{l}{r} = \frac{87}{0\cdot867} = 100 \text{ approximately}$$

By reference to Table 16.1 it will be seen that l/r of 100 corresponds to l/b of 29; and in this case $l/b = 87$ in./3 in. $= 29$. Thus, when designing timber posts of rectangular cross-section by reference to Table 16.1 it is immaterial whether the slenderness ratio is taken as effective height divided by least radius of gyration (l/r) or as effective height divided by least width (l/b).

Radius of Gyration of a Solid Circular Cross-section Column

In Fig. 16.10 $I_{vv} = I_{xx} = \dfrac{\pi D^4}{64}$

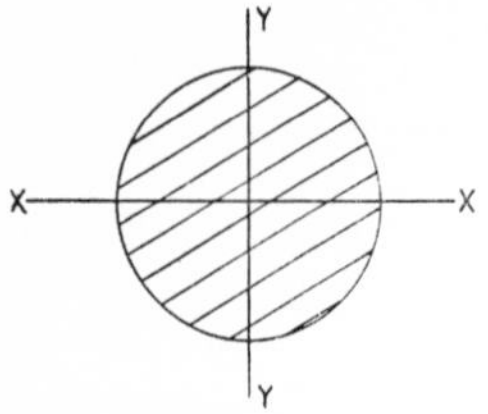

$A = \dfrac{\pi D^2}{4}$

$r_{vv} = \sqrt{\left(\dfrac{\pi D^4}{64} \times \dfrac{4}{\pi D^2}\right)}$

$= \sqrt{\left(\dfrac{D^2}{16}\right)} = \dfrac{D}{4}$

FIG. 16.10

i.e. the radius of gyration is one quarter the diameter of the circle, so that r for a 6 in. diameter solid round column is $1\frac{1}{2}$ in.

Radius of Gyration of a Hollow Circular Cross-section Column

In Fig. 16.11 $I_{vv} = I_{xx} = \dfrac{\pi}{64}(D^4 - d^4)$

$= \dfrac{\pi}{64}(D^2 + d^2)(D^2 - d^2)$

$A = \dfrac{\pi}{4}(D^2 - d^2)$

$r_{vv} = \sqrt{\left(\dfrac{\pi}{64}(D^2 + d^2)(D^2 - d^2)\right.}$

$\left. \times \dfrac{4}{\pi(D^2 - d^2)}\right)$

$= \sqrt{\left(\dfrac{D^2 + d^2}{16}\right)}$

$= \dfrac{\sqrt{(D^2 + d^2)}}{4}$

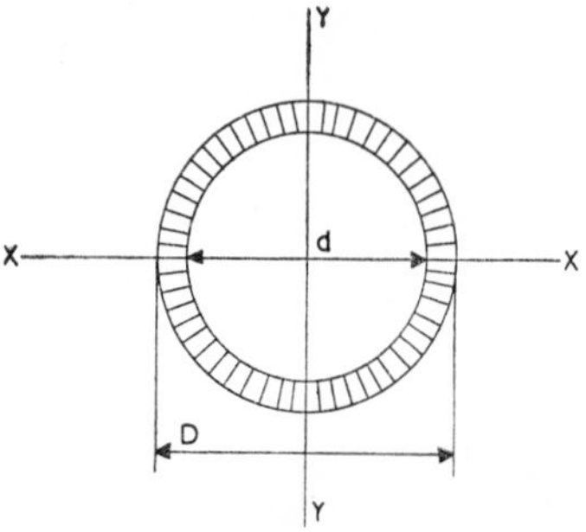

FIG. 16.11

For example, if $D = 6$ in. and $d = 4$ in.

$$r = \dfrac{\sqrt{(6^2 + 4^2)}}{4} = \dfrac{7 \cdot 2}{4} = 1 \cdot 8 \text{ in.}$$

It is interesting to note that the radius of gyration of a hollow section of 6 in. diameter is greater than that of a solid section of 6 in. diameter.

Increased Loads for Cased Columns

Many columns in buildings are cased in concrete which adds to their strength and stiffness. The radius of gyration of such cased columns is taken as $0.2 (B + 4)$ inches (see below) and the concrete casing is also allowed to take load.

B.S.449: 1959 states: "Struts of single $\mathtt{I}$ section or of two channels back to back in contact or spaced apart not less than $\frac{3}{4}$ in. or more than half their depth, and battened or laced in accordance with the requirements of clauses 35 and 36, may be designed as cased struts when the following conditions are fulfilled—

(i) The steel strut is unpainted and solidly encased in ordinary dense concrete, with $\frac{3}{8}$ in. aggregate (unless solidity can be obtained with a larger aggregate) and of a works strength not less than 3,000 lb/sq in. at 28 days when tested in accordance with B.S. 1881, *Methods for testing concrete:* Part 7 "Making and curing compression test cubes in the field," and Part 8, "Test for compressive strength of moulded cubes."

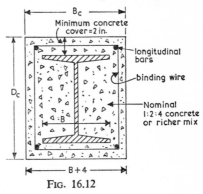

Fig. 16.12

(ii) The minimum width of solid casing is equal to $B + 4$ in., where B is the width overall of the steel flange or flanges in inches.

(iii) The surface and edges of the steel strut have a concrete cover of not less than 2 in.

(iv) The casing is effectively reinforced with wire to B.S. 785, *Rolled steel bars and hard-drawn steel wire for concrete reinforcement.* The wire shall be at least $\frac{3}{16}$ in. diameter and the reinforcement shall be in the form of stirrups or binding at not more than 6-in. pitch, so arranged as to pass through the centre of the covering of the edges and outer faces of the flanges and supported by and attached to longitudinal spacing bars not less than 4 in number.

The radius of gyration r of the strut section about the axis in the plane of its web or webs may be taken as $0.2 (B + 4)$ in. The radius of gyration about its other axis shall be taken as that of the uncased section.

In no case shall the axial load on a cased strut exceed twice that which would be permitted on the uncased section, nor shall the slenderness ratio of the uncased section, measured over its full length centre-to-centre of connexions, exceed 250. In computing the allowable axial load on the cased strut the concrete shall be taken as assisting in carrying the load over its rectangular cross-section; any cover in excess of 3 in. from the overall dimensions of the steel section of the cased strut being ignored. This cross-section of concrete shall be taken as assisting in carrying the load on the basis of a stress equal to the allowable stress in the steel (as given by p_c in Table 16.2 below) divided by 30 for steel to B.S. 15 and B.S. 2762 . . ."

"*Note:* This clause does not apply to steel struts of overall sectional dimensions greater than 30 in. $\times$ 18 in., the dimension of 30 in. being measured parallel to the web, or to box sections."

Thus, for uncased steel sections, the permissible axial load $= W = p_c A$ where p_c is the permissible compressive stress from Table 16.2 and A is the area of cross-section of the steel from Table 12.1A on page 252.

For cased stanchions, the permissible axial load is

$$W = p_c A + \frac{p_c}{30} \cdot B_c D_c$$

Note that $B_c D_c$ is the gross area of cross-section (*see* Fig. 16.12) and the area of the steel need not be deducted.

Permissible Compressive Stresses for Mild Steel Columns and Struts

The permissible axial stresses for mild steel complying with the requirements of B.S. 15, 1948, as given in B.S. 449:1959, are contained in Table 16.2 (for other types of steel see Table 17 in B.S. 449:1959).

TABLE 16.2

p_c = permissible compressive stress in tons/sq in.
l = effective height of column in inches.
r = least radius of gyration of column in inches.

$\frac{l}{r}$	p_c	$\frac{l}{r}$	p_c	$\frac{l}{r}$	p_c	$\frac{l}{r}$	p_c
0	9·50	70	5·83	140	2·61	210	1·28
10	8·98	80	5·30	150	2·33	220	1·17
20	8·45	90	4·77	160	2·08	230	1·08
30	7·93	100	4·24	170	1·87	240	1·00
40	7·40	110	3·75	180	1·69	250	0·93
50	6·88	120	3·32	190	1·54	300	0·66
60	6·35	130	2·94	200	1·40	350	0·49

Note: Intermediate values may be obtained by linear interpolation.

Maximum Slenderness Ratio

Although Table 16.2 gives values of permissible stresses for slenderness ratios up to 350, it is only in special cases that the slenderness ratio is allowed to exceed 180.

According to B.S.449: 1959, the ratio of the effective length, or of the length centre-to-centre of connexions, to the appropriate radius of gyration, shall not exceed the following values—

(i) For any member carrying loads resulting from dead weights with or without imposed loads and for single bolted or riveted single angle struts 180;

(ii) For any member carrying loads resulting from wind forces only, and provided that the deformation of such member does not cause an increase of stress, in any part of the structure, beyond the permissible stress . . . . 250.

For any member normally acting as a tie in a roof truss but subject to reversal of stress resulting from the action of wind, the ratio of the effective length to the least radius of gyration shall not exceed 350.

EXAMPLE 5

Calculate the safe axial load for a 10 in. × 8 in. × 55 lb uncased stanchion of 10 ft 6 in. effective height.

From Table 12.1B on page 253 least radius of gyration $(r) = 1.84$ in. and the area of cross-section $A = 16.18$ sq in.

$$\frac{l}{r} = \frac{126 \text{ in.}}{1.84 \text{ in.}} = 68.5, \text{ say } 69$$

From Table 16.2 permissible stress for $\frac{l}{r}$ of $60 = 6.35$ tons/sq in.

Permissible stress for $\frac{l}{r}$ of $70 = 5.83$ tons/sq in.

Difference for $\frac{l}{r}$ of . . . . . $10 = 0.52$ tons/sq in.

Difference for $\frac{l}{r}$ of . . . . . $1 = 0.052$ tons/sq in.

Permissible stress for $\frac{l}{r}$ of $69 = 5.83 + 0.052$

$$= 5.882 \text{ tons/sq in.}$$

Permissible axial load = permissible stress × area of cross-section

$$= 5.882 \times 16.18$$

$$= 95 \text{ tons (approximately)}$$

EXAMPLE 6

Calculate the safe axial load for a 12 in. × 6 in. × 44 lb cased stanchion of (*a*) 10 ft effective height; (*b*) 16 ft effective height.

(*a*) From Tables on pages 252 and 253, least radius of gyration of uncased section = 1·3 in. Area of cross-section = 13 sq in.

$$\text{Radius of gyration of cased section} = 0.2(B + 4)$$
$$= 0.2(6 + 4)$$
$$= 2 \text{ in.}$$

$$\text{Effective height} = 10 \text{ ft} = 120 \text{ in.}$$

For cased section, $\dfrac{l}{r} = \dfrac{120}{2} = 60$; $B_c = 10$ in.; $D_c = 16$ in.

From Table 16.2 permissible stress = 6·35 tons/sq in.

$$\text{Safe axial load } W = p_c A + \frac{p_c}{30} \cdot B_c D_c$$
$$= (6.35 \times 13) + \frac{6.35}{30} \times 10 \times 16$$
$$= 82.6 + 33.8$$
$$= 116.4 \text{ tons}$$

Before this load can be accepted it is necessary to determine whether it exceeds twice the load which would be permitted on the uncased section.

$$\frac{l}{r} = \frac{120}{1.3} = 92.4, \text{ say } 93$$

$$p_c \text{ for } \frac{l}{r} \text{ of } 90 = 4.77 \text{ tons/sq in.}$$

$$p_c \text{ for } \frac{l}{r} \text{ of } 100 = 4.24 \text{ tons/sq in.}$$

$$\text{Difference for } \frac{l}{r} \text{ of } 10 = 0.53 \text{ tons/sq in.}$$

$$\text{Difference for } \frac{l}{r} \text{ of } 1 = 0.053 \text{ tons/sq in.}$$

$$\text{Difference for } \frac{l}{r} \text{ of } 3 = 0.159 \text{ tons/sq in.}$$

$$\text{Permissible stress for } \frac{l}{r} \text{ of } 93 = 4.77 - 0.159$$
$$= 4.611 \text{ tons/sq in.}$$

$$\text{Safe axial load for uncased section} = p_c A$$
$$= 4.611 \times 13 = 60 \text{ tons}$$

Twice this load is 120 tons and, since the calculated safe load for the cased section does not exceed this value, the safe axial load for the cased stanchion is 116·4 tons. It should be noted that the safe loads for axially loaded stanchions can be read off directly from Tables 16.8 (A to D) on pages 338 to 341 but, for examination purposes, calculations would be required.

(b) Effective height = 16 ft = 192 in.

$$\frac{l}{r} = \frac{192}{2} = 96 \text{ (cased section)}$$

$$p_c \text{ for } \frac{l}{r} \text{ of } 90 = 4\cdot77 \text{ tons/sq in.}$$

$$p_c \text{ for } \frac{l}{r} \text{ of } 100 = 4\cdot24 \text{ tons/sq in.}$$

$$\text{Difference for } \frac{l}{r} \text{ of } 10 = 0\cdot53 \text{ tons/sq in.}$$

$$\text{Difference for } \frac{l}{r} \text{ of } 1 = 0\cdot053 \text{ tons/sq in.}$$

$$\text{Difference for } \frac{l}{r} \text{ of } 6 = 0\cdot318 \text{ tons/sq in.}$$

$$\text{Permissible stress for } \frac{l}{r} \text{ of } 96 = 4\cdot77 - 0\cdot318$$
$$= 4\cdot452 \text{ tons/sq in.}$$

$$\text{Apparent safe axial load} = p_c A + \frac{p_c}{30} B_c D_c$$
$$= (4\cdot452 \times 13) + \frac{4\cdot452}{30} \times 10 \times 16$$
$$= 58 + 23\cdot8$$
$$= 81\cdot8 \text{ tons}$$

Before this value can be accepted the safe load for the uncased section must be determined.

$$\frac{l}{r} = \frac{192 \text{ in.}}{1\cdot3} = 148$$

Permissible stress (from Table 16.2) = 2·386 tons/sq in.
Safe axial load = $p_c A$ = 2·386 × 13 = 31 tons

Twice this load $= 62$ tons and this is the maximum safe axial load for the cased stanchion and not $81 \cdot 8$ tons as calculated above. Tables 16.8A and 16.8C confirm the calculated results.

EXAMPLE 7

An uncased stanchion of ⊥ section is required to support an axial load of 100 tons. The effective height of the stanchion is 12 ft. Choose a suitable section.

From Table 16.8A it can be seen immediately that a suitable section is a 12 in. $\times$ 8 in. $\times$ 65 lb joist stanchion which is capable of supporting an axial load of 104 tons. When tables are not available it is necessary to make a guess at the size of the stanchion. For example, assuming a 10 in. $\times$ 8 in. $\times$ 55 lb joist stanchion and working from first principles, the safe axial load is $87 \cdot 2$ tons and this stanchion is therefore not adequate. Another guess would then be made and so on until a suitable stanchion is found.

Assuming a 12 in. $\times$ 8 in. $\times$ 65 lb stanchion, from Tables 12.1 and 16.8, $r = 1 \cdot 85$ in. and $A = 19 \cdot 12$ sq in.

$$\frac{l}{r} = \frac{12 \times 12}{1 \cdot 85} = 78$$

Permissible stress from Table 16.2 $= 5 \cdot 406$ tons/sq in.

Safe axial load $= p_c A = 5 \cdot 406 \times 19 \cdot 12$

$$= 104 \text{ tons nearly}$$

EXAMPLE 8

A hollow round steel column is $4\frac{1}{2}$ in. external diameter and the metal is $\frac{1}{4}$ in. thick. Calculate the safe axial load if the effective height is 10 ft.

External diameter, $D = 4\frac{1}{2}$ in.

Internal diameter, $d = 4$ in.

Area of cross-section $= \frac{\pi}{4}(D^2 - d^2)$

$$= \frac{\pi}{4}(4\tfrac{1}{2}^2 - 4^2)$$

$$= 3 \cdot 34 \text{ sq in.}$$

least $r = \dfrac{\sqrt{(D^2 + d^2)}}{4} = \dfrac{\sqrt{(4\tfrac{1}{2}^2 + 4^2)}}{4} = 1 \cdot 5$

Slenderness ratio $\quad = \dfrac{l}{r} = \dfrac{120}{1 \cdot 5} = 80$

Permissible stress $= 5 \cdot 3$ tons/sq in.

Permissible axial load $= 5 \cdot 3 \times 3 \cdot 34$

$$= 17 \cdot 7 \text{ tons}$$

EXAMPLE 9

A solid round steel column of 12 ft effective height is required to support an axial load of 65 tons. Choose a suitable section.

A column size must be assumed and checking calculations made. Assume a column 6 in. diameter.

$$\text{Area of cross-section} = \frac{\pi}{4} \times 6^2 = 28 \cdot 27 \text{ sq in.}$$

$$\text{radius of gyration} = \frac{D}{4} = 1 \cdot 5 \text{ in.}$$

$$\frac{l}{r} = \frac{144}{1 \cdot 5} = 96$$

Permissible stress (Table 16.2) $= 4 \cdot 452$ tons/sq in.

Permissible axial load $= 4 \cdot 452 \times 28 \cdot 27$

$$= 126 \text{ tons}$$

Since the load to be supported is only 65 tons, a smaller column will suffice.
Try a column 5 in. diameter.

$$\text{Area of cross-section} = \frac{\pi}{4} \times 5^2 = 19 \cdot 6 \text{ sq in.}$$

$$r = \frac{D}{4} = \frac{5}{4} = 1 \cdot 25 \text{ in.}$$

$$\frac{l}{r} = \frac{144}{1 \cdot 25} = 115 \cdot 2, \text{ say } 115$$

Permissible stress $= 3 \cdot 535$ tons/sq in.

Permissible axial load $= 3 \cdot 535 \times 19 \cdot 6$

$$= 69 \text{ tons}$$

This 5 in. diameter column is suitable since the axial load to be supported is 65 tons.

Effective Height (or Length) of Columns and Struts

B.S.449: 1959 states that for the purpose of calculating l/r (i.e. the slenderness ratio) an effective length should be assumed in accordance with Table 16.3 where L is the length of the strut from centre to centre of intersections with supporting members.

TABLE 16.3

Effective Length of Columns

Type	The effective length l of column
1. Effectively held in position and restrained in direction at both ends.	0·7L
2. Effectively held in position at both ends and restrained in direction at one end.	0·85L
3. Effectively held in position at both ends, but not restrained in direction.	L
4. Effectively held in position and restrained in direction at one end, and at the other partially restrained in direction but not held in position.	1·5L
5. Effectively held in position and restrained in direction at one end, but not held in position or restrained in direction at the other end.	2·0L

Explanation of Table

The reason why the effective height of a column may be less than or greater than its actual height in a building or structure is as follows: Only one table of permissible stresses (Table 16.2 on page 320) is given for the design of steel columns. The safe compressive stress for a column depends, however, not only on the actual height and cross-sectional dimensions of the column but also on the manner in which the ends of the column are restrained or fixed. Table 16.2 has been derived for one condition of end fixing (both ends pinned or hinged) and to make allowance for other conditions of end fixing, instead of constructing further tables of permissible stresses, adjustment is made by using a different height of column when calculating the slenderness ratio.

Before considering the end fixing of columns, it may be instructive to study the behaviour of beams as indicated in Fig. 16.13 (*a*), (*b*) and (*c*).

In Fig. 16.13 (*a*) both ends of the beam are free to bend upwards when the load is applied; in other words, the ends of the beam are not restrained in direction.

In Fig. 16.13 (*b*) one end of the beam is firmly fixed so that the

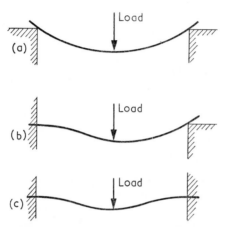

FIG. 16.13. (*a*) BOTH ENDS OF BEAM FREELY SUPPORTED (BENDING EXAGGERATED); (*b*) ONE END OF BEAM FIXED, ONE END FREELY SUPPORTED; (*c*) BOTH ENDS FIXED

end is restrained in direction, and in Fig. 16.13 (*c*) both ends of the beam are restrained in direction.

The load carrying capacities of these three beams will be different (other conditions being equal) because of the manner in which the ends of the beams are held or supported.

In a comparable manner, columns will buckle into different shaped curves according to the way in which the ends of the columns are held.

The columns of Fig. 16.14 are all restrained in position, i.e. the ends of the columns are not free to move sideways or backwards or forwards.

A greater load is required to cause column *b* to fail than column *a* and column *c* is the strongest. The length of curve marked *AB* in columns *b* and *c* is similar to the whole length of curve of column *a*, and this length is called the effective height of the column.

Column *a* is similar to case (3) of Table 16.3 on page 326, column *b* is similar to case (2) and column *c* is similar to case (1).

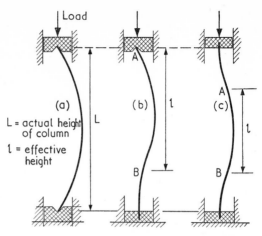

FIG. 16.14 (*a*) TOP AND BOTTOM OF COLUMN NOT RESTRAINED IN DIRECTION;
(*b*) TOP NOT RESTRAINED IN DIRECTION, BOTTOM RESTRAINED;
(*c*) TOP AND BOTTOM RESTRAINED IN DIRECTION

Case (5) in Table 16.3 can be explained by reference to Fig. 16.15. The tops of the columns are not restrained either in position or direction and will tend to buckle as shown. The effective height is therefore taken as twice the actual height of the column.

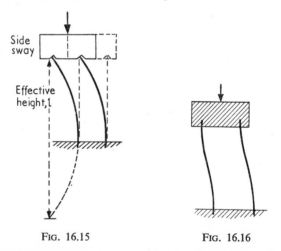

FIG. 16.15   FIG. 16.16

Fig. 16.16 represents columns which are restrained in position and direction at the bottom and direction only at the top. This case is a little better than case (4) of Table 16.3.

Practical Interpretation

B.S.449: 1959 gives typical examples of stanchions in multiple and single storey buildings and the effective lengths which may be used in their design. Since this chapter is concerned with *axial* loads on stanchions, only three examples (simplified) will be given.

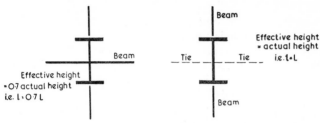

FIGS. 16.17 AND 16.18. PLAN OF CONNEXION AT TOP AND BOTTOM OF STANCHION

1. Interior stanchion in a steel framed building carrying four loaded beams (Fig. 16.17).

2. Interior stanchion carrying two loaded beams connected to the flanges of the stanchion and two non-loaded beams (tie beams) connected to the web (Fig. 16.18).

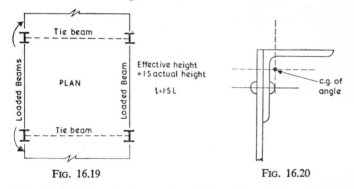

FIG. 16.19   FIG. 16.20

3. Stanchion in a single storey building of one bay as shown in Fig. 16.19 with load carrying beams on the flanges and a deep tie beam connecting the webs.

Angles as Struts

Struts in roof trusses and lattice girders frequently consist of single angle sections which are bolted or riveted by one leg to gusset plates. Since the centre of gravity of an angle section lies outside the legs of the angles (Fig. 16.20) and since the load is applied to the angle by means of the riveted or bolted connexion, this load is necessarily eccentric. In the past, various assumptions have been made to allow for the eccentricity of the load but B.S.449: 1959 has simplified design procedure by allowing the load to be considered as axial. The relevant clause in the B.S. is as follows—

Angles As Struts

For single angle discontinuous struts connected to gussets or to a section by either riveting or bolting by not less than two rivets or bolts in line along the angle at each end, or by their equivalent in welding, the eccentricity of the connexion with respect to the centroid of the strut may be ignored and the strut designed as an axially loaded member provided that the calculated average stress does not exceed the allowable stresses given in Table 17 (Table 16.2 in this book), in which l is taken as 0·85 times the length of the strut, centre to centre of intersections at each end, and r is the minimum radius of gyration.

Single angle struts with single bolted or riveted connexions shall be treated similarly, but the calculated stress shall not exceed 80 per cent of the values given in Table 17 (Table 16.2 in this book), and the full length l centre to centre of intersections shall be taken. In no case, however, shall the ratio of slenderness for such single angle struts exceed 180.

B.S.449: 1959 also contains clauses relating to double angle struts, back to back.

EXAMPLE 10

A 3 in. × 3 in. × ⅜ in. single angle section of length as shown in Fig. 16.21 has to transmit a compressive load of 6 tons. The length centre to centre of intersections is 7 ft. Check whether the angle is suitable.

From tables in structural steel handbooks,

$$\text{Area of cross-section} = 2 \cdot 11 \text{ sq in.}$$

$$\text{least } r = 0 \cdot 58 \text{ in.}$$

$$\frac{l}{r} = \frac{84 \times 0 \cdot 85}{0 \cdot 58} = 123$$

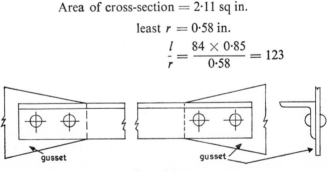

FIG. 16.21

Permissible stress, by interpolation, from Table 16.2.

$$= 3.206 \text{ tons/sq in.}$$

Permissible load = stress × area of cross-section

$$= 3.206 \times 2.11$$

$$= 6.7 \text{ tons}$$

Since this is greater than the actual load of 6 tons, the angle is suitable.

Reinforced Concrete Columns with Lateral Ties

Short Columns. C.P. 114 (1957) states that "Columns may be treated as short columns where the ratio of the effective length to least lateral dimension (i.e. least width) does not exceed 15."

The permissible stresses for concrete in direct compression as given in C.P.114 (1957) are contained in Table 16.4.

TABLE 16.4

Permissible concrete stresses C.P. 114 (1957)

Nominal mix	Permissible direct compressive stress
1 : 1 : 2	1140 lb/sq in.
1 : 1½ : 3	950 lb/sq in.
1 : 2 : 4	760 lb/sq in.

The L.C.C. By-laws (1952) give permissible column stresses for "quality A" concrete which are identical with those of Table 16.4 but for "ordinary grade" concrete the permissible stresses are lower (see Table 16.5).

TABLE 16.5

Permissible stresses for "ordinary grade" concrete.
L.C.C. By-laws (1952)

Designation of concrete	Nominal mix	Permissible direct compressive stress
Grade I	1 : 1 : 2	780 lb/sq in.
Grade II	1 : 1½ : 3	680 lb/sq in.
Grade III	1 : 2 : 4	600 lb/sq in.

Steel. The permissible stress for the longitudinal reinforcing bars (up to 1½ in. diameter) in axially loaded columns is 18,000 lb/sq in. for mild steel complying with B.S.785, 1938. Stronger steels are permitted higher stresses, up to a maximum of 23,000 lb/sq in.

Practical Requirements

Referring to Fig. 16.22—

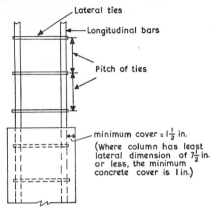

Fig. 16.22

LONGITUDINAL BARS: Minimum cross-sectional area =
0·8 per cent of gross cross-sectional area of column

$$= 0\cdot8 \text{ per cent of } A_g$$

Maximum cross-sectional area = 8 per cent of A_g
Minimum bar diameter $= \frac{1}{2}$ in.
Maximum bar diameter $= 2$ in.

LATERAL TIES: The object of the lateral ties is to prevent buckling of the longitudinal steel bars and to prevent shearing of the concrete on a diagonal plane.

Minimum bar diameter $= \frac{3}{16}$ in. or one-quarter of the diameter of the longitudinal reinforcement, whichever is the greater.

PITCH: The pitch (i.e. distance apart of lateral ties) shall not exceed the least of—

(a) The least lateral dimension (i.e. width) of the column;

(b) 12 times the diameter of the smallest longitudinal bar;

(c) 12 inches.

Design Details

Until the publication of C.P.114 in 1948, it was customary to assume that the stress in the steel was *m* times the permissible stress for the concrete where

$$m = \frac{\text{elastic modulus of steel}}{\text{elastic modulus of concrete}}$$

m was usually taken as 15, so that, if the permissible direct concrete stress was 760 lb/sq in. the permissible stress in the steel was 15×760, i.e. 11,400 lb/sq in.

Now, however, because of results of research into behaviour of loaded columns, ordinary mild steel is permitted to be stressed to 18,000 lb/sq in.

The permissible axial load *P* for a short reinforced concrete column is therefore—permissible stress for concrete times the area of concrete plus permissible stress for the steel times the steel area.

In symbols,

$$P = p_{cc}A_c + p_{sc}A_{sc}$$

Where *P* is the safe axial load in pounds. p_{cc} is the permissible stress for the concrete in direct compression (see Tables 16.4 and 16.5).

A_c is the area of concrete $= A_g - A_{sc}$ where A_g is the gross cross-sectional area p_{sc} is the permissible compression stress for column bars (18,000 lb/sq in. for mild steel).

A_{sc} is the cross-sectional area of the longitudinal steel.

EXAMPLE 11

A reinforced concrete column 10 in. square and 10 ft effective height contains four 1 in. diameter longitudinal bars. Calculate the safe axial load for the column if the permissible concrete stress is 760 lb/sq in. and the permissible steel stress is 18,000 lb/sq in.

Effective height of column $= 10$ ft $= 120$ in.

$$\frac{\text{Effective height}}{\text{least width}} = \frac{120}{10} = 12$$

therefore the column is short

Gross area of column $= 10 \times 10 = 100$ sq in.

Area of steel $= 4 \times 0.785$ $= 3.14$ sq in.

Area of concrete $= 96.86$ sq in.

Load taken by concrete = $760 \times 96{\cdot}86 = 73{,}613$ lb
Load taken by steel   = $18{,}000 \times 3{\cdot}14 = 56{,}520$ lb
Total safe axial load for column   = $130{,}133$ lb

or, by formula—

$$P = p_{cc}A_c + p_{sc}A_{sc}$$
$$p_{cc} = 760 \text{ lb/sq in.}$$
$$A_c = 100 - 3{\cdot}14 = 96{\cdot}86 \text{ sq in.}$$
$$p_{sc} = 18{,}000 \text{ lb/sq in.}$$
$$A_{sc} = 3{\cdot}14 \text{ sq in.}$$
$$P = (760 \times 96{\cdot}86) + (18{,}000 \times 3{\cdot}14)$$
$$= 130{,}133 \text{ lb}$$

Lateral Ties:

Minimum bar diameter = $\tfrac{1}{4}$ in.

Maximum pitch   = 10 in. (i.e. equal to width of column)

EXAMPLE 12

A short reinforced concrete column is required to carry an axial load of 100 tons. Design a square section column—(*a*) containing 0·8 per cent of steel; (*b*) containing 8 per cent of steel.

Permissible concrete stress is 760 lb/sq in.
Permissible steel stress is 18,000 lb/sq in.

(*a*)   Load = 100 tons = 224,000 lb

Let A_g = gross cross-sectional area of column

$A_g - A_{sc}$ = area of concrete

$$A_{sc} = \frac{0{\cdot}8}{100} A_g = 0{\cdot}008 A_g$$

Therefore $P = 760(A_g - 0{\cdot}008A_g) + (18{,}000 \times 0{\cdot}008A_g)$
$$= 760A_g - 6{\cdot}08A_g + 144A_g$$
$$= 898A_g$$

Therefore $A_g = \dfrac{P}{898} = \dfrac{224{,}000}{898} = 250$ sq in.

Length of side of square cross-section column = $\sqrt{250}$
$$= 15{\cdot}8, \text{ say } 16 \text{ in}$$

Steel area = $\dfrac{0{\cdot}8}{100} \times 250 = 2$ sq in.

Four $\frac{7}{8}$ in. diameter bars give 2·406 sq in.

(b)
$$A_{sc} = \frac{8}{100} A_g = 0.08 A_g$$

$$
\begin{aligned}
P &= 760(A_g - 0.08A_g) + (18,000 \times 0.08A_g) \\
&= 760A_g - 60.8A_g + 1,440A_g \\
&= 2,139A_g
\end{aligned}
$$

Therefore
$$A_g = \frac{P}{2,139} = \frac{224,000}{2,139} = 105 \text{ sq in.}$$

Length of side of square cross-section column

$$= \sqrt{105} = 10.2, \text{ say } 10\tfrac{1}{2} \text{ in.}$$

Steel area $= 8/100 \times 105 = 8.4$ sq in.

Four $1\frac{1}{4}$ in. diameter bars plus four $1\frac{1}{8}$ in. diameter bars give 8·885 sq in. (Fig. 16.23).

Fig. 16.23

Effective Height of Reinforced Concrete Columns

For axially loaded columns carrying four beams and two beams respectively as shown in Table 16.6, the effective heights of the columns may be assumed to be of the values given.

TABLE 16.6

Effective height of R.C. columns

L = actual height l = effective height

	Beams ↓ ↓ COL (col with four beams)	Beam COL Beam
Columns of one storey and top lengths of continuous columns	$l = 0.875L$	$l = 1.25L$
Columns continuing through two or more storeys, and bottom lengths of continuous columns	$l = 0.75L$	$l = L$

Long Columns

When the effective height exceeds fifteen times the least width of the column, the column must be considered as being long, and the safe axial loads for such columns are obtained by multiplying the safe load for a short column by the reduction coefficients given in Table 16.7.

TABLE 16.7

Reduction coefficients for stresses in long columns (C.P. 114, 1957)

Ratio of effective length to least lateral dimension of column	Coefficient*
15	1·0
18	0·9
21	0·8
24	0·7
27	0·6
30	0·5
33	0·4
36	0·35
39	0·3
42	0·25
45	0·2
48	0·15
51	0·1
54	0·05
57	0·0

*Intermediate values may be obtained by interpolation

EXAMPLE 13

An axially loaded column of 24 ft actual height and 12 in. square carries four beams, one on each face. The column contains four 1 in. diameter bars. Calculate the safe load for the column if the permissible stresses for a short column are, 760 lb/sq in. for the concrete and 18,000 lb/sq in. for the steel.

First, calculate the safe load for a short column.

$$P = 760(A_g - A_{sc}) + 18,000A_{sc}$$
$$A_g = 144 \text{ sq in.}$$
$$A_{sc} = 3\cdot14 \text{ sq in.}$$
$$P = 760(144 - 3\cdot14) + (18,000 \times 3\cdot14)$$
$$= 107,000 + 56,500$$
$$= 163,500 \text{ lb}$$

Assuming the column to be of one storey,
the effective height (from Table 16.6) $= 0.875 \times 24$

$$= 21 \text{ ft}$$
$$= 252 \text{ in.}$$

$$\frac{\text{effective height}}{\text{least width}} = \frac{252}{12} = 21$$

From Table 16.7 the reduction coefficient is 0.8.
Therefore

Safe axial load for the column $= 163,500 \times 0.8$

$$= 130,800 \text{ lb}$$

SUMMARY

Timber Columns. Permissible stresses for varying slenderness ratios are given in Table 16.1. If the column is of rectangular (solid) cross-section the slenderness ratio may be taken as: effective height divided by the least lateral dimension. If not of rectangular cross-section the slenderness ratio is: effective height divided by least radius of gyration. The effective height should be assumed in accordance with Table 16.3. The safe axial load for the column is obtained by multiplying the permissible stress by the area of cross-section of the column.

Steel Columns

$$\text{Slenderness ratio} = \frac{\text{effective height}}{\text{least radius of gyration}} = \frac{l}{r}$$

See Table 16.3 and pages 326–9 for a guide in estimating effective heights. Permissible stresses for varying slenderness ratios are given in Table 16.2.

The safe axial load is obtained by multiplying the permissible stress by the area of cross-section of the column.

least r for solid rectangular section $= 0.289b$

least r for solid circular section $= D/4$

least r for hollow circular section $= \dfrac{\sqrt{(D^2 + d^2)}}{4}$

least r for rolled sections, e.g. ⵉ sections, channels and angles can be obtained from Tables.

least r for cased beams of ⵉ section $= 0.2(B + 4)$

Reinforced Concrete Columns. A short column is one where the ratio of the effective column length to least lateral dimension does not exceed 15. A large number of columns in buildings are, therefore, "short."

$$\text{Safe axial load } P = p_{cc}A_c + p_{sc}A_{sc}$$

where $p_{cc} =$ permissible concrete stress (Table 16.4)

$A_c =$ area of cross-section of concrete

$\quad = A_g - A_{sc}$

$p_{sc} =$ permissible steel stress (usually 18,000 lb/sq in.)

$A_{sc} =$ area of steel

Guides to effective heights are given in Table 16.6. Reduction coefficients for long columns are given in Table 16.7.

TABLE 16.8A

Based on B.S.449: 1959

JOIST STANCHIONS: SAFE LOADS

(Reproduced by permission of the British Constructional Steelwork Association and the British Steel Makers)

Size $D \times B$ inches	Weight per foot in pounds	Safe Concentric Loads in Tons for Effective Lengths in Feet													
		6	7	8	9	10	11	12	13	14	15	16	18	20	2
24×7½	95	195	183	172	160	148	136	124	113	102	92·7	84·1	69·6	58·2	49
22×7	75	148	138	128	118	107	96·9	87·1	78·1	70·1	63·0	56·8	46·5	38·7	
20×6½	65	126	117	103	93·9	89·5	80·4	71·9	64·2	57·4	51·4	46·2	37·8		
18×6	55	103	94·7	86·3	77·8	69·3	61·4	54·3	48·1	42·8	38·2	34·2	27·8		
16×6	50	94·9	87·4	80·0	72·4	64·9	57·7	51·2	45·5	40·5	36·1	32·4	26·4		
15×6	45	85·1	78·3	71·5	64·7	57·8	51·4	45·5	40·4	35·9	32·1	28·8	23·4		
14×6	46	88·3	81·5	74·7	67·9	61·0	54·4	48·4	43·0	38·3	34·3	30·8	25·1		
14×5½	40	72·1	65·5	58·8	52·1	45·8	40·1	35·2	31·0	27·4	24·3	21·7			
13×5	35	60·1	53·7	47·3	41·2	35·7	30·9	26·9	23·6	20·7	18·4				
12×8	65	143	136	130	123	117	110	104	97·0	90·3	83·8	77·5	66·0	56·3	48
12×6	44	85·7	79·4	73·1	66·8	60·4	54·1	48·3	43·1	38·5	34·5	31·0	25·4		
12×5	32	54·4	48·5	42·5	36·8	31·8	27·5	23·9	20·9	18·4	16·3				

The above safe loads are tabulated for ratios of slenderness up to but not exceeding 1 Safe loads are calculated for the "effective lengths" of stanchions in accordance w Table 17 of B.S.449: 1959.

TABLE 16.8B

Joist Stanchions: Safe Loads
Based on B.S.449: 1959

(Reproduced by permission of the British Constructional Steelwork Association and the British Steel Makers)

Size D × B inches	Weight per foot in pounds	Safe Concentric Loads in Tons for Effective Lengths in Feet													
		3	4	5	6	7	8	9	10	11	12	13	14	16	18
×8	55	137	132	126	120	115	109	104	98·3	92·8	87·2	81·6	76·0	65·1	55·4
×6	40	95·5	90·0	84·6	79·1	73·7	68·2	62·7	57·2	51·7	46·5	41·7	37·4	30·3	24·8
×5	30	68·1	62·8	57·5	52·2	46·9	41·5	36·3	31·5	27·4	23·9	20·9	18·4		
×4½	25	55·0	50·1	45·2	40·3	35·3	30·4	26·0	22·2	19·1	16·5	14·4	12·6		
×4	21	44·5	39·7	35·0	30·2	25·5	21·3	17·8	15·0	12·7	10·9				
×6	35	83·7	79·0	74·3	69·6	64·9	60·2	55·5	50·8	46·0	41·5	37·2	33·5	27·1	22·3
×4	18	38·0	33·9	29·7	25·6	21·5	17·9	15·0	12·6	10·7	9·1				
×4	16	34·4	30·9	27·3	23·7	20·2	16·9	14·2	12·0	10·2	8·7				
×5	25	57·5	53·3	49·1	44·9	40·7	36·5	32·3	28·3	24·8	21·7	19·1	16·9	13·4	
×3	12	23·1	19·6	16·1	12·8	10·2	8·2	6·7							
×4½	20	45·4	41·9	38·4	34·9	31·4	27·9	24·4	21·2	18·5	16·1	14·1	12·4		
×3	10	19·6	16·9	14·1	11·4	9·1	7·3	6·0	5·0						

Each weight per foot is for the shaft only; weight of base, etc., to be added.

TABLE 16.9C

Based on B.S.449: 1959

CASED STANCHIONS: SAFE LOADS

(Reproduced by permission of the British Constructional Steelwork Association and the British Steel Makers)

Minimum Size $D_o \times B_o$ inches	Core Weight per foot in pounds	Safe Concentric Loads in Tons for Effective Lengths in Feet												
		6	8	10	12	14	16	18	20	22	24	26	28	30
28 × 11½	95	304	283	261	240	*205*	*168*	*139*	*116*	*98·6*	*84·3*	*72·9*	*63·6*	*5*
26 × 11	75	246	228	210	*175*	*140*	*114*	*93·1*	*77·5*	*65·3*	*55·6*	*48·0*	*41·8*	
24 × 10½	65	212	195	179	*144*	*115*	*92·7*	*75·7*	*62·8*	*52·8*	*45·0*	*38·8*		
22 × 10	55	179	164	*139*	*109*	*85·6*	*68·4*	*55·7*	*46·0*	*38·6*	*32·9*			
20 × 10	50	163	149	130	*103*	*81·1*	*65·0*	*52·9*	*43·8*	*36·8*	*31·3*			
19 × 10	45	149	137	*116*	*91·3*	*72·0*	*57·6*	*46·9*	*38·8*	*32·6*	*27·7*			
18 × 10	46	149	137	*122*	*97·0*	*76·9*	*61·7*	*50·2*	*41·6*	*35·0*	*29·8*	*25·6*		
18 × 9½	40	131	118	*91·7*	*70·4*	*54·7*	*43·5*	*35·2*	*29·1*	*24·4*				
17 × 9	35	114	*94·7*	*71·5*	*53·9*	*41·6*	*32·8*	*26·4*	*21·8*					
16 × 12	65	202	189	175	162	149	135	122	108	95·8	83·6	72·7	63·8	5
16 × 10	44	140	128	*116*	*96·7*	*77·1*	*62·1*	*50·8*	*42·1*	*35·4*	*30·2*	*26·0*		
16 × 9	32	105	*85·1*	*63·7*	*47·9*	*36·9*	*29·0*	*23·4*	*19·3*					
14 × 12	55	173	161	150	138	127	115	104	92·4	81·2	70·1	60·9	53·5	4
14 × 10	40	125	115	104	*93·1*	*75·0*	*60·6*	*49·7*	*41·4*	*34·8*	*29·7*	*25·6*	*22·3*	
14 × 9	30	96·6	83·0	*63·1*	*47·8*	*36·9*	*29·2*	*23·6*	*19·4*					
14 × 8½	25	*80·5*	*60·8*	*44·5*	*33·0*	*25·2*	*19·8*	*15·9*						
13 × 8	21		*60·4*	*42·6*	*30·0*	*21·9*	*16·6*	*12·9*						
12 × 10	35	109	99·8	90·8	81·8	*67·0*	*54·3*	*44·6*	*37·1*	*31·3*	*26·7*	*23·0*	*20·1*	
12 × 8	18		*51·2*	*35·9*	*25·2*	*18·4*	*13·9*	*10·9*						
11 × 8	16		*47·5*	*33·9*	*24·0*	*17·6*	*13·3*	*10·4*						
10 × 9	25	76·7	69·5	56·7	*43·5*	*33·8*	*26·8*	*21·7*	*17·9*	*15·0*				
10 × 7	12	*25·7*	*16·4*	*11·1*	*7·9*									
9 × 8½	20	*61·3*	*55·1*	*42·5*	*32·3*	*24·9*	*19·7*	*15·9*	*13·1*	*11·0*				
8 × 7	10	*22·8*	*14·8*	*10·0*	*7·2*									

The above safe loads are calculated for effective slenderness ratios not exceeding 180 the cased section and the term "effective length" at the head of the table is applicable to the cased section.

The slenderness ratio of the uncased section, measured over its full length centre to cen of connexions, should in no case exceed 250. Tabular loads are terminated in accorda with this limit, using for the purpose the lengths at the head of the table as actual leng

Tabular loads printed in italics are based on loads restricted to 100 per cent in exces those permitted on the uncased section.

TABLE 16.8D

Cased Stanchions: Dimensions and Properties
Based on B.S. 449: 1959

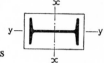

(Reproduced by permission of the British Constructional Steelwork Association and the British Steel Makers)

Core Composed of One Steel Joist	Core Area in square inches	Cased Section Area in square inches	Radius of Gyration			Section Modulus	
			Axis *y-y*		Axis *x-x*	Axis *y-y*	Axis *x-x*
			Cased Section	Core only	Core only		
24 × 7½ @ 95	27·94	322	2·30	1·50	9·52	16·68	211·09
22 × 7 @ 75	22·06	286	2·20	1·36	8·72	11·73	152·44
20 × 6½ @ 65	19·12	252	2·10	1·31	8·01	10·02	122·62
18 × 6 @ 55	16·18	220	2·00	1·21	7·21	7·88	93·53
16 × 6 @ 50	14·71	200	2·00	1·24	6·48	7·49	77·26
15 × 6 @ 45	13·24	190	2·00	1·23	6·10	6·62	65·59
14 × 6 @ 46	13·59	180	2·00	1·26	5·71	7·15	63·22
14 × 5½ @ 40	11·77	171	1·90	1·12	5·66	5·38	53·87
13 × 5 @ 35	10·30	153	1·80	1·03	5·25	4·33	43·62
12 × 8 @ 65	19·12	192	2·40	1·85	5·05	16·30	81·30
12 × 6 @ 44	13·00	160	2·00	1·30	4·94	7·37	52·79
12 × 5 @ 32	9·45	144	1·80	1·01	4·84	3·88	36·84
10 × 8 @ 55	16·18	168	2·40	1·84	4·22	13·69	57·74
10 × 6 @ 40	11·77	140	2·00	1·36	4·17	7·25	40·96
10 × 5 @ 30	8·85	126	1·80	1·05	4·06	3·89	29·25
10 × 4½ @ 25	7·35	119	1·70	0·94	4·08	2·88	24·47
9 × 4 @ 21	6·18	104	1·60	0·82	3·62	2·07	18·03
8 × 6 @ 35	10·30	120	2·00	1·38	3·34	6·51	28·76
8 × 4 @ 18	5·30	96	1·60	0·81	3·24	1·75	13·91
7 × 4 @ 16	4·75	88	1·60	0·84	2·89	1·69	11·29
6 × 5 @ 25	7·37	90	1·80	1·11	2·44	3·64	14·56
6 × 3 @ 12	3·53	70	1·40	0·64	2·44	0·97	7·00
5 × 4½ @ 20	5·88	76·5	1·70	1·06	2·06	2·93	10·01
4 × 3 @ 10	2·94	56	1·40	0·67	1·63	0·88	3·89

The weights per foot are for the main steel shaft only. Weights of bases and connexions are to be added and suitable allowances made where necessary for binding wire and casing.

The stanchions must be constructed to comply with the requirements of clause 30b of B.S. 449: 1959.

EXERCISE 16

1. Calculate the safe axial loads for the following posts all of Class B timber: (*a*) 3 in. square, 6 ft effective height; (*b*) 4 in. square, 8 ft effective height; (*c*) 6 in. square, 10 ft effective height.

2. Calculate the safe axial loads for the following posts of Class B timber all of 10 ft effective height: (*a*) 6 in. × 2 in. (*b*) 4 in. × 3 in. (*c*) 5 in. × 4 in. (*d*) 6 in. × 3 in.

3. A timber post of 12 ft effective height is required to support an axial load of 51,840 lb. Determine the length of side of a square section post of Class A timber.

4. A timber post of Class A timber has an effective height of 11 ft and is 12 in. diameter (solid circular cross-section). Calculate the value of the safe axial load.

5. A timber post of solid circular cross-section is of Class A timber and 10 ft effective height. It has to support an axial load of 68,500 lb. Determine the diameter of the post.

6. Two timber posts 8 in. × 3 in. in cross-section of Class B timber are placed side by side without being connected together to form a post 8 in. × 6 in. The effective height of the posts is 9 ft. Calculate the safe axial load for the compound post and compare this load with the safe axial load of one solid post 8 in. × 6 in. in cross-section of the same effective height.

7. Calculate the safe axial loads for a 8 in. × 6 in. × 35 lb uncased stanchion of ⊥ section for the following effective heights: 8 ft, 10 ft, 12 ft, 14 ft, 16 ft.

8. Repeat Question 7 assuming the stanchions to be adequately cased in concrete.

9. Calculate the safe axial loads for 10 in. × 8 in. × 55 lb cased stanchions of effective heights 10 ft, 12 ft, 14 ft, 16 ft, 18 ft.

10. Calculate the safe axial loads for 10 in. × 6 in. × 40 lb cased stanchions of effective heights 10 ft, 12 ft, 14 ft, 16 ft, 18 ft.

11. Determine the maximum permissible effective height of a 4 in. × 3 in. × 10 lb stanchion of ⊥ section assuming the stanchion is uncased. Calculate the safe axial load for such effective height.

12. Choose a suitable uncased stanchion of ⊥ section to support an axial load of 98 tons, the effective height being 10 ft.

13. Make calculations to determine which of the following stanchions is capable of supporting the greater axial load: (*a*) A stanchion consisting of two 8 in. × 4 in. × 18 lb uncased ⊥ sections placed side by side without being connected together; effective height = 8 ft. (*b*) One 8 in. ×6 in. × 35 lb uncased ⊥ section of 8 ft effective height.

14. Calculate the safe axial load for solid round steel columns of effective height 12 ft assuming the following diameters: 4 in., 6 in., 8 in., 10 in., 12 in.

15. Calculate the safe axial load for a 22 in. × 7 in. × 75 lb cased stanchion of ⊥ section of 10 ft effective height. Choose a stanchion of circular cross-section which is equivalent in load bearing capacity to the stanchion of ⊥ section.

16. Two 4 in. diameter solid round steel columns placed close together have an effective height of 11 ft. Calculate the safe axial load for the columns. Calculate the diameter of one column which would be equivalent in load carrying capacity to the two columns.

17. A hollow round steel column is 3 in. outside diameter and the metal is ¼ in. thick. Calculate the safe axial load for each of the effective heights specified: 4 ft, 6 ft, 8 ft, 10 ft.

18. A strut in a roof truss is a single angle section 3 in. × 3 in. × ¼ in. The

actual length of the strut is 6 ft and it is adequately secured to gussets at both ends by rivets and bolts as described on page 330. Calculate the safe load for the strut ($A = 1.44$ sq in. least $r = 0.59$ in.).

19. The reaction at the shoe of a roof truss is 4 tons as indicated in Fig. 16.24. Choose a suitable angle section for the strut marked A, which is 6 ft long between fastenings.

20. A bracket is fixed to the flange of a stanchion, as indicated in Fig. 16.25. Assuming the strength of the tie is more than adequate, calculate the maximum value of the load W. The strut is a $2\frac{1}{2}$ in. × $2\frac{1}{2}$ in. × $\frac{1}{4}$ in. single angle section ($A = 1.19$ sq in., least $r = 0.49$ in.).

21. Calculate the safe axial load for a 15 in. square "short" reinforced concrete column containing eight 1 in. diameter bars.

Fig. 16.24

$$p_{cc} = 760 \text{ lb/sq in.}; \qquad p_{sc} = 18,000 \text{ lb/sq in.}$$

22. Calculate the safe axial load for an 18 in. diameter "short" circular cross-section reinforced concrete column containing six $1\frac{1}{8}$ in. diameter bars.

$$p_{cc} = 760 \text{ lb/sq in.}; \qquad p_{sc} = 18,000 \text{ lb/sq in.}$$

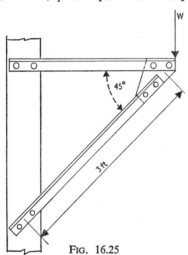

Fig. 16.25

23. Design a square cross-section column to support a load of 200 tons assuming 4 per cent of steel.

$$p_{cc} = 950 \text{ lb/sq in.}; \qquad p_{sc} = 18,000 \text{ lb/sq in.}$$

24. Repeat Question 23 for a circular cross-section column.

25. Design a short column to carry 250 tons, assuming: (a) $p_{cc} = 1,140$ lb/sq in., $p_{sc} = 20,000$ lb/sq in. 8 per cent steel. (b) $p_{cc} = 600$ lb/sq in., $p_{sc} = 18,000$ lb/sq in. 0.8 per cent steel.

26. Compare the load carrying capacities of a timber and a reinforced concrete column both 10 ft effective height and 12 in. square. The timber is Class A and the R.C. column contains eight 1 in. diameter bars.

$$p_{cc} = 760 \text{ lb/sq in.} \qquad p_{sc} = 18,000 \text{ lb/sq in.}$$

27. One dimension of a "short" R.C. column must not exceed 10 in. The column has to support an axial load of 289,900 lb. Assuming 4 per cent steel, design the column.

$$p_{cc} = 760 \text{ lb/sq in.} \qquad p_{sc} = 18,000 \text{ lb/sq in.}$$

28. The bottom length of a reinforced concrete column in a multi-storey building supports five floors and a flat roof. The area of each floor supported by the column is 400 sq ft and the *inclusive* loads are 150 lb/sq ft for the flat roof and 200 lb/sq ft for each floor. Design a suitable column ("short") assuming 4 per cent steel.

$$p_{cc} = 760 \text{ lb/sq in.} \qquad p_{sc} = 18,000 \text{ lb/sq in.}$$

29. A column is 15 in. square and 30 ft effective height and it contains eight 1 in. diameter bars. Calculate the safe axial load assuming

$$p_{cc} = 760 \text{ lb/sq in. and } p_{sc} = 18,000 \text{ lb/sq in.}$$

30. A "short" column is 18 in. square and it has to support an axial load of 200 tons. Calculate the area of steel required.

$$p_{cc} = 760 \text{ lb/sq in.} \qquad p_{sc} = 18,000 \text{ lb/sq in.}$$

CHAPTER 17

Riveted and Bolted Connexions

General

A RIVET or bolt may be considered as simply a *peg* inserted in holes drilled in two or more thicknesses of steel to prevent relative movement. For example, the two steel plates in Fig. 17.1 tend to slide

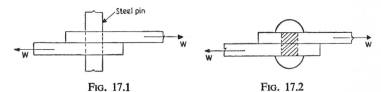

FIG. 17.1   **FIG. 17.2**

over each other, but could be prevented from doing so by a suitable steel pin inserted in the holes in each plate, as shown. In order to prevent the *steel pin* from slipping out of the holes, rivet heads are, of course, formed, and these produce an effective joint (Fig. 17.2).

The rivet heads (or bolt heads and nuts) do, in fact, strengthen the joint by pressing the two thicknesses of plate together, but their strength cannot be determined easily, and so the rivet strength is calculated on the assumption that the shank of the rivet (shown shaded) only is used in building up its strength.

Single Shear

If the loads W in Fig. 17.2 are large enough, the rivet could fail, as in Fig. 17.3, by the rivet *shearing* or breaking by the sliding of its

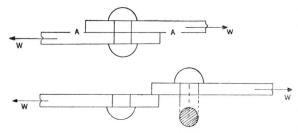

FIG. 17.3

fibres along line $A–A$. This type of rivet or bolt failure is known as failure in single shear, and the student should note that the area of steel rivet resisting this failure is the circular area of the rivet shank, as seen in plan.

i.e. $\dfrac{\pi}{4} \times$ (diameter of rivet)^2 or $0\cdot7854d^2 = A$

The safe allowable stress in single shear is given in B.S.449: 1959 as—

(*a*) 5 tons/sq in. for ordinary black bolts;

(*b*) 6 tons/sq in. for power-driven field rivets;

(*c*) 6·5 tons/sq in. for power-driven shop rivets;

(*d*) 6 tons/sq in. for close tolerance and turned bolts.

Black bolts are manufactured from rolled steel bars and, owing to the difficulties in rolling round black bars to the exact required diameter, it is customary to drill the holes in the plates, etc., $\frac{1}{16}$ in. greater in diameter than the specified diameter of the bolt.

Turned and fitted bolts are made from rolled steel bars which are greater in diameter than the required size of the bolt. The bars are then turned down to the required diameter. These bolts give a better fit in the holes than black bolts and are therefore allowed higher stresses. It is customary to drill the holes $\frac{1}{32}$ in. greater in diameter than the specified size of the bolt.

Shop driven rivets are driven in the fabricating shop and they are usually driven by a special machine. The rivets and the rivet heads are formed more accurately than is possible in the case of site rivets and they are therefore permitted a higher stress. The holes are drilled $\frac{1}{16}$ in. larger in diameter than the specified sizes of the rivets.

Nominal Diameter and Gross Diameter:

The nominal diameter refers to the specified size of the rivet shank, i.e. the diameter of the rivet when it is cold. When the rivet is heated until it is soft, inserted in the hole and the rivet head formed, the rivet metal fills the hole completely so that the gross diameter is $\frac{1}{16}$ in. larger than the specified diameter (i.e. nominal diameter) of the rivet. B.S.449: 1959, allows the strength of a rivet to be estimated on its *gross* diameter.

For example, the safe load in single shear (safe stress × area) of a $\frac{3}{4}$ in. diameter shop rivet is

$$0\cdot7854 \times \left(\dfrac{13}{16}\right)^2 \times 6\cdot5$$

$$= 0\cdot5185 \times 6\cdot5 = 3\cdot37 \text{ tons}$$

For bolts the gross diameter is, of course. equal to the nominal diameter, therefore the safe load in single shear, or single shear value (S.S.V.) of a $\frac{3}{4}$ in. diameter turned bolt is

$$0\cdot7854 \times (\tfrac{3}{4})^2 \times 6 = 0\cdot4418 \times 6$$
$$= 2\cdot651 \text{ tons}$$

S.S.V. of one $\frac{3}{4}$ in. diameter site rivet (or field rivet), power-driven,

$$= 0\cdot7854 \times (\tfrac{13}{16})^2 \times 6$$
$$= 0\cdot5185 \times 6 = 3\cdot11 \text{ tons}$$

S.S.V. of one $\frac{3}{4}$ in. diameter black bolt is

$$0\cdot7854 \times (\tfrac{3}{4})^2 \times 5$$
$$= 0\cdot4418 \times 5 = 2\cdot21 \text{ tons}$$

Table 17.1 gives the areas of circles for the diameters which are usually encountered in rivet and bolt calculations.

TABLE 17.1

AREAS OF CIRCLES

Diameter (in.)	$\frac{3}{8}$	$\frac{7}{16}$	$\frac{1}{2}$	$\frac{9}{16}$	$\frac{5}{8}$	$\frac{11}{16}$	$\frac{3}{4}$	$\frac{13}{16}$	$\frac{7}{8}$	$\frac{15}{16}$	1	$1\frac{1}{16}$
Area (in.²)	0·1104	0·1503	0·1964	0·2485	0·3068	0·3712	0·4418	0·5185	0·6013	0·6903	0·7854	0·8866

Rivets of $\frac{3}{4}$ in. diameter and $\frac{7}{8}$ in. diameter are common for beams and stanchions and their connexions. $\frac{1}{2}$ in, $\frac{5}{8}$ in., $\frac{3}{4}$ in., $\frac{7}{8}$ in. diameter may be used for roof trusses, etc., depending on the size of the truss; 1 in. diameter rivets and bolts are used only for large constructions, e.g. bridges.

Double Shear

In the type of connexion shown for example in Fig. 17.4 (a double cover butt joint), the rivet or rivets on one side of the joint would have to shear across *two* planes, as shown, and this is known as failure in double shear.

A rivet or bolt under these circumstances will need twice as much load to break it compared with a rivet or bolt in single shear, so the safe load on a rivet in double shear is twice that on the same rivet in single shear. Thus, using the circular area of the rivet shank as before, the safe load in double shear = area × 2 × single shear safe stress.

The safe load for a $\frac{7}{8}$ in. diameter black bolt

$$= 2 \times \text{area} \times \text{shear stress}$$
$$= 2 \times 0.6013 \times 5$$
$$= 6.01 \text{ tons}$$

The safe load or double shear value (D.S.V.) of a $\frac{3}{4}$ in. diameter site rivet $= 2 \times 0.5185 \times 6 = 6.22$ tons

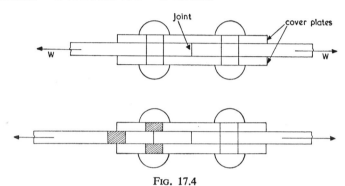

Fig. 17.4

Bearing

The two main ways in which the rivet or bolt itself may fail have been discussed. This type of failure assumes, however, fairly thick steel plates capable of generating sufficient stress to shear the rivet.

Consider Fig. 17.5, for example. The heavy load of 12 tons taken

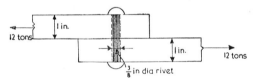

Fig. 17.5

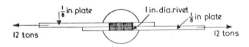

Fig. 17.6

by the 1 in. steel plates would certainly shear the $\frac{3}{8}$ in. diameter rivet (single shear).

Now consider the opposite type of case, as in Fig. 17.6, where a thick steel rivet (1 in. diameter) is seen connecting two very thin steel plates.

The steel plates in this case are much more likely to be torn by the rivet than the rivet to be sheared by the weaker steel plates.

This type of failure is known as bearing (or tearing), and the student should again note the area which is effective in resisting this type of stress (Fig. 17.7). The area of contact of the rivet with

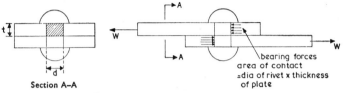

Section A–A

FIG. 17.7

the plate on one side of it is actually semi-cylindrical, but since the bearing stress is not uniform, it is assumed that the area of contact is the thickness of plate times diameter of rivet. This area is shown shaded in section *A–A* of Fig. 17.7.

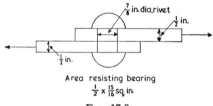

Area resisting bearing
$\frac{1}{2} \times \frac{15}{16}$ sq. in.

FIG. 17.8

For bearing purposes as for shear, the gross diameter of the rivet can be taken as the nominal diameter plus $\frac{1}{16}$ in.

When two plates of the same thickness are being connected, then of course *either* plate could tear, and the area resisting bearing would be thickness of one plate times diameter of rivet (Fig. 17.8). Where plates of different thicknesses are used, then the thinner of

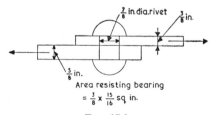

Area resisting bearing
$= \frac{3}{8} \times \frac{15}{16}$ sq. in.

FIG. 17.9

the two plates would tear first, so the area resisting bearing or tearing would be thickness of thinner plate times the diameter of rivet (Fig. 17.9). Where three thicknesses are concerned, as in Fig. 17.10, the two $\frac{5}{8}$ in. plates are acting together and the 1 in. plate would tear before the two $\frac{5}{8}$ in. plates, so the area resisting tearing would be 1 in. times $\frac{13}{16}$ in. It should be noted, however, that B.S.449: 1959,

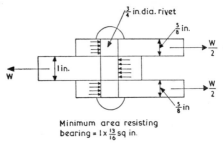

Minimum area resisting
bearing $= 1 \times \frac{13}{16}$ sq in.

Fig. 17.10

permits a higher bearing stress on the middle plate than on the outer plates (see below).

Safe Stresses in Bearing

The allowable safe stresses in bearing according to amendment made in 1961 to B.S.449: 1959 are—

(*a*) Power-driven shop rivets 19 tons/sq in.

(*b*) Power-driven field rivets 17·5 tons/sq in.

(*c*) Close tolerance and turned bolts 19 tons/sq in.

(*d*) Black bolts 12·5 tons/sq in.

These stresses apply when the bolts or rivets are in double shear. When they are in single shear, the permissible bearing stress must be reduced by 20 per cent.

Examples. Safe load in bearing in a $\frac{3}{8}$ in. plate of a $\frac{3}{4}$ in. diameter black bolt (single shear)

$$= \tfrac{3}{4} \times \tfrac{3}{8} \times 80\% \text{ of } 12\cdot5 = 2\cdot82 \text{ tons}$$

Safe load in bearing of a $\frac{7}{8}$ in. diameter shop rivet connecting a $\frac{3}{8}$ in. plate and a $\frac{1}{2}$ in. angle (rivets in single shear)

$$= \frac{15}{16} \times \tfrac{3}{8} \times 80\% \text{ of } 19 = 5\cdot34 \text{ tons}$$

Criterion Value

It will be seen that rivets (or bolts) may be designed on the basis of (*a*) their strength in shear, or (*b*) their strength in bearing.

In actual design the lesser of these two values will, of course, have to be used, and the student should ask himself—

1. If the connexion fails by shear, will it be in single or double shear?

2. What is the safe appropriate shear load on one rivet or bolt?

3. What is the safe bearing load on one rivet or bolt? The actual safe load on one rivet will be the lower (the criterion) of the values given by (2) or (3).

Examples of Riveted and Bolted Joints and Connexions

EXAMPLE 1

Calculate the safe load W on the lap joint shown in Fig. 17.11 in terms of the shear or bearing values.

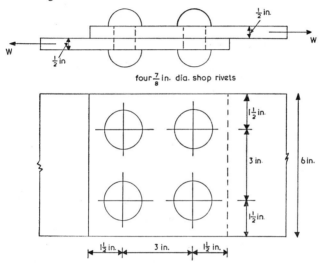

four $\frac{7}{8}$ in. dia. shop rivets

FIG. 17.11

There are only two plates, therefore, single shear, or the bearing value in a $\frac{1}{2}$ in. plate, will be the criterion.

Single shear value of one $\frac{7}{8}$ in. diameter rivet ($\frac{15}{16}$ in. diameter gross)

$$= 0 \cdot 6903 \times 6 \cdot 5 = 4 \cdot 49 \text{ tons}$$

Bearing value in a $\frac{1}{2}$ in. plate $= \left(\frac{15}{16} \times \frac{1}{2} \right) \times 80\%$ of 19

$$= 7 \cdot 13 \text{ tons}$$

Criterion value is the shear value, i.e. 4·49 tons

Therefore, value of one rivet = 4·49 tons

Value of four rivets = $4 \times 4 \cdot 49 = 17 \cdot 96$ tons

EXAMPLE 2

What is the safe load W which the internal truss members shown in Fig. 17.12 may take, in terms of the rivet groups A and B?

Rivets A: In single shear, or bearing in a $\frac{5}{8}$ in. plate

$$\text{S.S.V. of one rivet} = 0.5185 \times 6.5 = 3.37 \text{ tons}$$

$$\text{B.V. of one rivet in } \tfrac{5}{8} \text{ in. plate} = \frac{13}{16} \times \frac{5}{8} \times 0.8 \times 19 = 7.72 \text{ tons}$$

$$\text{Criterion} = \text{single shear value} = 3.37 \text{ tons}$$

$$\text{Value of two rivets } A = 2 \times 3.37 = 6.74 \text{ tons}$$

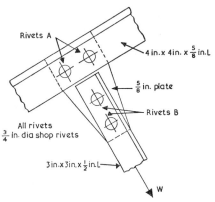

FIG. 17.12

Rivets B: In single shear, or bearing in a $\frac{1}{2}$ inch angle
Safe value of one rivet in single shear is as before 3·37 tons.
Safe value of one rivet in bearing in $\frac{1}{2}$ in. thickness

$$= \frac{13}{16} \times \frac{1}{2} \times 0.8 \times 19 = 6.18 \text{ tons}$$

$$\text{Criterion} = \text{single shear value} = 3.37 \text{ tons}$$

$$\text{Value of two rivets } B = 2 \times 3.37 \text{ tons} = 6.74 \text{ tons}$$

Thus the safe pull $W = 6.74$ tons

EXAMPLE 3

What is the safe load W in tons on the tie shown in Fig. 17.13 with respect to rivets A and rivets B?

Rivets A: D.S.V. of one $\frac{3}{4}$ in. diameter rivet ($\frac{13}{16}$ in. gross)

$$= 2 \times 0.5185 \times 6.5 = 6.74 \text{ tons}$$

Permissible stress in bearing in the middle plate ($\frac{3}{8}$ in. thick gusset)

$$= 19 \text{ tons/sq in.}$$

B.V. of one rivet

$$= \frac{13}{16} \times \frac{3}{8} \times 19 = 5 \cdot 79 \text{ tons}$$

Criterion value $= 5 \cdot 79$ tons

Total value of rivets A

$$= 5 \cdot 79 \times 3 = 17 \cdot 37 \text{ tons}$$

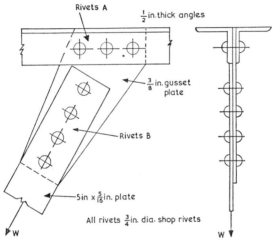

Fig. 17.13

Rivets B: S.S.V. of one rivet

$$= 0 \cdot 5185 \times 6 \cdot 5 = 3 \cdot 37 \text{ tons}$$

B.V. of one rivet in $\frac{5}{16}$ in. plate

$$= \frac{13}{16} \times \frac{5}{16} \times 80\% \times 19 = 3 \cdot 86 \text{ tons}$$

Criterion value $= 3 \cdot 37$ tons

Total value of rivets B

$$= 3 \cdot 37 \times 4 = 13 \cdot 48 \text{ tons}$$

It appears, therefore, that the safe load W is decided by rivets B

and is 13·48 tons. The strength of the plate in tension, however, should be investigated before 13·48 tons is accepted as the safe load. The 5 in. × $\frac{5}{16}$ in. plate is weakened by one rivet hole $\frac{13}{16}$ in. diameter (Fig. 17.14).

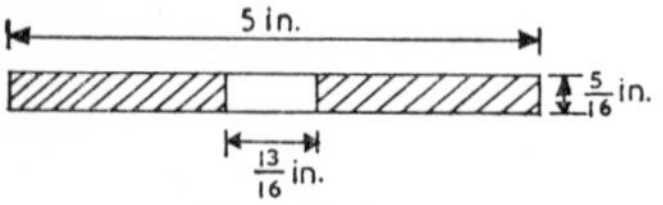

FIG. 17.14

Net area of cross-section

$$= \left(5 \times \frac{5}{16}\right) - \left(\frac{13}{16} \times \frac{5}{16}\right)$$

$$= 1\cdot308 \text{ sq in.}$$

The permissible tension stress for ordinary mild steel is 9·5 tons/sq in. for plates up to $\frac{3}{4}$ in. thick. Therefore the tension value of the plate

$$= 1\cdot308 \times 9\cdot5 = 12\cdot4 \text{ tons}$$

The actual safe load W for the connexion is therefore 12·4 tons (assuming the $\frac{1}{2}$ in. thick angles are adequately strong).

EXAMPLE 4

Referring to Example 3 and Fig. 17.13, calculate the safe load W, assuming $\frac{3}{4}$ in. diameter turned bolts are used instead of the shop rivets.

Here, the gross diameter of the bolt is the same as the nominal diameter so calculations must be made on a diameter of $\frac{3}{4}$ in. and not on a diameter of $\frac{13}{16}$ in. When calculating the strength of the plate in tension the hole is, however, taken as $\frac{13}{16}$ in. diameter.

Bolts A: D.S.V. of one bolt $= 2 \times 0\cdot4418 \times 6 = 5\cdot3$ tons

B.V. of one bolt in the middle plate ($\frac{3}{8}$ in. thick)

$$= \frac{3}{4} \times \frac{3}{8} \times 19 = 5\cdot34 \text{ tons}$$

Total value of bolts $A = 5\cdot3 \times 3 = 15\cdot9$ tons

Bolts B: S.S.V. of one bolt $= 0\cdot4418 \times 6 = 2\cdot65$ tons

B.V. of one bolt in $\frac{5}{16}$ in. plate $= \frac{3}{4} \times \frac{5}{16} \times 0\cdot8 \times 19 = 3\cdot56$ tons

Total value of bolts $B = 2\cdot65 \times 4 = 10\cdot60$ tons

The tensile strength of the plate is as before 12·4 tons, therefore the safe load W is 10·6 tons.

EXAMPLE 5

A compound bracket, as shown in Fig. 17.15, is shop riveted to a 0·54 in. thick stanchion web and carries a reaction of 18 tons from a steel joist as shown.

The bracket is as shown, and there are two rows of $\frac{3}{4}$ in. diameter shop rivets (6 rivets in all). Is the connexion strong enough in terms of the rivets?

Note: There are three thicknesses, but the rivets would fail (in terms of shear) by the complete bracket sliding down plane *A–A*, so the criterion will thus be the least of (*a*) single shear, or (*b*) bearing in the 0·54 in. web.

Value of one rivet in single shear ($\frac{13}{16}$ in. hole)

$$= 0\cdot5185 \times 6\cdot5 = 3\cdot37 \text{ tons}$$

Value of one rivet in bearing

$$= \left(\frac{13}{16} \times 0\cdot54\right) \times 0\cdot8 \times 19$$

$$= 6\cdot67 \text{ tons}$$

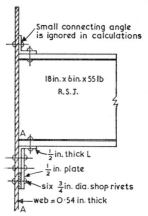

Criterion is single shear value of 3·37 tons. Therefore

safe load $= 6$ rivets at 3·37 tons

$$= 20\cdot22 \text{ tons}$$

As the actual load is 18 tons, the actual stresses in the rivets are less than the safe allowable stresses, i.e. the connexion is adequate.

Fig. 17.15

Double Cover Butt Joints

In designing butt joints and other similar types of connexions, the student should bear in mind that not only can failure occur through an insufficient number of rivets being provided, but that the member

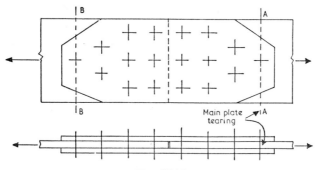

Fig. 17.16

itself may fail in tension. Consider, for example, the splice shown in Fig. 17.16.

To consider one possible chance of failure: the plate being jointed would fail by tearing across face *A–A* (or face *B–B*) under a certain heavy load and, therefore, no matter how many rivets are employed, the safe strength in tension across this and other faces could never be exceeded.

The strength of the rivets must obviously be approximately equal to the strength of the member for the joint to be considered economical.

Consider this effect in the following example.

EXAMPLE 6

A 6 in. × ⅝ in. steel plate used as a tension member in a structural frame has to be jointed using a double cover butt joint with two ⅜ in. thick cover plates and ¾ in. diameter shop rivets. The safe stress in tension in the steel plate is 9·5 tons/sq in. Design a suitable joint.

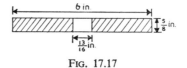

FIG. 17.17

However the rivets are arranged, the section will certainly be weakened by having at least one rivet hole (Fig. 17.17), so the net area of the plate being jointed

$$= \left(6 - \frac{13}{16}\right)\frac{5}{8} = 3\cdot242 \text{ sq in.}$$

and as the safe tension stress is 9·5 tons/sq in., the safe load on the plate itself cannot exceed

$$3\cdot242 \times 9\cdot5, \quad \text{i.e. } 30\cdot8 \text{ tons}$$

The rivets will be in double shear, and bearing in the ⅝ in. plate at 19 tons/sq in. D.S.V. of one rivet ($\frac{13}{16}$ in. diameter gross)

$$= 2 \times 0\cdot5185 \times 6\cdot5 = 6\cdot74 \text{ tons}$$

B.V. of one rivet in ⅝ in. middle plate

$$= \frac{13}{16} \times \frac{5}{8} \times 19 = 9\cdot65 \text{ tons}$$

Therefore, criterion value of one rivet = 6·74 tons
Number of rivets required on each side of joint

$$= \frac{\text{total load}}{\text{value of one rivet}}$$

$$= \frac{30\cdot8}{6\cdot74} = 4\cdot6, \text{ say 5 rivets}$$

These will be arranged as in Fig. 17.18.

Strength of plate ($\frac{5}{8}$ in. thick): At the section *A–A* the value of the plate is (as has been seen) the area (less one rivet hole) multiplied by 9.5 tons/sq in., i.e. the strength of the plate is 30·8 tons.

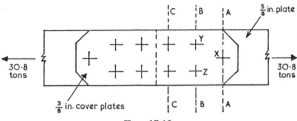

Fig. 17.18

At the section *B–B* the plate is weakened by *two* rivet holes, but it should be noted that in the event of the plate actually tearing across *B–B*, the joint would not fail until the one rivet marked *X* also had failed (in double shear in this case).

Thus, the strength across *B–B* = the area (less two rivet holes) × 9·5 + the value of one rivet (*X*), and, similarly, the strength of the plate at *C–C* = the area (less two rivet holes) × 9·5 + the value of three rivets (*x, y, z*).

The strength at $B–B = \left\{ 6 - 2 \left(\frac{13}{16} \right) \right\} \frac{5}{8} \times 9 \cdot 5 + 6 \cdot 74$

$$= 26 + 6 \cdot 74$$

$$= 32 \cdot 74 \text{ tons}$$

Obviously, the strength at *C–C* would be even greater and the actual value need not be calculated as we are concerned with the strength at the weakest point.

One more point remains to be checked. If the rivets were amply strong and the main plate sound across sections *A–A, B–B,* etc., the joint could still fail if the cover plates were too thin and a tension failure in the covers would occur where they are weakened most, i.e. across section *C–C*.

Strength of cover plates across *C–C*

$$= \left\{ 6 - 2 \left(\frac{13}{16} \right) \right\} \frac{3}{4} \times 9 \cdot 5$$

$$= 31 \cdot 2 \text{ tons}$$

which is slightly more than the safe load for the $\frac{5}{8}$ in. plate (30·8 tons).

Note: Engineers sometimes talk about the "efficiency" of a joint as being the

$$\frac{\text{safe load for the joint}}{\text{original value of the undrilled plate}} \times 100$$

to express as a percentage.

Here, the efficiency $= \dfrac{30 \cdot 8}{6 \times \frac{5}{8} \times 9 \cdot 5} \times 100 = 86 \cdot 5$ per cent

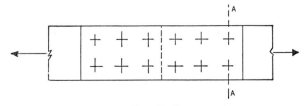

Fig. 17.19

The reader should note carefully that increasing the number of rivets above the number actually required may, in some cases, actually weaken the joint.

In the case just dealt with (Example 6), had six rivets been used, as in Fig. 17.19, instead of five as required, the value of the plate at

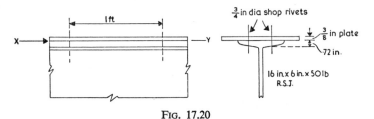

Fig. 17.20

section *A–A* would now only be the plate less two holes, i.e.

$$\left\{ 6 - 2\left(\frac{13}{16}\right) \right\} \frac{5}{8} \times 9 \cdot 5$$

$$= 26 \text{ tons}$$

as against 30·8 tons when five rivets were used.

EXAMPLE 7

Fig. 17.20 shows a section and part elevation of a compound girder, the top flange consisting of a 0·72 in. thick flange and a ⅜ in. thick plate.

There is a tendency in bending for the plate to slide along the joist flange at the line xy and this sliding force in this case is assumed to be (from calculations) 10·5 tons per foot of beam length. At what pitch must $\frac{3}{4}$ in. diameter shop rivets (in two rows) be placed to resist this sliding?

$$\text{S.S.V. of one rivet} = 3\cdot37 \text{ tons}$$

$$\text{B.V. of one rivet} = \frac{13}{16} \times \frac{3}{8} \times 0\cdot8 \times 19 = 4\cdot63 \text{ tons}$$

$$\text{Criterion} = 3\cdot37 \text{ tons}$$

$$\text{No. of rivets per foot run} = \frac{\text{total load per foot}}{\text{value of one rivet}}$$

$$= \frac{10\cdot5}{3\cdot37} = 3\cdot12$$

Pitch of rivets (if one line only existed) would be

$$\frac{12}{\text{no. per ft}} = \frac{12}{3\cdot12} = 3\cdot85 \text{ in.}$$

Pitch of rivets in two rows $= 2 \times 3\cdot85 = 7\cdot70$ in. pitch in each line.

It is usual not to exceed a pitch of 6 in. in such construction, therefore each row of rivets would have a pitch of 6 in.

SUMMARY

$$\text{S.S.V. of one rivet or bolt} = Af_s$$
$$\text{D.S.V. of one rivet or bolt} = 2Af_s$$

B.V. of one rivet or bolt in a plate of thickness t inches $= dtf_b$

A is the area of cross-section of the rivet shank or bolt shank.

For rivets, A may be taken as the area of a circle $\frac{1}{16}$ in. greater in diameter than the specified diameter (nominal diameter).

For bolts, A is the area calculated from the nominal diameter.

d is the diameter of the rivet or bolt.

For rivets, d = nominal diameter plus $\frac{1}{16}$ in.

For bolts, d = nominal diameter

$$f_s = \text{permissible shear stress}$$
$$f_b = \text{permissible bearing stress.}$$

In certain problems, the strength of the plate in tension may have to be investigated. The permissible tension stress for ordinary mild steel is 9·5 tons/sq in.

When deducting the areas of rivet or bolt holes to determine the strength of a plate, the diameter of the hole is taken as $\frac{1}{16}$ in. greater than the nominal diameter of the rivet or bolt.

TABLE 17.2A

SHEARING AND BEARING VALUES FOR POWER-DRIVEN SHOP RIVETS
(Based on B.S.449: 1959; as amended 1961)

Gross Dia. of Rivet after driving in inches	Area in square inches	Shearing Value @ 6·5 tons/inch²		Simple Bearing Value @ 80% of 19 tons/inch² and Enclosed Bearing Value @ 19 tons/inch² (See footnote) Thickness in inches of plate passed through or of enclosed plate										
		Single Shear	Double Shear	$\frac{3}{16}$	$\frac{1}{4}$	$\frac{5}{16}$	$\frac{3}{8}$	$\frac{7}{16}$	$\frac{1}{2}$	$\frac{9}{16}$	$\frac{5}{8}$	$\frac{11}{16}$	$\frac{3}{4}$	
$\frac{3}{8}$	0·1104	0·72	1·44	**1·07**	**1·43**	*1·78*	*2·14*							
				1·34	*1·78*	*2·23*								
$\frac{7}{16}$	0·1503	0·98	1·95	**1·25**	**1·66**	*2·08*	*2·49*							
				1·56	*2·08*	*2·60*								
$\frac{1}{2}$	0·1963	1·28	2·55	**1·43**	**1·90**	**2·38**	*2·85*	*3·33*						
				1·78	**2·38**	*2·97*	*3·56*							
$\frac{9}{16}$	0·2485	1·62	3·23	**1·60**	**2·14**	**2·67**	**3·21**	*3·74*	*4·28*					
				2·00	**2·67**	*3·34*	*4·01*							
$\frac{5}{8}$	0·3068	1·99	3·99	**1·78**	**2·38**	**2·97**	**3·56**	*4·16*	*4·75*					
				2·23	**2·97**	**3·71**	*4·45*	*5·20*						
$\frac{11}{16}$	0·3712	2·41	4·83	**1·96**	**2·61**	**3·27**	**3·92**	**4·57**	*5·23*	*5·88*				
				2·45	**3·27**	**4·08**	*4·90*	*5·71*						
$\frac{3}{4}$	0·4418	2·87	5·74	**2·14**	**2·85**	**3·56**	**4·28**	**4·99**	**5·70**	*6·41*	*7·13*			
				2·67	**3·56**	**4·45**	**5·34**	*6·23*	*7·13*					
$\frac{13}{16}$	0·5185	3·37	6·74	**2·32**	**3·09**	**3·86**	**4·63**	**5·40**	**6·18**	*6·95*	*7·72*			
				2·89	**3·86**	**4·82**	**5·79**	*6·75*	*7·72*					
$\frac{7}{8}$	0·6013	3·91	7·82	**2·49**	**3·33**	**4·16**	**4·99**	**5·82**	**6·65**	**7·48**	*8·31*	*9·14*		
				3·12	**4·16**	**5·20**	**6·23**	**7·27**	*8·31*	*9·35*				
$\frac{15}{16}$	0·6903	4·49	8·97	**2·67**	**3·56**	**4·45**	**5·34**	**6·23**	**7·13**	**8·02**	**8·91**	*9·80*	*10·69*	
				3·34	**4·45**	**5·57**	**6·68**	**7·79**	**8·91**	*10·02*	*11·13*			
1	0·7854	5·11	10·21	**2·85**	**3·80**	**4·75**	**5·70**	**6·65**	**7·60**	**8·55**	**9·50**	*10·45*	*11·40*	
				3·56	**4·75**	**5·94**	**7·13**	**8·31**	**9·50**	*10·69*	*11·88*			
$1\frac{1}{16}$	0·8866	5·76	11·53	**3·03**	**4·04**	**5·05**	**6·06**	**7·07**	**8·08**	**9·08**	**10·09**	**11·10**	*12·11*	*14*
				3·79	**5·05**	**6·31**	**7·57**	**8·83**	**10·09**	**11·36**	*12·62*	*13·88*		

Upper line of Bearing Values for each diameter of rivet are Simple Bearing Values.
Lower line of Bearing Values for each diameter of rivet are Enclosed Bearing Values.
For areas to be deducted from a bar for one hole, see table on page 365.
For explanation of table, see Notes on page 365.

TABLE 17.2B

SHEARING AND BEARING VALUES FOR POWER-DRIVEN FIELD RIVETS
(Based on B.S.449: 1959; as amended 1961)

Cross Dia. of rivet after driving in inches	Area in square inches	Shearing Value @ 6 tons/inch²		Simple Bearing Value @ 80% of 17·5 tons/inch² and Enclosed Bearing Value @ 17·5 tons/inch² (See footnote) Thickness in inches of plate passed through or of enclosed plate										
		Single Shear	Double Shear	3/16	1/4	5/16	3/8	7/16	1/2	9/16	5/8	11/16	3/4	7/8
3/8	0·1104	0·66	1·33	**0·98**	**1·31**	*1·64*	*1·97*							
				1·23	*1·64*	*2·05*								
7/16	0·1503	0·90	1·80	**1·15**	**1·53**	*1·91*	*2·30*							
				1·44	*1·91*	*2·39*								
1/2	0·1963	1·18	2·36	**1·31**	**1·75**	**2·19**	**2·63**	*3·06*						
				1·64	**2·19**	*2·73*	*3·28*							
9/16	0·2485	1·49	2·98	**1·48**	**1·97**	**2·46**	**2·95**	*3·45*	*3·94*					
				1·85	**2·46**	*3·08*	*3·69*							
5/8	0·3068	1·84	3·68	**1·64**	**2·19**	**2·73**	**3·28**	*3·83*	*4·38*					
				2·05	**2·73**	**3·42**	*4·10*	*4·79*						
11/16	0·3712	2·23	4·45	**1·80**	**2·41**	**3·01**	**3·61**	**4·21**	*4·81*	*5·41*				
				2·26	**3·01**	**3·76**	*4·51*	*5·26*						
3/4	0·4418	2·65	5·30	**1·97**	**2·63**	**3·28**	**3·94**	**4·59**	**5·25**	*5·91*	*6·56*			
				2·46	**3·28**	**4·10**	**4·92**	*5·74*	*6·56*					
13/16	0·5185	3·11	6·22	**2·13**	**2·84**	**3·55**	**4·27**	**4·98**	**5·69**	*6·40*	*7·11*			
				2·67	**3·55**	**4·44**	**5·33**	**6·22**	*7·11*	*8·00*				
7/8	0·6013	3·61	7·22	**2·30**	**3·06**	**3·83**	**4·59**	**5·36**	**6·13**	**6·89**	*7·66*	*8·42*		
				2·87	**3·83**	**4·79**	**5·74**	**6·70**	*7·66*	*8·61*				
15/16	0·6903	4·14	8·28	**2·46**	3·28	**4·10**	**4·92**	**5·74**	**6·56**	**7·38**	**8·20**	*9·02*	*9·84*	
				3·08	**4·10**	**5·13**	**6·15**	**7·18**	**8·20**	*9·23*	*10·25*			
1	0·7854	4·71	9·42	**2·63**	**3·50**	**4·38**	**5·25**	**6·13**	**7·00**	**7·88**	**8·75**	*9·63*	*10·50*	
				3·28	**4·38**	**5·47**	**6·56**	**7·66**	**8·75**	*9·84*	*10·94*			
1 1/16	0·8866	5·32	10·64	**2·79**	**3·72**	**4·65**	**5·58**	**6·51**	**7·44**	**8·37**	**9·30**	**10·23**	*11·16*	*13·02*
				3·49	**4·65**	**5·81**	**6·97**	**8·13**	**9·30**	**10·46**	*11·62*	*12·78*		

Upper line of Bearing Values for each diameter of rivet are Simple Bearing Values.
Lower line of Bearing Values for each diameter of rivet are Enclosed Bearing Values.
For areas to be deducted from a bar for one hole, see table on page 365.
For explanation of table, see Notes on page 365.

TABLE 17.2C

SHEARING AND BEARING VALUES FOR HAND-DRIVEN RIVETS
(Based on B.S. 449: 1959; as amended 1961)

Gross Dia. of Rivet after driving in inches	Area in square inches	Shearing Value @ 5.5 tons/inch²		Simple Bearing Value @ 80% of 16 tons/inch² and Enclosed Bearing Value @ 16 tons/inch² (See footnote) — Thickness in inches of plate passed through or of enclosed plate										
		Single Shear	Double Shear	3/16	1/4	5/16	3/8	7/16	1/2	9/16	5/8	11/16	3/4	13/16
3/8	0·1104	0·61	1·21	**0·90**	**1·20**	*1·50*	*1·80*							
				1·13	*1·50*	*1·88*								
7/16	0·1503	0·83	1·65	**1·05**	**1·40**	*1·75*	*2·10*							
				1·31	*1·75*	*2·19*								
1/2	0·1963	1·08	2·16	**1·20**	**1·60**	**2·00**	*2·40*	*2·80*						
				1·50	**2·00**	*2·50*	*3·00*							
9/16	0·2485	1·37	2·73	**1·35**	**1·80**	**2·25**	**2·70**	*3·15*	*3·60*					
				1·69	**2·25**	*2·81*	*3·38*							
5/8	0·3068	1·69	3·37	**1·50**	**2·00**	**2·50**	**3·00**	*3·50*	*4·00*					
				1·88	**2·50**	**3·13**	*3·75*	*4·38*						
11/16	0·3712	2·04	4·08	**1·65**	**2·20**	**2·75**	**3·30**	**3·85**	*4·40*	*4·95*				
				2·06	**2·75**	**3·44**	*4·13*	*4·81*						
3/4	0·4418	2·43	4·86	**1·80**	**2·40**	**3·00**	**3·60**	**4·20**	**4·80**	*5·40*	*6·00*			
				2·25	**3·00**	**3·75**	**4·50**	*5·25*	*6·00*					
13/16	0·5185	2·85	5·70	**1·95**	**2·60**	**3·25**	**3·90**	**4·55**	**5·20**	*5·85*	*6·50*			
				2·44	**3·25**	**4·06**	**4·88**	**5·69**	*6·50*	*7·31*				
7/8	0·6013	3·31	6·61	**2·10**	**2·80**	**3·50**	**4·20**	**4·90**	**5·60**	**6·30**	*7·00*	*7·70*		
				2·63	**3·50**	**4·38**	**5·25**	**6·13**	*7·00*	*7·88*				
15/16	0·6903	3·80	7·59	**2·25**	**3·00**	**3·75**	**4·50**	**5·25**	**6·00**	**6·75**	**7·50**	*8·25*	*9·00*	
				2·81	**3·75**	**4·69**	**5·63**	**6·56**	**7·50**	*8·44*	*9·38*			
1	0·7854	4·32	8·64	**2·40**	**3·20**	**4·00**	**4·80**	**5·60**	**6·40**	**7·20**	**8·00**	*8·80*	*9·60*	
				3·00	**4·00**	**5·00**	**6·00**	**7·00**	**8·00**	*9·00*	*10·00*			
1 1/16	0·8866	4·88	9·75	**2·55**	**3·40**	**4·25**	**5·10**	**5·95**	**6·80**	**7·65**	**8·50**	**9·35**	*10·20*	*11*
				3·19	**4·25**	**5·31**	**6·38**	**7·44**	**8·50**	**9·56**	*10·63*	*11·69*		

Upper line of Bearing Values for each diameter of rivet are Simple Bearing Values.
Lower line of Bearing Values for each diameter of rivet are Enclosed Bearing Values.
For areas to be deducted from a bar for one hole, see table on page 365.
For explanation of table, see Notes on page 365.

TABLE 17.2D

SHEARING AND BEARING VALUES FOR CLOSE TOLERANCE AND TURNED BOLTS
(Based on B.S.449: 1959; as amended 1961)

Dia. Bolt shank inches	Area in square inches	Shearing Value @ 6·0 tons/inch² Single Shear	Shearing Value @ 6·0 tons/inch² Double Shear	$\frac{3}{16}$	$\frac{1}{4}$	$\frac{5}{16}$	$\frac{3}{8}$	$\frac{7}{16}$	$\frac{1}{2}$	$\frac{9}{16}$	$\frac{5}{8}$	$\frac{11}{16}$	$\frac{3}{4}$
$\frac{3}{8}$	0·1104	0·66	1·33	**1·07**	*1·43*	*1·78*							
				1·34	*1·78*								
$\frac{7}{16}$	0·1503	0·90	1·80	**1·25**	**1·66**	*2·08*	*2·49*						
				1·56	*2·08*	*2·60*							
$\frac{1}{2}$	0·1963	1·18	2·36	**1·43**	**1·90**	*2·38*	*2·85*						
				1·78	*2·38*	*2·97*							
$\frac{9}{16}$	0·2485	1·49	2·98	**1·60**	**2·14**	**2·67**	*3·21*	*3·74*					
				2·00	**2·67**	*3·34*	*4·01*						
$\frac{5}{8}$	0·3068	1·84	3·68	*1·78*	**2·38**	**2·97**	**3·56**	*4·16*	*4·75*				
				2·23	**2·97**	*3·71*	*4·45*						
$\frac{11}{16}$	0·3712	2·23	4·45	*1·96*	**2·61**	**3·27**	**3·92**	*4·57*	*5·23*				
				2·45	**3·27**	**4·08**	*4·90*	*5·71*					
$\frac{3}{4}$	0·4418	2·65	5·30	*2·14*	**2·85**	**3·56**	**4·28**	**4·99**	*5·70*	*6·41*			
				2·67	**3·56**	**4·45**	*5·34*	*6·23*					
$\frac{13}{16}$	0·5185	3·11	6·22	*2·32*	**3·09**	**3·86**	**4·63**	**5·40**	**6·18**	*6·95*	*7·72*		
				2·89	**3·86**	**4·82**	**5·79**	*6·75*	*7·72*				
$\frac{7}{8}$	0·6013	3·61	7·22	*2·49*	**3·33**	**4·16**	**4·99**	**5·82**	**6·65**	*7·48*	*8·31*		
				3·12	**4·16**	**5·20**	**6·23**	*7·27*	*8·31*				
$\frac{15}{16}$	0·6903	4·14	8·28	*2·67*	**3·56**	**4·45**	**5·34**	**6·23**	**7·13**	**8·02**	*8·91*	*9·80*	
				3·34	**4·45**	**5·57**	**6·68**	**7·79**	**8·91**	*10·02*			
1	0·7854	4·71	9·42	*2·85*	**3·80**	**4·75**	**5·70**	**6·65**	**7·60**	**8·55**	*9·50*	*10·45*	
				3·56	**4·75**	**5·94**	**7·13**	**8·31**	**9·50**	*10·69*			
$1\frac{1}{16}$	0·8866	5·32	10·64	*3·03*	**4·04**	**5·05**	**6·06**	**7·07**	**8·08**	**9·08**	**10·09**	*11·10*	*12·11*
				3·79	**5·05**	**6·31**	**7·57**	**8·83**	**10·09**	*11·36*	*12·62*		

Upper line of Bearing Values for each diameter of bolt are Simple Bearing Values.
Lower line of Bearing Values for each diameter of bolt are Enclosed Bearing Values.
For areas to be deducted from a bar for one hole, see table on page 365.
For explanation of table, see Notes on page 365.

TABLE 17.2E

SHEARING AND BEARING VALUES FOR BLACK BOLTS
(Based on B.S.449: 1959; as amended 1961)

Dia. of Bolt Shank in inches	Area in square inches	Shearing Value @ 5·0 tons/inch²		Simple Bearing Value @ 80% of 12·5 tons/inch² and Enclosed Bearing Value @ 12·5 tons/inch² (See footnote) Thickness in inches of plate passed through or of enclosed plate									
		Single Shear	Double Shear	$\frac{3}{16}$	$\frac{1}{4}$	$\frac{5}{16}$	$\frac{3}{8}$	$\frac{7}{16}$	$\frac{1}{2}$	$\frac{9}{16}$	$\frac{5}{8}$	$\frac{11}{16}$	$\frac{3}{4}$
$\frac{3}{8}$	0·1104	0·55	1·10	0·70	0·94	*1·17*	*1·41*						
				0·88	*1·17*	*1·46*							
$\frac{7}{16}$	0·1503	0·75	1·50	0·82	1·09	1·37	*1·64*	*1·91*					
				1·03	1·37	*1·71*	*2·05*						
$\frac{1}{2}$	0·1963	0·98	1·96	0·94	1·25	1·56	1·88	*2·19*	*2·50*				
				1·17	1·56	1·95	*2·34*	*2·73*					
$\frac{9}{16}$	0·2485	1·24	2·49	1·05	1·41	1·76	2·11	2·46	*2·81*	*3·16*			
				1·32	1·76	2·20	2·64	*3·08*					
$\frac{5}{8}$	0·3068	1·53	3·07	1·17	1·56	1·95	2·34	2·73	*3·13*	*3·52*			
				1·46	1·95	2·44	2·93	*3·42*	*3·91*				
$\frac{11}{16}$	0·3712	1·86	3·71	1·29	1·72	2·15	2·58	3·01	3·44	*3·87*	*4·30*		
				1·61	2·15	2·69	3·22	*3·76*	*4·30*				
$\frac{3}{4}$	0·4418	2·21	4·42	1·41	1·88	2·34	2·81	3·28	3·75	4·22	*4·69*	*5·16*	
				1·76	2·34	2·93	3·52	4·10	*4·69*	*5·27*			
$\frac{13}{16}$	0·5185	2·59	5·18	1·52	2·03	2·54	3·05	3·55	4·06	4·57	5·08	*5·59*	*6·09*
				1·90	2·54	3·17	3·81	4·44	5·08	*5·71*	*6·35*		
$\frac{7}{8}$	0·6013	3·01	6·01	1·64	2·19	2·73	3·28	3·83	4·38	4·92	5·47	*6·02*	*6·56*
				2·05	2·73	3·42	4·10	4·79	5·47	*6·15*	*6·84*		
$\frac{15}{16}$	0·6903	3·45	6·90	1·76	2·34	2·93	3·52	4·10	4·69	5·27	5·86	6·45	*7·03*
				2·20	2·93	3·66	4·39	5·13	5·86	6·59	*7·32*	*8·06*	
1	0·7854	3·93	7·85	1·88	2·50	3·13	3·75	4·38	5·00	5·63	6·25	6·88	7·50
				2·34	3·13	3·91	4·69	5·47	6·25	7·03	7·81	*8·59*	*9·38*
$1\frac{1}{16}$	0·8866	4·43	8·87	1·99	2·66	3·32	3·98	4·65	5·31	5·98	6·64	7·30	7·97
				2·49	3·32	4·15	4·98	5·81	6·64	7·47	8·30	*9·13*	*9·96*

Upper line of Bearing Values for each diameter of bolt are Simple Bearing Values.
Lower line of Bearing Values for each diameter of bolt are Enclosed Bearing Values.
For areas to be deducted from a bar for one hole, see table on page 365.
For explanation of tables, see Notes on page 365.

TABLE 17.2F

AREAS IN SQUARE INCHES TO BE DEDUCTED FOR ONE HOLE THROUGH A MEMBER

Diameter of hole in inches	Thickness of Member at Hole in Inches										
	1/4	5/16	3/8	7/16	1/2	9/16	5/8	11/16	3/4	7/8	1
7/16	0·094	0·117	0·141	0·164	0·188						
1/2	0·109	0·137	0·164	0·191	0·219	0·246					
9/16	0·125	0·156	0·188	0·219	0·250	0·281	0·313				
5/8	0·141	0·176	0·211	0·246	0·281	0·316	0·352	0·387			
11/16	0·156	0·195	0·234	0·273	0·313	0·352	0·391	0·430	0·469		
3/4	0·172	0·215	0·258	0·301	0·344	0·387	0·430	0·473	0·516	0·602	
13/16	0·188	0·234	0·281	0·328	0·375	0·422	0·469	0·516	0·563	0·656	0·750
7/8	0·203	0·254	0·305	0·355	0·406	0·457	0·508	0·559	0·609	0·711	0·813
15/16	0·219	0·273	0·328	0·383	0·438	0·492	0·547	0·602	0·656	0·766	0·875
1	0·234	0·293	0·352	0·410	0·469	0·527	0·586	0·645	0·703	0·820	0·938
1 1/16	0·250	0·313	0·375	0·438	0·500	0·563	0·625	0·688	0·750	0·875	1·000
1 1/8	0·266	0·332	0·398	0·465	0·531	0·598	0·664	0·730	0·797	0·930	1·063

NOTES ON TABLES OF RIVETS AND BOLTS

Permissible Stresses. Permissible stresses on gross areas of rivets and bolts—

	Single Shear Tons/inch^2	Bearing Tons/inch^2
Power Driven Shop Rivets	6·5	19·0
Power Driven Field Rivets	6·0	17·5
Hand Driven Rivets	5·5	16·0
Close Tolerance and Turned Bolts	6·0	19·0
Black Bolts	5·0	12·5

Multiple Shear. For rivets and bolts in double shear, the area to be assumed shall be twice the for single shear.

here the rivets or bolts are in single shear, the permissible bearing stress shall be reduced) per cent.

Critical Values. Bearing values printed in ordinary type are less than single shear. In these , the bearing values are the determining factors.

aring values printed in prominent type are greater than single and less than double shear, at in the case of (*a*) single shear, the shearing value is the criterion; (*b*) double shear, the ng value is the criterion.

aring values printed in *italics* are equal to or greater than double shear. In these cases, the ring values are the criterion.

EXERCISE 17

(*Note:* permissible tension stress for mild steel = 9·5 tons/sq in.)

1. A flat bar of steel 3 in. wide and $\frac{3}{8}$ in. thick is to be connected by a simple lap joint to a $\frac{3}{8}$ in. thick gusset plate. The flat bar has to sustain a tension load of 6 tons. Calculate the number of $\frac{3}{4}$ in. diameter shop rivets required.

2. Centre lines of the members meeting at the shoe of a roof truss are given in Fig. 17.21. The strut is a 3 in. × 3 in. × $\frac{3}{8}$ in. angle section and the tie is a

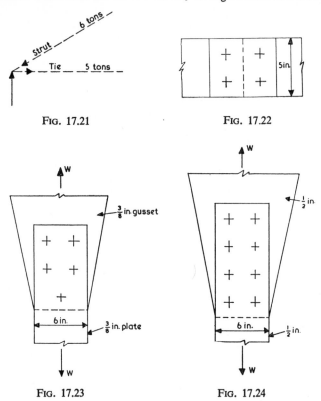

FIG. 17.21   FIG. 17.22

FIG. 17.23   FIG. 17.24

$2\frac{1}{2}$ in. × $2\frac{1}{2}$ in. × $\frac{1}{4}$ in. angle section. Calculate the number of $\frac{5}{8}$ in. diameter shop rivets required to connect the members to a $\frac{3}{8}$ in. thick gusset plate.

3. The size of each plate in a simple lap joint is 4 in. × $\frac{1}{2}$ in. and there are six $\frac{3}{4}$ in. diameter turned bolts in a single line. Calculate the safe load in tension.

4, In a double cover butt joint, the jointed plate is 5 in. × $\frac{1}{2}$ in. and the cover plates are 5 in. × $\frac{5}{16}$ in. (Fig. 17.22). There are two $\frac{3}{4}$ in. diameter shop rivets each side of the join (four rivets in all). Calculate the maximum safe tension for the plates.

5. A simple lap joint with five $\frac{7}{8}$ in. diameter site rivets is shown in Fig. 17.23. Calculate the maximum safe pull, W.

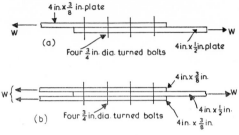

Fig. 17.25

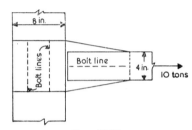

Fig. 17.26

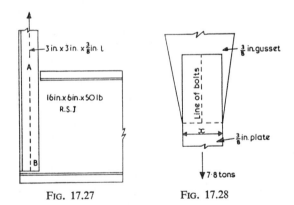

Fig. 17.27   Fig. 17.28

6. Eight black bolts, $\frac{7}{8}$ in. diameter, connect a flat bar to a gusset plate as shown in Fig. 17.24. Calculate the safe load W.

7. Fig. 17.25 gives two different bolted connexions (*a*) and (*b*). In each case, calculate the safe load W.

8. A 4 in. wide plate is connected, by means of a $\frac{3}{8}$ in. gusset plate to the flange of a 10 in. × 8 in. × 55 lb stanchion, as shown in Fig. 17.26. Calculate the required thickness of the plate and the number of $\frac{7}{8}$ in. diameter black bolts.

13—(T. 779)

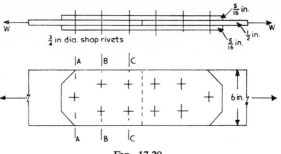

FIG. 17.29

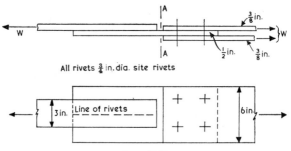

FIG. 17.30

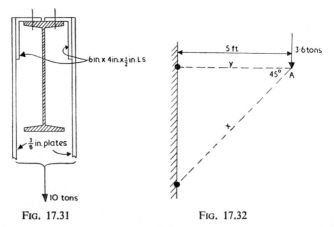

FIG. 17.31   FIG. 17.32

9. The end of a beam is supported by a hanger consisting of a 3 in. × 3 in. × ⅜ in. angle section, as shown in Fig. 17.27. The load at the end of the beam is 10 tons. Calculate the number of ¾ in. diameter turned bolts required along the line *AB* and check the strength in tension of the angle section. (Gross area of angle = 2·11 sq in.)

10. A ⅜ in. thick tie member is to be connected to a ⅜ in. thick gusset plate, as indicated in Fig. 17.28. Calculate the necessary width *x* of the tie and calculate the number of ⅝ in. diameter black bolts to connect the tie to the gusset.

11. Fig. 17.29 shows a joint in a tension member which is 6 in. wide and ½ in. thick. Determine the safe load *W*. (Calculations are required for the strength of the middle plate at sections *A–A* and *B–B*; the strength of the cover plate at *C–C*, and the strengths of the rivets in shear and bearing.)

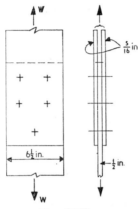

FIG. 17.33

12. Referring to Fig. 17.30, calculate the maximum safe load *W*, confining the calculations to that part of the connexion which lies to the right of line *A–A* (tension stress = 9·5 tons/sq in.). Then, using this load, find the required thickness of the 3 in. wide plate at 9 tons per sq in. and the necessary number of ¾ in. diameter site rivets.

13. It is proposed to suspend a load of 10 tons from an existing B.S.B. in a building by the means shown in Fig. 17.31, using ¾ in. diameter turned bolts. Calculate the width of plate required and the number of bolts.

14. Two members *X* and *Y* form a bracket from a wall and are to be connected by means of a ⅜ in. gusset plate at *A* by ⅝ in. diameter shop rivets (Fig. 17.32) The member *X* is a 3 in. × 3 in. × ½ in. angle section and may be assumed to be amply strong in compression. Assuming member *Y* to be a flat bar ¼ in. thick, calculate the minimum width required and determine the number of rivets to connect *X* and *Y* to the gusset plate.

15. Calculate the value of the maximum permissible load *W* for the connexion shown in Fig. 17.33. The rivets are ¾ in. diameter (shop).

16. Design a suitable connexion between a 24 in. × 7½ in. × 95 lb rolled steel joist and the flange of a 10 in. × 8 in. × 55 lb stanchion, using ¾ in. diameter shop rivets in the vertical leg of the seating angle. The load transmitted by the beam to the stanchion is 20 tons.

CHAPTER 18

Addition of Direct and Bending Stress

PREVIOUS chapters have dealt largely with two main types of stress They are—

1. Direct or Axial Stress: This occurs when a load (tensile or compressive) is spread evenly across a section, as in the case of a short column axially loaded. Here, the unit stress or stress per square inch is found by dividing the total load by the sectional area of the member, i.e.

$$\text{Direct stress} = f_a = W/A$$

2. Bending Stress: In this case, the stress has been seen to vary— having different values at different distances from the neutral axis of the section, and the stress at a distance y from the neutral axis $= f_b = M \times y/I$, **or** where the stress at the extreme fibres is required f_b max. $= M/Z$.

Cases frequently arise, however, where *both* these types of stress occur at the same time, and the stress intensity due to the addition of the two stresses is to be determined.

Consider, for example, the short timber post shown in plan in Fig. 18.1. The load passes through the centroid of the section, and

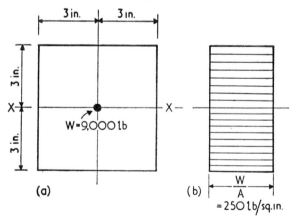

FIG. 18.1.(*a*) LOADING; (*b*) STRESS DISTRIBUTION

370

the resulting stress is pure axial stress, and its intensity $= W/A =$ 9,000/36 $=$ 250 lb/sq in.

The stress has the same intensity at all points of the section, and this is shown by the rectangular shape of the "stress distribution diagram."

Fig. 18.2(*a*) shows the same section with a load of 9,000 lb as before, but this time the load, whilst still on the *X–X* axis, lies $\frac{1}{2}$ in. away from the *Y–Y* axis.

There will still be a direct stress everywhere on the section as before of $W/A = 9,000/36 = 250$ lb/sq in., but the eccentricity of the load with regard to the *Y–Y* axis causes a moment of 9,000 $\times \frac{1}{2}$ $= 4,500$ lb-in., which has the effect of increasing the compression on the area to the right of *Y–Y* (shaded) and decreasing the direct compression on the portion to the left of *Y–Y*.

Fig. 18.2(*b*) shows the direct stress W/A in compression.

Fig. 18.2(*c*) shows the bending stress of

$$\frac{M}{Z} = \frac{4,500}{36} = 125 \text{ lb/sq in. compression at } BC$$

and 125 lb/sq in. tension at *AD*.

Fig. 18.2(*d*) shows how these two stress distribution diagrams (*b,c*) are superimposed, giving the final diagram as shown. The compressive stress on the edge *BC*

$$= \frac{W}{A} + \frac{M}{Z} = 250 + 125 = 375 \text{ lb/sq in.}$$

whilst the stress on edge *AD*

$$= \frac{W}{A} - \frac{M}{Z} = 250 - 125 = 125 \text{ lb/sq in.}$$

Note: The stress is still compressive at any point, but it varies in intensity from face *AD* to face *BC*.

The stress at section *Z–Z* (1 in. from *Y–Y*) is

$$\frac{W}{A} + \frac{M \cdot y}{I_{yy}} \quad \text{where } y = 1 \text{ in.}$$

$$= 250 + \frac{4,500 \times 1}{108}$$

$$= 250 + 41 \cdot 67 = 291 \cdot 67 \text{ lb/sq in.}$$

Fig. 18.3(*a*) shows the same short column as in the previous

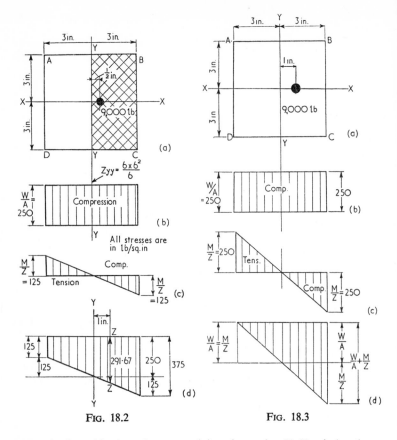

FIG. 18.2   FIG. 18.3

example, but this time the eccentricity about the $Y-Y$ axis has been increased to 1 in. As before,

$$\text{the direct stress} = \frac{W}{A} = \frac{9{,}000}{36} = 250 \text{ lb/sq in.}$$

but the M is now 9,000 lb-in.

and
$$Z_{yy} = \frac{bd^2}{6} = 36 \text{ in.}^3,$$

Thus
$$\frac{M}{Z} = \frac{9{,}000}{36},$$

which is 250 lb/sq in.

Figs. 18.3(*b*) and 18.3(*c*) show the direct and bending stresses respectively, whilst in Fig. 18.3(*d*) the two diagrams have been superimposed, showing—

(1) that the stress on face BC

$$= \frac{W}{A} + \frac{M}{Z}$$
$$= 250 + 250$$
$$= 500 \text{ lb/sq in.}$$

(2) that the stress on face AD

$$= \frac{W}{A} - \frac{M}{Z}$$
$$= 250 - 250$$
$$= 0$$

The original compression of W/A on face AD has been cancelled out by the tension at AD caused by the eccentricity of the loading away from that face, and the stress intensity at $AD = 0$, whilst that on face $BC = 500$ lb/sq in.

This interesting example demonstrates a general rule that, in the case of square or rectangular sections, the load may be eccentric from one axis by no more than $\frac{1}{6}$th of the width unless tension on one face is permissible.

In the case of a steel, timber or reinforced concrete, column tension would be allowable within reasonable limits, but, in a brick wall, tension would be undesirable and the resultant load or thrust in a masonry structure should not depart more than $d/6$ (or $b/6$) from the axis.

This is sometimes called the *Law of the Middle Third*, i.e. if the load or the resultant thrust cuts a rectangular section at a point not further than $d/6$ from the centre line (i.e. within the middle third), then the stress everywhere across the section will be compressive.

In the previous examples, the stress being determined was the stress within the material, i.e. in the column itself. Sometimes, however, it is the stress intensity between the faces of two materials resting against each other that is being considered.

Consider the masonry retaining wall shown in Fig. 18.4(*a*). The earth pressure and the weight W of the wall combine to form a resultant R which cuts the base, as shown, at a distance s from the centre-line of the base.

The vertical component V of the resultant causes a moment of $V \times s$, which adds compressive stress between the wall and the earth below at A, and reduces the pressure between the surfaces at B.

If V cuts within the middle third of the base width d, then the stress everywhere between A and B will be compressive, as in Fig. 18.4(*b*).

Note: As the wall itself may be of any length, it is customary in design to consider only one foot length of wall, i.e. to estimate the weight of one foot of wall and the earth pressure on one foot of length also.

Thus, if the rectangle shown in Fig. 18.4(*c*) represents the area of wall resting on the base *AB* (as seen in a plan), then the eccentricity of the load *V* will tend to rotate this area about the axis *Y–Y*, so that,

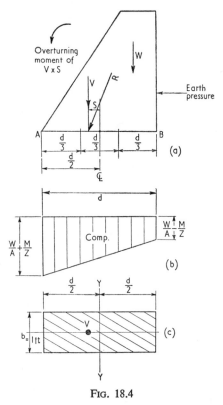

FIG. 18.4

in calculating *Z*, the value $bd^2/6$ will be in effect $1 \times d^2/6 = \frac{1}{6}$th of d^2, and will be normally in ft³ units.

Eccentricity about Both Axes

The short pier shown (Fig. 18.5) carries one load only, eccentric to both *X–X* and *Y–Y* axes. The stress at corner *C* will be

$$\frac{W}{A} + \frac{M_{xx}}{Z_{xx}} + \frac{M_{yy}}{Z_{yy}}$$

for the load has moved towards *C* from both axes.

Stress at corner B will be

$$\frac{W}{A} + \frac{M_{yy}}{Z_{yy}} - \frac{M_{xx}}{Z_{xx}},$$

for the load is away from the $Y–Y$ axis on the same side as B, but is away from the $X–X$ axis on the side furthest from B.

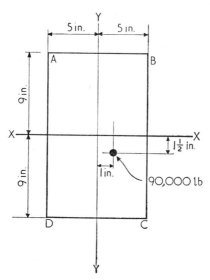

FIG. 18.5

Similarly, stress at corner $A = \dfrac{W}{A} - \dfrac{M_{xx}}{Z_{xx}} - \dfrac{M_{yy}}{Z_{yy}}$, and

stress at corner $D = \dfrac{W}{A} + \dfrac{M_{xx}}{Z_{xx}} - \dfrac{M_{yy}}{Z_{yy}}$.

The solution is outlined below:

$$\frac{W}{A} = \frac{90,000}{180} = 500 \text{ lb/sq in.}$$

$$\frac{M_{xx}}{Z_{xx}} = \frac{90,000 \times 1\frac{1}{2}}{\dfrac{10 \times 18^2}{6}} = 250 \text{ lb/sq in.}$$

$$\frac{M_{yy}}{Z_{yy}} = \frac{90,000 \times 1}{\dfrac{18 \times 10^2}{6}} = 300 \text{ lb/sq in.}$$

Stress at corner $A = 500 - 300 - 250 = -50$ lb/sq in.
(tension)
Stress at corner $B = 500 + 300 - 250 = +550$ lb/sq in.
(compression)
Stress at corner $C = 500 + 300 + 250 = +1{,}050$ lb/sq in.
(compression)
Stress at corner $D = 500 - 300 + 250 = +450$ lb/sq in.
(compression)

Miscellaneous Examples

EXAMPLE 1

A short stanchion carries three loads, as shown in Fig. 18.6. Calculate the intensity of stress at corners A, B, C and D.

Area $= 16 \cdot 18$ in.^{2}
$Z_{xx} = 57 \cdot 74$ in.^{3}
$Z_{yy} = 13 \cdot 7$ in.^{3}

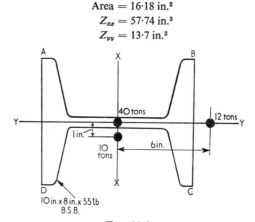

FIG. 18.6

1st Method.

Direct stress $= \dfrac{W}{A} = \dfrac{40 + 10 + 12}{16 \cdot 18} = \dfrac{62}{16 \cdot 18} = 3 \cdot 84$ tons/sq in.

Bending stress $\dfrac{M_{xx}}{Z_{xx}} = \dfrac{12 \times 6}{57 \cdot 74} = 1 \cdot 246$ tons/sq in.

Bending stress $\dfrac{M_{yy}}{Z_{yy}} = \dfrac{10 \times 1}{13 \cdot 7} = 0 \cdot 73$ tons/sq in.

Stress at $A = \dfrac{W}{A} - \dfrac{M_{xx}}{Z_{xx}} - \dfrac{M_{yy}}{Z_{yy}} = 3 \cdot 84 - 1 \cdot 246 - 0 \cdot 73$
$= 1 \cdot 864$ tons/sq in.

Stress at $B = \dfrac{W}{A} + \dfrac{M_{xx}}{Z_{xx}} - \dfrac{M_{yy}}{Z_{yy}} = 3 \cdot 84 + 1 \cdot 246 - 0 \cdot 73$
$= 4 \cdot 356$ tons/sq in.

Stress at $C = \dfrac{W}{A} + \dfrac{M_{xx}}{Z_{xx}} + \dfrac{M_{yy}}{Z_{yy}} = 3 \cdot 84 + 1 \cdot 246 + 0 \cdot 73$

$$= 5 \cdot 816 \text{ tons/sq in.}$$

Stress at $D = \dfrac{W}{A} - \dfrac{M_{xx}}{Z_{xx}} + \dfrac{M_{yy}}{Z_{yy}} = 3 \cdot 84 - 1 \cdot 246 + 0 \cdot 73$

$$= 3 \cdot 324 \text{ tons/sq in.}$$

2nd Method. The amount and position of the resultant of the three loads can be calculated (Fig. 18.7) and the resultant load

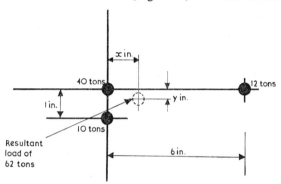

FIG. 18.7

applied to the column in place of the three loads.

$$62x = 6 \times 12, \qquad x = \frac{72}{62} = 1 \cdot 161 \text{ in.}$$

$$62y = 10 \times 1 \qquad y = \frac{10}{62} = 0 \cdot 1611 \text{ in.}$$

Thus the resultant would be as in Fig. 18.8.

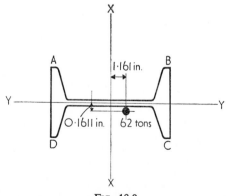

FIG. 18.8

$$\text{Stress at } A = \frac{62}{16 \cdot 18} - \frac{62 \times 1 \cdot 161}{57 \cdot 74} - \frac{62 \times 0 \cdot 1611}{13 \cdot 7}$$

$$= 3 \cdot 84 - 1 \cdot 246 - 0 \cdot 73 = 1 \cdot 864 \text{ tons/sq in.}$$

Stress at $B = 3 \cdot 84 + 1 \cdot 246 - 0 \cdot 73 = 4 \cdot 356$ tons/sq in.

Stress at $C = 3 \cdot 84 + 1 \cdot 246 + 0 \cdot 73 = 5 \cdot 816$ tons/sq in.

Stress at $D = 3 \cdot 84 - 1 \cdot 246 + 0 \cdot 73 = 3 \cdot 324$ tons/sq in.

EXAMPLE 2

An eccentric load of W lb applied to a short circular pier, as shown in Fig. 18.9, causes a total stress of 1,790 lb/sq in. at the point C. What is the value of the load W in pounds?

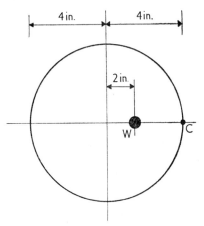

FIG. 18.9

$$\text{Area of section} = \frac{\pi D^2}{4} = \frac{\pi \times 64}{4} = 16\pi = 50 \cdot 25 \text{ in.}^2$$

$$\text{Section modulus } Z = \frac{\pi D^3}{32} = \frac{\pi \times 8^3}{32} = 16\pi = 50 \cdot 25 \text{ in.}^3$$

As stress at $C = 1,790$ lb/sq in.

$$\frac{W}{A} + \frac{M}{Z} = \frac{W}{A} + \frac{W \times 2}{Z} = 1,790 \text{ lb/sq in.}$$

so

$$\frac{W}{50 \cdot 25} + \frac{2W}{50 \cdot 25} = \frac{3W}{50 \cdot 25} = 1,790$$

and

$$W = \frac{1,790 \times 50 \cdot 25}{3}$$

$$W = 30,000 \text{ lb}$$

SUMMARY

Maximum combined stress = direct stress + bending stress.
When load W is eccentric to axis X–X only:

$$\text{Maximum stress} = \frac{W}{A} + \frac{We_x}{Z_{xx}}$$

When load W is eccentric to axis Y–Y only:

$$\text{Maximum stress} = \frac{W}{A} + \frac{We_y}{Z_{yy}}$$

When load W is eccentric to both axes:

$$\text{Maximum stress} = \frac{W}{A} + \frac{We_x}{Z_{xx}} + \frac{We_y}{Z_{yy}}$$

EXERCISE 18

1. A short timber post carries a load of 8,000 lb eccentric from one axis only as shown in Fig. 18.10. Calculate the intensity of stress—(a) at face BC (f_{bc}) (b) at face AD (f_{ad}).

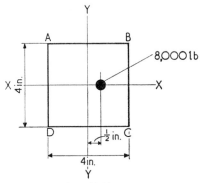

FIG. 18.10

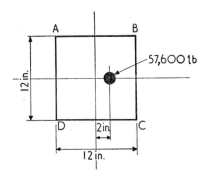

FIG. 18.11

2. Calculate the compression stress on the faces BC and AD of the short timber post, as shown in Fig. 18.11.

3. Repeat Question 2, but increasing the eccentricity to 3 inches.

4. Calculate the stress at the corner C of the short timber post shown in Fig. 18.12.

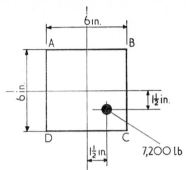

Fɪɢ. 18.12

5. A short steel stanchion consists of a 10 in. × 8 in. R.S.J. and carries loads as shown in Fig. 18.13. Calculate the stress at faces AD and BC.

$$\text{Area} = 16{\cdot}18 \text{ in.}^2$$
$$Z_{xx} = 57{\cdot}74 \text{ in.}^3$$
$$Z_{yy} = 13{\cdot}69 \text{ in.}^3$$

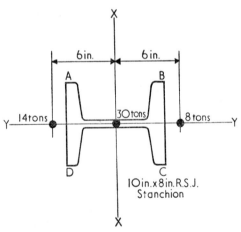

Fɪɢ. 18.13

6. A short steel post consisting of a 10 in. × 6 in. × 40 lb R.S.J. carries three loads, as shown in Fig. 18.14. Calculate the stress at each of the corners A, B, C and D.

7. The short steel post, as shown in Fig. 18.15, is a 10 in. × 6 in. × 40 lb R.S.J. There is a central point load of 12 tons and an eccentric load of W tons as shown. The maximum stress on the face BC is $4{\cdot}72$ tons/sq in. What is the value of the load W?

8. A concrete beam 6 in. × 12 in., as shown in Fig. 18.16 is pre-stressed by

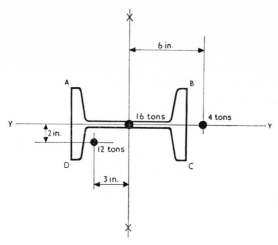

FIG. 18.14

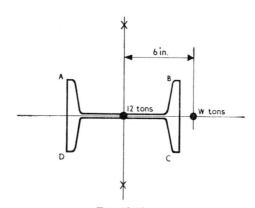

FIG. 18.15

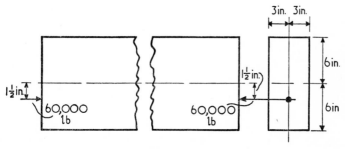

FIG. 18.16

the application of two loads of 60,000 lb applied at points $1\frac{1}{2}$ in. below the neutral axis of the section. (*a*) What are the stresses at the upper and lower faces of the beam? (*b*) At what distance below the neutral axis would the loads have to be applied for there to be no stress at all at the top face of the beam?

Note: Neglect self-weight of beam.

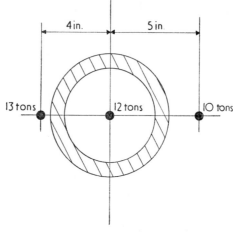

Fig. 18.17

9. A hollow metal tube used as a short column is 6 in. external and 5 in. internal diameter. The column is loaded as shown in Fig. 18.17. Calculate the maximum fibre stress on the column.

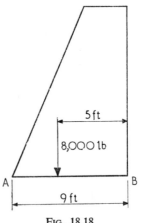

Fig. 18.18

10. The vertical resultant load on the earth from a foot run of retaining wall is 8,000 lb applied as shown in Fig. 18.18. Calculate the intensity of vertical stress under the wall at *A* and *B*.

11. A 6 in. × 4 in. timber beam subjected to horizontal thrusts at each end, as shown in Fig. 18.19, is loaded with a central concentrated load of 1,000 lb. The beam itself weighs 30 lb. What is the maximum (*a*) compressive stress? (*b*) tensile stress?

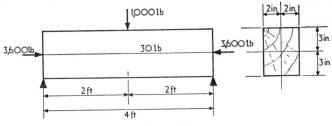

FIG. 18.19

12. A circular steel column 4 in. diameter is rigidly fixed at the lower end and is free from restraint at the top. It carries a vertical load of 14 tons and a horizontal thrust of 0·4 ton, as shown in Fig. 18.20. Calculate the maximum compression stress, ignoring secondary stresses.

13. A double angle rafter member in a steel truss is subjected to an axial

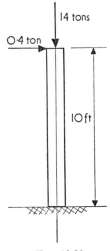

FIG. 18.20

compression of 6 tons and also to bending moment from a point load of 1 ton, as shown in Fig. 18.21. The member is composed of two 3 in. × 3 in. × ½ in. angles, as shown, for which the properties (given for the double angle section) are

$$A = 5·5 \text{ in.}^2$$

$$I_{xx} = 4·36 \text{ in.}^4$$

Calculate the maximum compressive stress in the member.

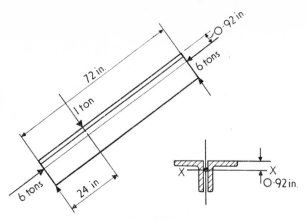

FIG. 18.21

14. A 9 in. × 7 in. × 50 lb R.S.J. stanchion carries four loads, as shown in Fig. 18.22. The properties of the section are—

$$\text{Area} = 14 \cdot 71 \text{ in.}^2$$
$$Z_{xx} = 46 \cdot 25 \text{ in.}^3$$
$$Z_{yy} = 11 \cdot 48 \text{ in.}^3$$

Calculate the intensities of stress at the four corners.

15. A short stanchion is of a 9 in. × 7 in. × 50 lb R.S.J. with properties as

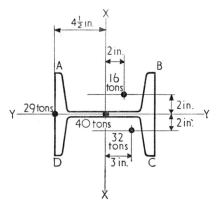

FIG. 18.22

given for Question 14. It carries one single load *W* eccentric to both axes, as shown in Fig. 18.23, and the maximum stress at corner *C* is found to be 4·282 tons/sq in. What is the value in tons of the load *W*?

16. A triangular mass wall, as shown in section in Fig. 18.24, weighs 120 lb/cu ft and rests on a flat base *AB*. What is the intensity of vertical bearing stress at *A* and *B* per foot length of wall?

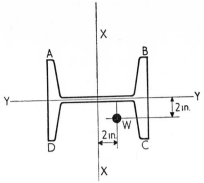

FIG. 18.23

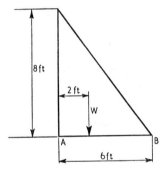

FIG. 18.24

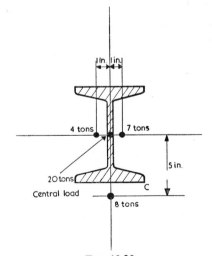

FIG. 18.25

385

17. An 8 in. × 6 in. × 35 lb R.S.J. stanchion carries a central point load and three other point loads, as shown in Fig. 18.25. The R.S.J. has the following properties—

$$\text{Area} = 10\cdot3 \text{ in.}^2$$

$$I_{xx} = 115\cdot1 \text{ in.}^4$$

$$I_{yy} = 19\cdot54 \text{ in.}^4$$

Determine the maximum stress in the stanchion.

18. If the 4 ton load is removed from the stanchion as described in Question 17, all three other loads remaining as before, what will now be the maximum stress in the stanchion, and at which corner will this maximum stress occur?

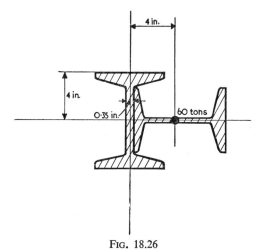

FIG. 18.26

19. A compound stanchion is built up of two 8 in. × 6 in. × 35 lb R.S.J.s, as shown in Fig. 18.26, and carries a single point load of 60 tons. The properties of one single R.S.J. are—

$$\text{Area} = 10\cdot3 \text{ in.}^2$$

$$I_{xx} = 115\cdot1 \text{ in.}^4$$

$$I_{yy} = 19\cdot54 \text{ in.}^4$$

What is the maximum stress in the compound stanchion?

CHAPTER 19

Dams and Earth-retaining Walls

THE previous chapter has been concerned mainly with the addition of direct and bending stress when these two types of stress occur within a material, e.g. the variation of stress across the face of a column section which arises due to eccentricity of loading.

The principles involved in those cases are used in much the same way on occasions where, for example, a wall, resting on earth or on a concrete footing and acted upon by horizontal forces, is transmitting to the earth or footing stresses which consist of—

1. Direct stress from the wall's weight.
2. Stress due to the overturning moment.

Before these resultant stresses are considered, it will be necessary to study the effect of earth pressure, water pressure and wind pressure upon vertical and non-vertical surfaces.

Water Pressure

Consider the vertical surface AB, shown in Fig. 19.1, to be the face

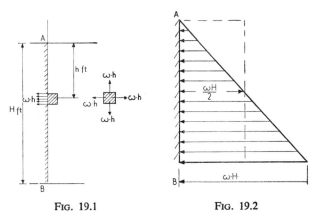

FIG. 19.1   FIG. 19.2

of a water retaining wall. It can be shown that a cubic foot of water weighing 62·5 pounds, and situated at a depth h below the surface, exerts a pressure of $(62·5 \times h)$ pounds outwards on all of its six side surfaces.

If w represents the weight of 1 cu ft of water, then the outward pressure in every direction $= w \cdot h$ lb/sq ft. Thus the intensity of outward pressure varies directly as the depth, and will be a maximum amount of $w \cdot H$ (where H is the maximum depth) lb/sq ft (Fig. 19.2).

At the surface of the water (where $h = 0$), the pressure will be zero. So, as the maximum is wH lb/sq ft, the average pressure between A and $B = wH/2$ lb/sq ft.

In dealing with retaining walls generally, it is convenient to consider the forces acting on one foot length of wall, that is, an area of wall H ft high and 1 ft measured perpendicular to the plane of the diagrams, Figs. 19.1 and 19.2. Thus, as the "wetted area" concerned is H sq ft, the total water pressure on a one foot strip of wall

$$= \text{``wetted area''} \times \text{average rate of pressure}$$

$$= H \times wH/2$$

$$= \frac{wH^2}{2} \text{ lb}$$

This resultant pressure on the wall's vertical surface from the water is (as will be seen from Fig. 19.2) the resultant of a large number of forces which range from zero at the top to wH at the base, and the resultant will therefore act at a point $\frac{1}{3}$rd of H from the base, as shown in Fig. 19.3.

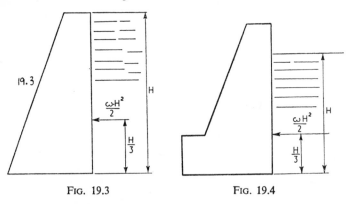

FIG. 19.3   FIG. 19.4

Note: If the water does not reach the top of the wall, as, for example, in Fig. 19.4, then the resultant pressure is calculated with H as the depth of the water and not as the height of the wall. The pressure is again $wH^2/2$ and it acts at a point $H/3$ (one-third the water depth) from the wall's base.

EXAMPLE 1

A masonry dam 12 ft high retains water on its vertical face. The water weighs 62·5 lb/cu ft, and reaches to the top of the wall. What is the total resultant water pressure per foot run of wall?

$$\text{Resultant pressure} = P = wH^2/2 = \frac{62 \cdot 5 \times 12 \times 12}{2}$$

$$= 4{,}500 \text{ lb acting 4 ft above base of wall}$$

EXAMPLE 2

A masonry dam retains water on its vertical face. The wall is, as shown in Fig. 19.5, 14 ft high, but the water level reaches only 3 ft from the top of the wall.

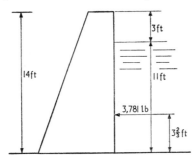

FIG. 19.5

What is the resultant water pressure per foot run of wall?

$$P = \frac{wH^2}{2} = \frac{62 \cdot 5 \times 11 \times 11}{2}$$

$$= 3{,}781 \text{ lb acting } 3\tfrac{2}{3} \text{ ft above base}$$

In cases where the wall in contact with the water is not vertical, as is the case shown in Fig. 19.6, the wetted area will be larger than

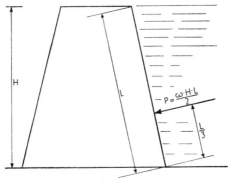

FIG. 19.6

in the case of a vertical back, and the resultant pressure will thus be increased to $w . H . L/2$ (i.e. the wetted area will be L sq ft instead of H sq ft considering one foot run of wall).

Earth Pressure

It is obvious that pressures on walls from retained earth cannot be determined with quite the same accuracy as was the case with water. Earths vary in weight and character; they behave quite differently under varying conditions of moisture, etc., and in general, the resultant pressures on vertical and non-vertical surfaces from earths are obtained from various earth pressure theories. Numerous theories exist for the calculation of earth pressures, and these theories vary in the assumptions which they make and the estimated pressures which they determine. A great deal of modern research is at present being directed upon this subject, but most of this is beyond the scope of a volume of this type, and therefore only one or two well tried theories will be dealt with in detail.

Rankine's Theory of Earth Pressure

It has been seen that a cubic foot of water at a depth of h below the surface presses outwards horizontally by an amount of $w . h$ lb/sq ft (w being the weight of a cubic foot of water). In the case of earth weighing w lb/cu ft, the outward pressure at a depth of h below the surface will be less than $w . h$ lb/sq ft, since some of the earth is "self-supporting."

ANGLE OF REPOSE: Consider, for example, the earth retained by the vertical face AB in Fig. 19.7. If the retaining face AB was removed,

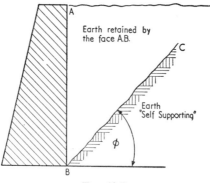

FIG. 19.7

then some of the earth would probably collapse at once, and in the course of time the earth would assume a line BC, as shown. The angle ϕ made between the horizontal and the line BC varies with different types of earth, and is called the angle of repose of the earth. It is obvious, therefore, that only part of the earth was in fact being retained by the wall and was exerting pressure on the wall. Thus, it follows that the amount of pressure on the wall from the earth depends upon the angle of repose for the type of earth concerned, and Rankine's theory states in general terms that the outward pressure per square foot at a depth of h ft due to a level fill of earth is

$$wh\left[\frac{1-\sin\phi}{1+\sin\phi}\right]\text{ lb/sq ft}$$

as compared with (wh) lb/sq ft in the case of water. Thus, by similar reasoning as was used in the case of water pressure, the maximum pressure at the bottom of the wall

$$=wH\left[\frac{1-\sin\phi}{1+\sin\phi}\right]\text{ lb/sq ft}$$

and the average pressure $=\dfrac{wH}{2}\left[\dfrac{1-\sin\phi}{1+\sin\phi}\right]$ lb/sq ft

The earth acts at this average rate on an area of H sq ft of wall, so the total resultant pressure per foot run of wall

$$=\frac{wH^2}{2}\left[\frac{1-\sin\phi}{1+\sin\phi}\right]\text{ lb}$$

and this acts as shown in Fig. 19.8.

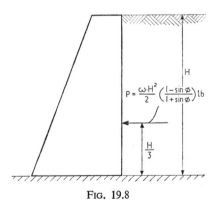

Fig. 19.8

EXAMPLE 3

Earth weighing 90 lb/cu ft and having an angle of repose ϕ of 30°, exerts pressure on a 12 ft high vertical face. What is the resultant horizontal force per foot run of wall?

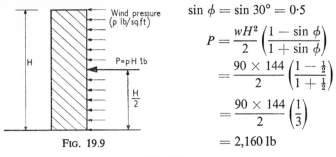

$\sin \phi = \sin 30° = 0·5$

$$P = \frac{wH^2}{2}\left(\frac{1 - \sin \phi}{1 + \sin \phi}\right)$$

$$= \frac{90 \times 144}{2}\left(\frac{1 - \frac{1}{2}}{1 + \frac{1}{2}}\right)$$

$$= \frac{90 \times 144}{2}\left(\frac{1}{3}\right)$$

$$= 2,160 \text{ lb}$$

Fig. 19.9

Wind Pressure

The pressure from wind, unlike water and earth pressure, does not, of course, increase nearer to the lower part of the wall. The pressure per sq ft p remains constant and thus the resultant force P acts at half the height of the wall (Fig. 19.9), and $P = pH$ lb/ft of wall.

Distribution of Pressure over Base of Wall

When the weight of a wall per foot W and the resultant pressure from the earth or water P have been calculated, these two forces may be compounded to a resultant, as in Fig. 19.10, and it will be shown that the position along the base at which this resultant cuts (i.e. at S) has an important bearing on the stability of the wall and on the pressures exerted by the wall upon the earth beneath.

Consider now the wall shown in Fig. 19.11. The values in pounds of W and P are as shown, and W acts through the centroid of the wall section.

From the similar triangles ASC and ADE

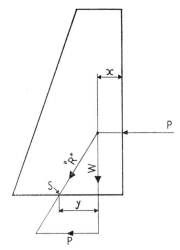

Fig. 19.10

$$\frac{y}{4} = \frac{2,160}{5,600}, \quad y = \frac{2,160 \times 4}{5,600}$$

$$y = 1·54 \text{ ft}$$

Thus the resultant force R cuts the base at $(3 + 1·54) = 4·54$ ft from the point G, the heel of the wall.

It has been seen that the resultant pressure R cuts the base at point S, as shown in Figs. 19.11 and 19.12.

In considering the effect of this resultant on the earth or concrete under the base FG, it is normally convenient to split the force R

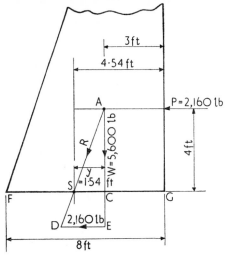

FIG. 19.11

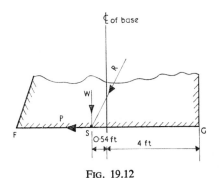

FIG. 19.12

into the vertical and horizontal components W and P from which this resultant was compounded. (Note that the vertical component of the resultant is equal to the weight W of the wall only when the earth pressure is horizontal.)

These two component forces W and P are shown again in Fig. 19.12. Component force P tends to *slide* the wall along the plane FG, so need not be considered when calculating the pressure on the earth beneath FG. Component force W, however, does exert pressure on the earth or concrete under *FG*, and as the point *S* is to the left of the centre line of the base the earth under the left hand part of the base will have greater pressure exerted upon it than the earth under the right hand half.

The student should by now be able to appreciate why this chapter on stresses under walls is linked with the addition of direct and bending stress.

Here, the direct stress $= \dfrac{W}{A}$

$$= \frac{\text{weight of wall}}{\text{area of base}}$$

$$= \frac{5,600 \text{ lb}}{8 \text{ sq ft}} = 700 \text{ lb/sq ft}$$

The moment due to the eccentricity of the resultant

$$= W \times 0{\cdot}54 = 5,600 \times 0{\cdot}54 = 3,020 \text{ lb/ft}$$

$$= W \times \text{distance of } S \text{ from the centre of the base}$$

and $Z =$ section modulus about an axis through the centre line of the base $= \dfrac{bd^2}{6} = \dfrac{1 \times 8^2}{6} = 10{\cdot}67 \text{ ft}^3$

$$\text{Bending stress} = \frac{M}{Z} = \frac{3,020}{10{\cdot}67} = 284 \text{ lb/sq ft.}$$

Thus, intensity of pressure under wall at *F*

$$= \frac{W}{A} + \frac{M}{Z} = 700 + 284$$

$$= 984 \text{ lb/sq ft}$$

Intensity of pressure under wall at *G*

$$= \frac{W}{A} - \frac{M}{Z} = 700 - 284$$

$$= 416 \text{ lb/sq ft}$$

as shown in the stress distribution diagram of Fig. 19.13.

EXAMPLE 4

A masonry dam wall is as shown in Fig. 19.14 and weighs 150 lb/cu ft. It retains on its vertical face water weighing 62·5 lb/cu ft. The water reaches the

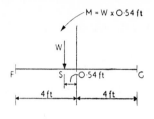

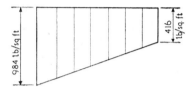

FIG. 19.13

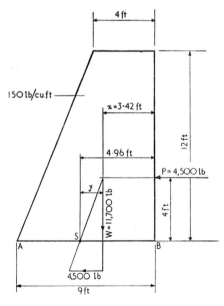

FIG. 19.14

top of the wall. Calculate the intensity of stress under the wall at the heel and the toe.

$$W = \left(\frac{4+9}{2}\right)12 \times 150 = 11,700 \text{ lb}$$

$$P = \frac{wH^2}{2} = \frac{62 \cdot 5 \times 144}{2} = 4,500 \text{ lb}$$

To determine the centroid of the wall,

$$x = \frac{(4 \times 12 \times 2) + (5 \times 12/2 \times 5\frac{2}{3})}{78}$$

$$= \frac{96 + 170}{78} = \frac{266}{78} = 3 \cdot 42 \text{ ft}$$

By similar triangles $\quad \dfrac{y}{4} = \dfrac{4,500}{11,700}$

and $y = \dfrac{4 \times 4,500}{11,700} = 1 \cdot 54 \text{ ft}$

Thus, the resultant pressure cuts at $3 \cdot 42 + 1 \cdot 54 = 4 \cdot 96$ ft from B at S, or $0 \cdot 46$ ft to the centre line of the base.

Thus, the pressure intensity at $A = \dfrac{W}{A} + \dfrac{M}{Z}$

$$= \frac{11,700}{9} + \frac{11,700 \times 0 \cdot 46}{\dfrac{1 \times 9^2}{6}}$$

$$= 1,300 + 399 = 1,699 \text{ lb/sq ft}$$

And the pressure intensity at $B = \dfrac{W}{A} - \dfrac{M}{Z} = 1,300 - 399$

$$= 901 \text{ lb/sq ft}$$

Note: In calculating distance y (i.e. the position at which the resultant cuts, measured from the centroid of the section) the distance was obtained by similar triangles, i.e.

$$\frac{y}{4} = \frac{4,500}{11,700}$$

The student should, however, note that this could have been obtained from first principles, as follows—

Considering Fig. 19.15, if the wall had *no* horizontal force P acting on it the wall's weight W would cut the base at D, and the resultant upward pressure from the earth would also act upwards at *D* and be of the amount *W*.

When a force of *P* acts horizontally on the wall, however, it causes an anticlockwise overturning moment of *PH/3*. The earth, which can only press upwards with a force of *W*, must therefore

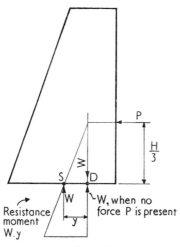

Fig. 19.15

resist this with a clockwise moment of the same amount, and thus the resultant force *W* from the earth is moved from *D* to *s* (a distance *y*) to cause a clockwise moment *W . y*.

Thus $W \times y = P \times \dfrac{H}{3}$

and $y = \dfrac{P \times H/3}{W}$ as before

from similar triangles.

Law of the Middle Third

The previous examples have been chosen so that the resultant pressure has cut the base within the middle third. Hence, although the pressures at *B* and *A* (the heel and toe of the base) have been of different amounts, the stresses have been compressive at both points.

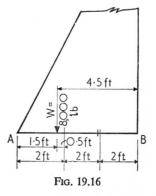

Fig. 19.16

Consider, however, the case shown in Fig. 19.16. The resultant here cuts outside the middle third and thus there will be a tendency to tension at B, i.e. M/Z will exceed W/A.

If the joint at B is capable of resisting tensile stress then

$$\text{the stress at } A \text{ will be } \frac{W}{A} + \frac{M}{Z}$$

$$= \frac{8{,}000}{6} + \frac{8{,}000 \times 1 \cdot 5 \times 6}{6 \times 6}$$

$$= 1{,}333 + 2{,}000 = 3{,}333 \text{ lb/sq ft compression}$$

$$\text{and the stress at } B \text{ will be } \frac{W}{A} - \frac{M}{Z} = 1{,}333 - 2{,}000$$

$$= -667 \text{ lb/sq ft or } 667 \text{ lb/sq ft tension}$$

The diagram of pressure distribution under the base will be as in Fig. 19.17.

If the joint at B is not capable of resisting tension, then there will be a tendency for the base to lift where tension would occur.

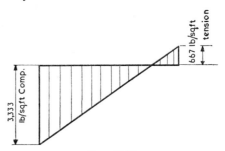

FIG. 19.17

In this case, the point at which the resultant cuts the base should be considered the middle third point, as in Fig. 19.18(*b*), so that the effective width of the base becomes three times the distance

$$AS = (3 \times 1 \cdot 5) = 4 \cdot 5 \text{ ft}$$

The stress at A (the toe) then becomes

$$\frac{W}{A} + \frac{M}{Z} = \frac{8{,}000}{4 \cdot 5} + \frac{8{,}000 \times 0 \cdot 75 \times 6}{4 \cdot 5^2}$$

$$= 1{,}780 + 1{,}780 = 3{,}560 \text{ lb/sq ft}$$

and the pressure distribution diagram is as shown in Fig. 19.18(*c*).

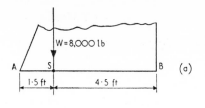

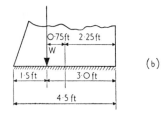

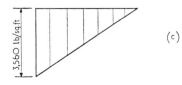

Fig. 19.18

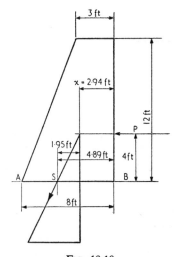

Fig. 19.19

399

Miscellaneous Retaining Wall Examples

EXAMPLE 5

A masonry dam is 12 ft high and weighs 140 lb/cu ft. It retains water to the full depth, as shown in Fig. 19.19. Calculate intensities of vertical pressure under the base (*a*) when the water reaches the top of the wall; (*b*) when the dam is empty.

(*a*) Weight of wall $W = \left(\dfrac{11}{2} \times 12 \times 140\right)$

$$= 9{,}240 \text{ lb}$$

$$P = \frac{wH^2}{2} = \frac{62 \cdot 5 \times 144}{2} = 4{,}500 \text{ lb}$$

$$x = \frac{(3 \times 12 \times 1 \cdot 5) + (2 \cdot 5 \times 12 \times 14/3)}{66}$$

$$= 2 \cdot 94 \text{ ft}$$

$$\frac{y}{4} = \frac{4{,}500}{9{,}240}, \quad y = \frac{45 \times 4}{92 \cdot 4} = 1 \cdot 95 \text{ ft}$$

Therefore, the resultant cuts the base 0·89 ft to the left of the centre line of the base, as in Fig. 19.19.

Therefore intensity of stress at $A = \dfrac{W}{A} + \dfrac{M}{Z}$

$$= \frac{9{,}240}{8} + \frac{9{,}240 \times 0 \cdot 89 \times 6}{8^2}$$

$$= 1{,}155 + 770$$

$$= 1{,}925 \text{ lb/sq ft}$$

and intensity of stress at *B*

$$= \frac{W}{A} - \frac{M}{Z}$$

$$= 1{,}155 - 770$$

$$= 385 \text{ lb/sq ft}$$

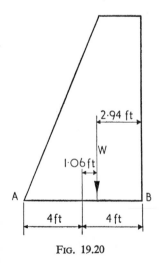

FIG. 19.20

(*b*) When dam is empty. There is now no pressure *P* on the side of the wall, so the resultant thrust (the weight of the wall alone) acts through the centroid, as shown in Fig. 19.20, and cuts the base 1·06 ft to the right of the centre line of the base. Thus, the pressure on the soil will be at its greatest at *B* and

$$f_b = \frac{W}{A} + \frac{M}{Z} = \frac{9{,}240}{8} + \frac{9{,}240 \times 1{\cdot}06 \times 6}{8^2}$$

$$= 1{,}155 + 918 = 2{,}073 \text{ lb/sq ft}$$

$$\text{and } f_a = \frac{W}{A} - \frac{M}{Z} = 1{,}155 - 918 = 237 \text{ lb/sq ft}$$

EXAMPLE 6

A trapezoidal dam wall, as shown in Fig. 19.21, weighs 120 lb/cu ft. It retains on its vertical face water weighing 62·5 lb/cu ft. (*a*) If the water reaches the top of the wall, will the resultant pressure cut the base *AB* outside its middle third?

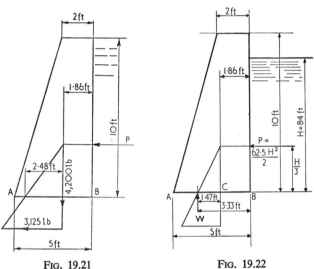

FIG. 19.21   FIG. 19.22

(*b*) If the answer to (*a*) is affirmative, what reduced depth of water would cause the resultant pressure to cut the base at the middle third? (See Fig. 19.22.)

(*a*) $W = (3{\cdot}5 \times 10)120 = 4{,}200 \text{ lb}$

$$P = \frac{wH^2}{2} = \frac{62{\cdot}5 \times 100}{2} = 3{,}125 \text{ lb}$$

$$x = \frac{(2 \times 10 \times 1) + (1\frac{1}{2} \times 10 \times 3)}{35} = 1{\cdot}86 \text{ ft}$$

$$\frac{y}{10/3} = \frac{3{,}125}{4{,}200}, \quad y = \frac{3{,}125 \times 10}{3 \times 4{,}200} = 2{\cdot}48 \text{ ft}$$

Thus, the resultant pressure cuts the base at

$$1{\cdot}86 + 2{\cdot}48 = 4{\cdot}34 \text{ ft from } B$$

i.e. outside the middle third.

(*b*) By taking moments about *C* (Fig. 19.22)

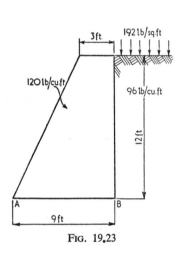

FIG. 19.23

$$\frac{(31{\cdot}25H^2)H}{3} = 4{,}200 \times 1{\cdot}47$$

$$\text{Therefore } H^3 = \frac{4{,}200 \times 1{\cdot}47 \times 3}{31{\cdot}25}$$

$$= 592$$

$$\text{Thus } H = \sqrt[3]{592} = 8{\cdot}4 \text{ ft}$$

EXAMPLE 7

A trapezoidal wall, as shown in Fig. 19.23, weighs 120 lb/cu ft and retains on its vertical face earth weighing 96 lb/cu ft and having an angle of repose ϕ of 30°. The earth being retained has a superimposed vertical load equal to 192 lb/sq ft. Determine the intensities of vertical pressure under the base *AB*.

The super load of 192 lb/sq ft may be considered as equivalent to a further 2 ft depth of earth at 96 lb/cu ft, as in Fig. 19.24,

i.e. $$h_1 = \frac{\text{intensity of super load/sq ft}}{\text{weight of earth/cu ft}}$$

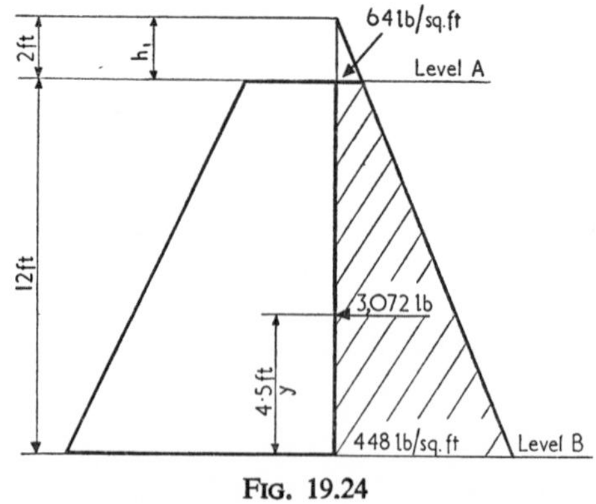

FIG. 19.24

The intensity of pressure at level A

$$= w \cdot h_1 \left(\frac{1 - \sin \phi}{1 + \sin \phi} \right)$$
$$= 96 \times 2 \times \tfrac{1}{3} = 64 \text{ lb/sq ft}$$

The intensity of pressure at level B

$$= w(h_1 + H) \left(\frac{1 - \sin \phi}{1 + \sin \phi} \right)$$
$$= 96 \times 14 \times \tfrac{1}{3} = 448 \text{ lb/sq ft}$$

The pressure P on the vertical face of the wall is found from the area of the pressure trapezoid, shown shaded, and it acts at the centroid of the trapezoid, as shown.

Pressure P = area of shaded trapezoid $= \left(\dfrac{64 + 448}{2} \right) 12$

$$= 3{,}072 \text{ lb}$$

The pressure P acts at distance y from the base, where

$$y = \frac{(64 \times 12 \times 6) + (384 \times 6 \times 4)}{3{,}072} = \frac{4{,}608 + 9{,}216}{3{,}072}$$

$$= \frac{13{,}824}{3{,}072} = 4 \cdot 5 \text{ ft}$$

and the overturning moment caused by the earth

$$= 3{,}072 \times 4 \cdot 5 \text{ ft} = 13{,}824 \text{ lb-ft}$$
$$W = 6 \times 12 \times 120 = 8{,}640 \text{ lb}$$
$$x = \frac{(3 \times 12 \times 1 \cdot 5) + (3 \times 12 \times 5)}{72}$$
$$= \frac{54 + 180}{72} = \frac{234}{72} = 3 \cdot 25 \text{ ft}$$

By similar triangles (Fig. 19.25)

$$\frac{y}{4 \cdot 5} = \frac{3{,}072}{8{,}640}$$
$$y = \frac{3{,}072 \times 4 \cdot 5}{8{,}640} = 1 \cdot 6 \text{ ft}$$

Thus, the resultant cuts the base at $3 \cdot 25 + 1 \cdot 6 = 4 \cdot 85$ ft from B, i.e. $0 \cdot 35$ ft to left of centre line of base, as in Fig. 19.25.

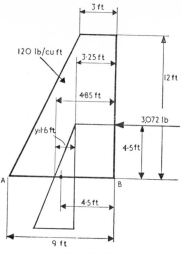

FIG. 19.25

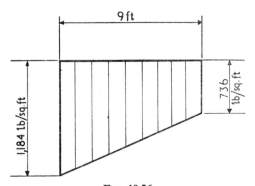

FIG. 19.26

Thus, intensity of stress at $A = \dfrac{W}{A} + \dfrac{M}{Z}$

$$= \frac{8,640}{9} + \frac{8,640 \times 0\cdot35 \times 6}{81}$$

$$= 960 + 224 = 1,184 \text{ lb/sq ft}$$

And intensity of stress at $B = \dfrac{W}{A} - \dfrac{M}{Z} = 960 - 224$

$$= 736 \text{ lb/sq ft}$$

The pressure distribution is as shown in Fig. 19.26.

Resistance to Sliding

The previous examples have been concerned with calculations to show the effects of the horizontal pressure as regards the overturning tendency, and the consequent stress on the earth under the wall. There is, however, the possibility that the wall might tend to slide along the base line X–X, as shown in Fig. 19.27, unless the weight of the wall is sufficient to prevent such sliding.

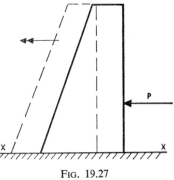

FIG. 19.27

The resistance to sliding depends upon—(*a*) the weight of the wall, and (*b*) the coefficient of friction of the materials concerned.

The principles involved are as follows: Consider a wooden block of weight W resting on a steel surface, as in Fig. 19.28(*a*). The steel surface presses upwards in reaction to the downward weight of the block, as shown.

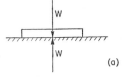

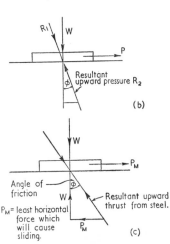

FIG. 19.28

If, however, a small load P (not sufficient to move the block) is also placed on the block, as in Fig. 19.28(*b*), then the resultant of the forces W and P will be R_1, as shown, and the resultant upward pressure from the steel surface will also be inclined as shown (R_2). This resultant upward pressure will be inclined at an angle (ϕ), as indicated.

If the force P is now gradually increased, the angle ϕ will also increase, until at a certain load (which depends on the nature of the two surfaces in contact and on the weight W) the block will move horizontally.

The angle ϕ which the resultant upward thrust makes with the vertical at the stage where the block starts to slide is known as the *angle of friction* between the two surfaces.

The tangent of $\phi = \dfrac{P_M}{W}$, see Fig. 19.28(*c*).

$$= \frac{\text{the least force which will cause sliding}}{\text{weight of block}} \quad \dots\dots (1)$$

and tan ϕ is known as the *coefficient of friction* for the two materials concerned.

For most materials this coefficient of friction will vary between 0·4 to 0·7, and it will be appreciated from equation (1) that

$$P_M = \text{the least force that will cause sliding}$$

$$= W \times \text{coefficient of friction}$$

In the case of earth or water retaining walls, P_M, the force which would cause sliding, can be calculated as $W \times$ coefficient of friction, and the horizontal force P of the retained earth or water should not exceed approximately half of the force P_M.

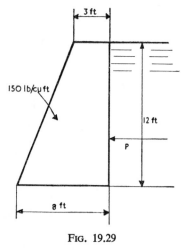

FIG. 19.29

EXAMPLE 8

The masonry dam, shown in Fig. 19.29, retains water to the full depth, as shown. The coefficient of friction between the base of the wall and the earth underneath = 0·7. Test to see if the wall is safe against sliding.

$P =$ actual horizontal pressure on side of wall

$$= \frac{wH^2}{2} = \frac{62 \cdot 5 \times 144}{2}$$

$$= 4{,}500 \text{ lb}$$

$P_M =$ horizontal force which would just cause sliding

$$P_M = 0 \cdot 7 \times W = 0 \cdot 7(150 \times 5 \cdot 5 \times 12)$$

$$= 0 \cdot 7(9{,}900) = 6{,}930 \text{ lb}$$

The actual pressure (4,500 lb) exceeds half the value of P_M, and the factor of safety against sliding is less than 2, which is undesirable.

SUMMARY

Total pressure per foot run of vertical wall due to a fluid $= \dfrac{wH^2}{2}$ lb

where $w =$ weight of fluid in lb/cu ft

$H =$ height of water in feet.

Total pressure per foot run of vertical wall due to a level fill of earth

$$= \frac{wH^2}{2}\left(\frac{1 - \sin \phi}{1 + \sin \phi}\right) \text{ lb}$$

where $w =$ weight of retained earth in lb/cu ft

$H =$ height of earth in feet

$\phi =$ angle of repose of earth

Least force that will cause sliding = total vertical pressure × coefficient of friction.

EXERCISE 19

1. Calculate the resultant force P on the wall, as shown in Fig. 19.30, acted upon by water weighing 62·5 lb/cu ft if the height H is (*a*) 8 ft; (*b*) 10 ft; (*c*) 12 ft; (*d*) 16 ft; (*e*) 40 ft.

2. Calculate the resultant force P from the earth pressure against the wall, as shown in Fig. 19.31, if the height H is as for Question 1 above.

Weight of earth = 90 lb/cu ft.

Angle of repose = $\phi = 30°$.

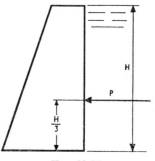

Fig. 19.30

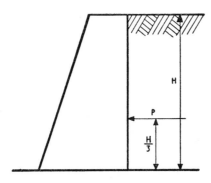

Fig. 19.31

3. The resultant force at the base of a retaining wall has a magnitude of 20,000 lb per foot run of wall (Fig. 19.32). Calculate the intensity of vertical stress at A and B.

4. The resultant force of 16,000 lb at the base of a masonry wall cuts the base, as shown in Fig. 19.33. Calculate the intensity of vertical stress under the wall at A and at B.

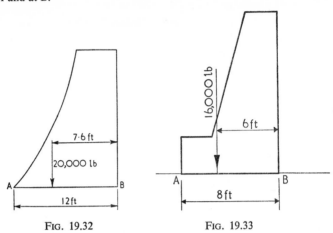

FIG. 19.32   FIG. 19.33

5. Calculate the intensity of vertical pressure at A and B for the wall shown in Question 4 if the resultant cuts the base at 6·3 ft from B.

6. The wall shown weighs 10,000 lb and this weight, together with the side thrust P acts as shown in Fig. 19.34. Calculate the intensity of vertical stress

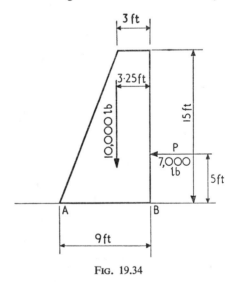

FIG. 19.34

under the wall at A and B.

7. Recalculate Question 6, assuming the weight of the wall to be 12,000 lb. instead of 10,000 lb.

8. The wall, shown in Fig. 19.35, has a resultant vertical pressure of 11,400 lb per foot length, due to the weight of the wall and the pressure *P*. Calculate the intensity of pressure at the toe (point *A*).

9. A masonry retaining wall is trapezoidal, being 12 ft high, 4 ft wide at the top and 6 ft at the base. The masonry weighs 120 lb/cu ft, and the wall retains on its vertical face earth weighing 95 lb/cu ft and having an angle of repose of 40°. Calculate the maximum pressure intensity under the wall.

10. A brick pier *H* ft high is 18 in. × 12 in. in section and weighs 100 lb/cu ft. It has a uniform wind pressure of 15 lb/sq ft on one side, as shown in Fig. 19.36, and rests on a concrete block to which it is not connected. How high is the wall if the resultant pressure cuts through the point *A*?

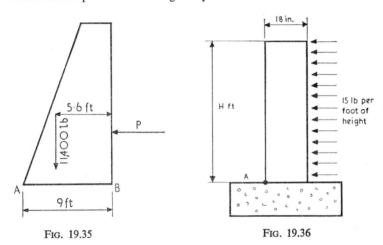

Fig. 19.35   Fig. 19.36

11. A concrete wall of trapezoidal section, 12 ft high, has a top width of 2 ft and a base width of 8 ft with one face vertical and a uniform batter on the other face. There is water pressure on the vertical face, with top water level 2 ft below the top of the wall. If the water weighs 62·5 lb/cu ft and the masonry 150 lb/cu ft, calculate the maximum and minimum pressures on a horizontal plane 6 ft above the base of the wall.

12. A brick wall 18 in. thick and 10 feet high is built on a level solid concrete base slab. The wall weighs 120 lb/cu ft. Assuming no tension at the bed joint, calculate the intensity of the uniformly distributed horizontal wind force in lb/sq ft over the full height of the wall that would just cause overturning of the wall.

13. A concrete retaining wall is as shown in Fig. 19.37. Using the Rankine formula, calculate the pressure under the wall at *A* and *B*. Assume the earth to weigh 100 lb/cu ft, and the natural angle of repose of the earth to be 30°. The concrete weighs 150 lb/cu ft.

14. Fig. 19.38 shows the section of a mass concrete retaining wall, weighing 150 lb/cu ft. The position and amount of the resultant earth pressure of 1,500 lb is as shown. Calculate the vertical pressures under the wall at *A* and *B*, assuming (*a*) tension stresses are permitted, (*b*) no tension stresses can develop.

15. A small mass concrete retaining wall, 6 ft high, is trapezoidal in section, 1 ft wide at the top and 4 ft wide at the base. The wall weighs 140 lb/cu ft and it retains on its vertical face earth weighing 90 lb/cu ft and having an angle of

repose of 30°. Calculate the pressure intensity under the base of the wall at the heel and at the toe.

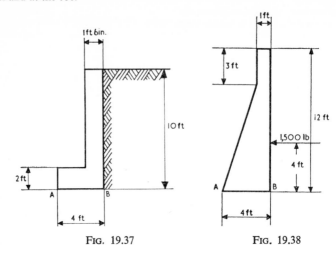

FIG. 19.37   FIG. 19.38

16. A 9 in. thick wall, weighing 120 lb/cu ft, rests on a solid foundation. It has a uniform horizontal pressure of 15 lb/sq ft on one face. If the resultant pressure at the base just cuts at the edge of the wall (i.e. if overturning is just about to take place), how high is the wall?

17. How high will a wall, similar to that mentioned in Question 16, be if the resultant pressure at the base cuts at the middle third, i.e. if tension is about to occur?

18. An L- shaped retaining wall is 12 ft high and is as shown in Fig. 19.39.

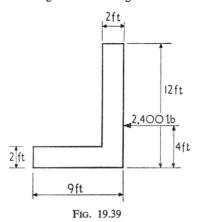

FIG. 19.39

On each foot length of wall a horizontal force of 2,400 lb is applied, as shown. The masonry weighs 90 lb/cu ft. Calculate the maximum and minimum pressures under the wall in lb/sq ft.

Answers to Exercises

EXERCISE 1

1. Reaction = 50 lb upwards; tension = 50 lb. **2.** 300 lb. **3.** Total downward weight = 160 lb; reaction of ground on box = 140 lb; compression = 140 lb. **4.** 50 tons. **5.** 102 tons; 112 tons. **6.** Reaction = $1\frac{1}{2}$ tons; tension = $1\frac{1}{2}$ tons. **7.** 28 lb; 56 lb; 244 lb. **8.** 103 lb; $102\frac{1}{2}$ lb; $105\frac{1}{2}$ lb. **9.** 8 st; 18 st; 30 st. **10.** 120 lb; 190 lb; 238 lb. **11.** 5 lb; $9\frac{1}{4}$ lb; reaction = $9\frac{1}{2}$ lb. **12.** 100 lb downwards; 200 lb upwards; 100 lb. **13.** 100 lb upwards; 100 lb upwards; 50 lb. **14.** 51 lb; 51 lb; 104 lb; 51 lb. **15.** 200 lb; 50 lb; 100 lb; 50 lb.

EXERCISE 2

Most of the following answers have been obtained by drawing and since accuracy in drawing varies a little from student to student, the reader must not expect his answers always to agree exactly with the given answers.
1. (a) $10\frac{1}{2}$ lb; $14\frac{1}{2}$ lb. (b) $36\frac{1}{2}$ lb; 45 lb. (c) 116 lb; 58 lb. **2.** $14\frac{1}{2}°$. **3.** $L = 1·75$ cwt; $R = 1$ cwt; reaction $= 2·8$ cwt. **4.** $L = 4$ cwt; $R = 1·5$ cwt; $W = 5·7$ cwt. $M = 2·15$ cwt. **5.** 2 tons at 60° from horizontal. **6.** 14·6 cwt at 25° from vertical. **7.** 19·3 cwt at $9\frac{1}{2}°$ from horizontal. **8.** 35 cwt; 33° from horizontal. **9.** $14\frac{1}{2}$ cwt at 20° from horizontal. **10.** 112 lb at 67° from horizontal. **11.** 135 lb at 17° from vertical. **12.** 153 lb; 109 lb; 158 lb. **13.** (a) Tie, 3·5 tons; strut, 4 tons. (b) 16 cwt; 16 cwt. (c) $34\frac{1}{2}$ cwt; 20 cwt. **14.** 18·4 cwt; $22\frac{1}{2}°$; strut, 16·9 cwt; tie, 6·9 cwt. **15.** 5 cwt; 8·7 cwt; L.H. hor. comp. = 4·3 cwt; L.H. vert. comp. = 2·5 cwt; R.H. hor. comp. = 4·3 cwt; R.H. vert. comp. = 7·5 cwt. **16.** 13·4 cwt; 11 cwt; 9·5 cwt at L.H. support, 5·5 cwt at R.H. support. **17.** Tie, 10 cwt; strut 10 cwt; vert. comp. = 8·7 cwt; hor. comp. = 5 cwt. **18.** *BC*, 20 lb; *AB*, 35 lb; hor. comp. = $17\frac{1}{2}$ lb; vert. comp. = 30 lb. **19.** 10 cwt; 12·2 cwt; 13·7 cwt. **20.** $82\frac{1}{2}°$; 12·25 cwt. **21.** 5·8 cwt. **22.** *A*, 0·9 cwt; *B*, 0·74 cwt. **23.** 0·58 cwt. **24.** 8 cwt in inclined members, 4·6 cwt in horizontal member, 4·6 cwt in cable; vertical reaction = 4 cwt. **25.** 6 cwt in *BC* and *CD*; 6·9 cwt in *BD*; 3·45 cwt in *AB* and *AD*; reaction at *A* = 6 cwt. **26.** (a) $X = 12·9$ cwt; $Y = 16·4$ cwt, both forces acting away from meeting point. (b) $X = 0·8$ lb; $Y = 4·3$ lb, both acting away from meeting point. (c) $X = 3·2$ cwt; $Y = 6·5$ cwt. (d) $X = 0·8$ cwt; $Y = 2·5$ cwt. (e) $X = 3·85$ tons. (f) $X = 4·1$ tons. **27.** Strut, 26·4 cwt; tie 19·3 cwt. **28.** Tension = 76 lb; vert. comp. = 38 lb. **29.** $X = 127$ lb; $Y = 107$ lb; strut, 160 lb; tie, 224 lb. **30.** Left post, 120 lb at 37° from horizontal; centre post 58 lb at 28° from vertical. Right post, 50 lb at 29° from horizontal.

EXERCISE 3

Most of the following answers have been obtained by drawing and are therefore approximate.
1. $R_A = 10·6$ cwt; $R_B = 7·9$ cwt. **2.** $R_A = 1·73$ tons; $R_B = 2$ tons; hor. member, 1·73 tons; inclined member, 2 tons; vert. member, 1 ton; hor. comp. 1·73 tons, vert. comp. 1 ton. **3.** Top hinge, $\frac{3}{4}$ cwt; bottom hinge, $1\frac{1}{4}$ cwt; hor. comp. $\frac{3}{4}$ cwt; vert. comp., 1 cwt. **4.** 3·89 cwt; 3·89 cwt.

5. Cable, 2·89 cwt; hinge, 2·89 cwt. **6.** $R_A = 100$ lb; $R_B = 173$ lb. **7.** $R_A = 1\frac{1}{3}$ cwt; $R_B = 2·404$ cwt; hor. comp. $= 1\frac{1}{3}$ cwt; vert. comp. $= 2$ cwt. **8.** Tension $= 195$ lb; reaction $= 175$ lb. **9.** Tension $= 12$ cwt; reaction $= 11·9$ cwt. **10.** 100 lb at wall; 100 lb at hinge. **11.** Cable, 2·27 cwt; Hinge, 3 cwt. **12.** Tension $= 1·4$ tons; reaction $= 2·23$ tons. **13.** Tension $= 7·2$ cwt; reaction $= 15·9$ cwt. **14.** Resultant $= 7·7$ cwt; cable, 16·1 cwt; reaction $= 17·5$ cwt· **15.** $R_A = 15·3$ cwt; $R_B = 11·5$ cwt; $AB = 20$ cwt; $AC = 5·7$ cwt; $BC = 11·5$ cwt. **16.** $x = 21°$ approx. **17.** Tension $= 35·35$ lb; reaction $= 50$ lb. **18.** Reaction at hinge $= 66$ cwt; reaction at wall $= 44$ cwt. **19.** $R_A = 63$ lb; $R_B = 38$ lb. **20.** $R_A = 0·74$ cwt; $R_B = 1·58$ cwt. **21.** Resultant $= 85$ lb; tension $= 126$ lb; reaction $= 174$ lb. **22.** Resultant $= 9·4$ cwt; tie $= 8·5$ cwt; reaction at hinge $= 5$ cwt. **23.** $R_A = 12·6$ cwt; $R_B = 5·8$ cwt. **24.** (a) 12·4 lb at 22° from horizontal, cutting bottom side of square at approx. 6 in. from bottom right hand corner. (b) 12·1 lb, cutting base of triangle at approx. 8 in. from left hand corner. (c) 15·1 lb, cutting base of triangle at approx. 1 ft, 1½ in from left hand corner. **25.** 8·45 cwt, cutting mast at approx. 6 ft, 11 in. from foot. **26.** 12 cwt at 18 ft from foot of mast. **27.** 20 tons at 6·75 ft from L. **28.** $R_B = 3·8$ tons; $R_L = 4·15$ tons at 32½° from vertical. **29.** $R_B = 5·95$ tons; $R_L = 4·2$ tons at 17° from vertical. **30.** $R_X = 22·5$ cwt; $R_Y = 13$ cwt at 6½° from horizontal. **31.** $R_L = 2·24$ tons at 64° from vertical; $R_B = 5$ tons. **32.** $R_L = 5·5$ tons; $R_B = 6·5$ tons. **33.** $R_B = 0·44$ tons; $R_L = 1·14$ tons at 41½° from vertical. **34.** $R_B = 0·58$ tons at 40½° from vertical. $R_L = 0·94$ tons at 24° from vertical. **35.** $R_B = 0·84$ tons; $R_L = 1·66$ tons at 10° from horizontal **36.** $R_B = 1·16$ tons at 45° from horizontal; $R_L = 0·87$ tons at 19° from horizontal. **37.** $R_B = 4·4$ tons; $R_L = 4·9$ tons at 20½° from vertical. **38.** $R_B = 4·4$ tons at 11½° from vertical; $R_B = 4·75$ tons at 10½° from vertical. **39.** $R_B = 1·54$ tons at 27° from vertical; $R_L = 1·32$ tons. **40.** $R_B = 4·05$ tons at 6½° from vertical; $R_L = 5·7$ tons at 5½° from vertical.

EXERCISE 4

1. $W = 22$ lb; reaction $= 41$ lb. **2.** 4·5 in. **3.** Tension $= 76\frac{2}{3}$ lb; reaction $= 43\frac{1}{3}$ lb upwards. **4.** 1·4 in.; 53 lb. **5.** 9¼ in. **6.** Prop, 332·5 lb upwards; hinge, 207·5 lb upwards. **7.** Prop, 832 lb upwards; hinge, 292 lb downwards. **8.** $W = 4\frac{1}{2}$ lb; reaction at $A = 85$ lb downwards; reaction at $B = 47\frac{1}{2}$ lb upwards. **9.** $R_A = 240$ lb downwards; $R_B = 360$ lb upwards. **10.** 500 lb. **11.** (a) 200 lb; (b) 125 lb. **12.** 2·828 tons. **13.** See Answers to Exercise 3. **14.** Tension $= 2·887$ cwt; reaction $= 4·725$ cwt at 17°47′ from vertical. **15.** Tension $= 4·907$ cwt; reaction $= 3·511$ cwt at 64°43′ from vertical. **16.** Tension in guy rope $= 3·06$ tons; force, in mast $= 3·5$ tons, in jib $= 4·3$ tons, in tie $= 2·5$ tons. **17.** 1,200 lb; 1,070 lb acting downwards at 76°28′ from vertical. **18.** 779·4 lb; 1,375 lb. **19.** 815·7 lb; 623 lb at 67°12′ from vertical. **20.** 69·28 lb; 200 lb; 69·28 lb. **21.** (a) $R_A = 7$ cwt; $R_B = 11·4$ cwt at 37°52′ from vertical. (b) $R_A = 1$ ton; $R_B = 2·24$ tons at 26°34′ from vertical. (c) $R_A = 2·25$ tons; $R_B = 2·85$ tons at 52°7′ from vertical.

EXERCISE 5

1. (a) $R_A = 5$ tons; $R_B = 7$ tons. (b) $R_A = 11$ tons; $R_B = 13$ tons. (c) $R_A = 12$ tons; $R_B = 1$ ton. (d) $R_A = 5·5$ tons; $R_B = 24·5$ tons. (e) $R_A = 7$ tons; $R_B = 15$ tons. **2.** (a) $R_A = 25$ tons; $R_B = 15$ tons. (b) $R_A = 18$ tons; $R_B = 23$ tons. (c) $R_A = 36$ tons; $R_B = 12$ tons. (d) $R_A = 19·2$ tons; $R_B = 12·8$ tons. (e) $R_A = 23·5$ tons; $R_B = 6·5$ tons. (f) $R_A = 26·75$ tons; $R_B = 1125$ tons. (g) $R_A = 57·125$ tons; $R_B = 24·875$ tons. **3.** $R_0 = 4$; $R_D = 1$;

$R_E = 2\frac{2}{3}$; $R_F = 1\frac{1}{3}$ tons. **4.** 14,970 lb. **5.** $12\frac{1}{4}$ cwt; $55\frac{1}{2}$ cwt; 2·46 ft. **6.** 2·17. **7.** 1·48. **8.** 57·6 ft. **9.** 1·58 ft. **10.** 2·035. **11.** 1·5. **12.** 1·25; 0·44 (i.e. structure will overturn); 3·66. **13.** 2·34; 2,691·5 lb; 548·5 lb. **14.** 10·48 ft. **15.** 4; 2,700 lb; 900 lb. **16.** 1·6; 225 lb; 4575 lb. **17.** 841·5 lb; 3,158·5 lb. **18.** 2·598; 2,446·4 lb; 553·6 lb. **19.** $1\frac{2}{3}$; 800 lb; 8,800 lb. **20.** 90,000 lb; 30,195 lb; 54,000 lb; 7·21 ft. **21.** (*a*) 3,200 lb; 3,200 lb. (*b*) $3,373\frac{1}{3}$ lb; $2,626\frac{2}{3}$ lb. (*c*) 9,400 lb approx.; 2,800 lb approx. **22.** 1·72; $5,333\frac{1}{3}$ lb; $1,866\frac{2}{3}$ lb.

EXERCISE 6

1. (*a*) $8\frac{1}{4}$ in. from hinge; 47·14 lb; 44·01 lb. (*b*) $8\frac{1}{4}$ ft along rod from hinge ; 9·622 cwt; 13·17 cwt. (*c*) $5\frac{3}{8}$ ft from hinge; 6·01 cwt; 11·56 cwt. **2.** (*a*) $9\frac{1}{3}$ ft horizontally from hinge; 7 cwt; 11·4 cwt. (*b*) 7·2 ft from B; 3 cwt; 3·905 cwt. (*c*) 10·28 ft from B; 2·25 tons; 2·85 tons; (*d*) 9 ft from line AB; 1 ton; 2·236 tons. **3.** Resultant is midway between loads; $R_A = 0.9925$ tons; $R_B = 0.65$ tons. **4.** $8\frac{5}{8}$ in. horizontally from A and $8\frac{5}{8}$. in. vertically from A. **5.** 5·33 in. from line AB; 3·73 in. from line AD. **6.** 12 in.; 360 lb-in. **7.** (*a*) $\frac{29}{32}$ in. (0·906 in.). (*b*) $2\frac{1}{4}$ in. (*c*) $3\frac{2}{7}$ in. (3·286 in.). (*d*) $4\frac{1}{6}$ in. (4·166 in.). **8.** (*a*) $\bar{x} = 2.083$ in.; $\bar{y} = 8.125$ in. (*b*) $\bar{x} = 2.8$ in.; $\bar{y} = 2.4$ in. (*c*) $\bar{x} = 5.387$ in.; $\bar{y} = 2.516$ in. (*d*) $\bar{x} = 1.58$ in.; $\bar{y} = 1.52$ in. (*e*) $\bar{x} = 7.625$ ft; $\bar{y} = 4.955$ ft. (*f*) $\bar{x} = 8.385$ in.; $\bar{y} = 14.85$ in. (*g*) $\bar{x} = 5.486$ in.; $\bar{y} = 4.172$ in. (*h*) $\bar{x} = 3.7$ ft; $\bar{y} = 8.11$ ft. **9.** 9·79 in. **10.** (*a*) $\bar{x} = 4.19$ in.; $\bar{y} = 6.25$ in. (*b*) $\bar{x} = 3.16$ in.; $\bar{y} = 4.84$ in. (*c*) $\bar{x} = 3.998$ in.; $\bar{y} = 3$ in. **11.** (*a*) $\bar{x} = 5.75$ ft; F.S. = 2·07. (*b*) $\bar{x} = 3\frac{1}{2}$ ft; F.S. = 2·4. (*c*) $\bar{x} = 5\frac{4}{11}$ ft (5·363 ft); F.S. = 2·36. **12.** (*a*) $\bar{x} = 8.11$ ft; $P = 9,855$ lb. (*b*) $\bar{x} = 3.52$ ft; $P = 2,640$ lb. **13.** $\bar{x} = 2.99$ ft; F.S. = 2·55. **14.** $R_A = 20$ lb; $R_B = 53.85$ lb. **15.** $R_A = 4,860$ lb; $R_B = 5,940$ lb.

EXERCISE 7

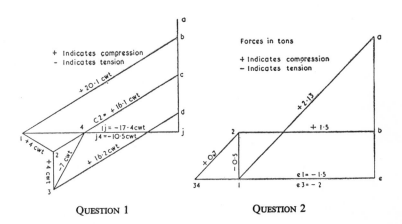

QUESTION 1   QUESTION 2

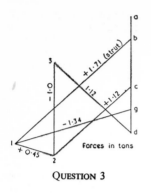

QUESTION 3

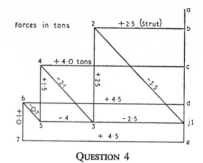

QUESTION 4

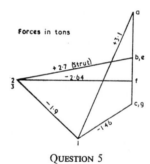

QUESTION 5

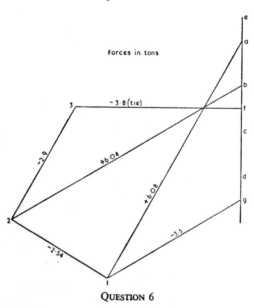

QUESTION 6

414

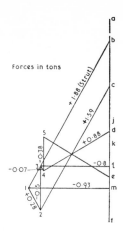

Forces in tons

+1·88 (Strut)
+1·59
+0·88
-0·38
-0·07
-0·8
-0·15
+0·20
-0·93

Question 7

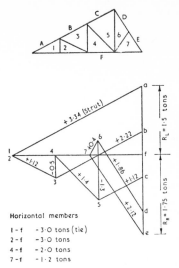

+3·34 (Strut)
+2·22
+1·12
+0·5
+0·4
+1·4
+1·86
+1·12
+2·12

$R_L = 1·5$ tons

$R_R = 1·75$ tons

Horizontal members

1 - f	- 3·0 tons (tie)
2 - f	- 3·0 tons
4 - f	- 2·0 tons
7 - f	- 1·2 tons

Question 8

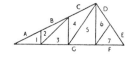

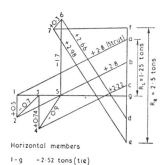

+0·3
+2·66
+2·8 (Strut)
+2·98
-1·7
+2·8
+2·22
+0·5
+0·7
+0·74
+0·9

$R_L = 1·25$ tons

$R_R = 2·5$ tons

Horizontal members

1 - g	- 2·52 tons (tie)
3 - g	- 2·00 tons
5 - g	- 1·50 tons
7 - f	- 1·70 tons

Question 9

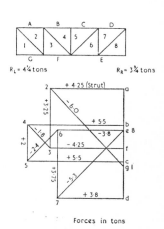

$R_L = 4¼$ tons $R_R = 3¾$ tons

+ 4·25 (Strut)
+3·25
-6·0
+5·5
-1·8
-3·8
+2
-2·4
- 4·25
+5·5
+3·75
-5·3
+ 3·8

Forces in tons

Question 10

415

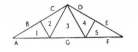

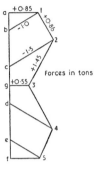

Forces in tons

QUESTION 11

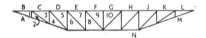

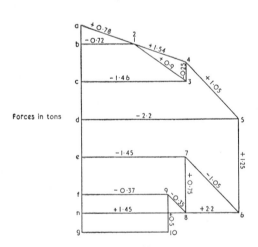

Forces in tons

QUESTION 12

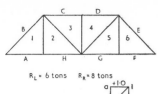

R_L = 6 tons R_R = 8 tons

QUESTION 13

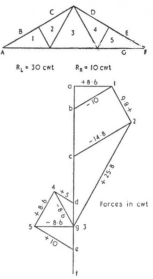

R_L = 30 cwt R_R = 10 cwt

Forces in cwt

QUESTION 14

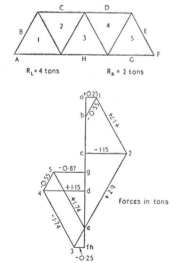

R_L = 4 tons R_R = 2 tons

Forces in tons

QUESTION 15

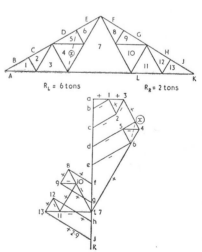

R_L = 6 tons R_R = 2 tons

QUESTION 16

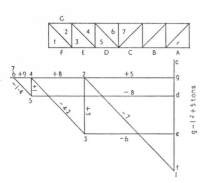

QUESTION 17

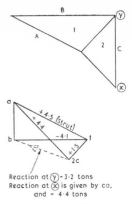

Reaction at (y) = 3·2 tons
Reaction at (x) is given by ca,
and = 4·4 tons

QUESTION 18

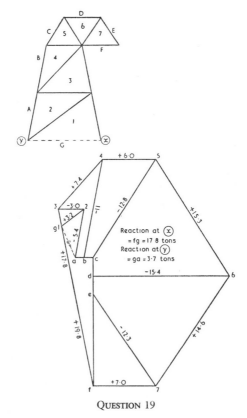

Reaction at (x)
= fg = 17·8 tons
Reaction at (y)
= ga = 3·7 tons

QUESTION 19

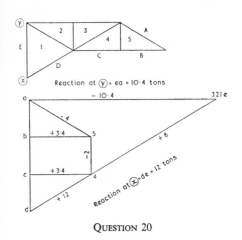

Reaction at Ⓨ = ea = 10·4 tons

Reaction at Ⓧ = de = 12 tons

QUESTION 20

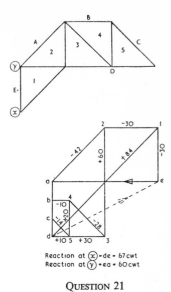

Reaction at Ⓧ = de = 67 cwt
Reaction at Ⓨ = ea = 60 cwt

QUESTION 21

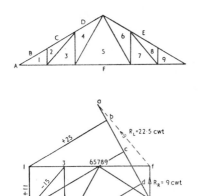

R_L = 22·5 cwt

R_R = 9 cwt

Note :- Only enough forces
are given to enable
student to check his
method.

QUESTION 22

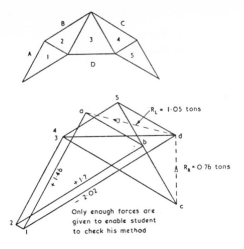

QUESTION 23

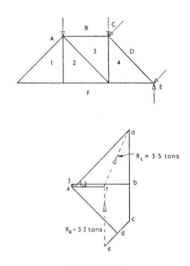

QUESTION 24

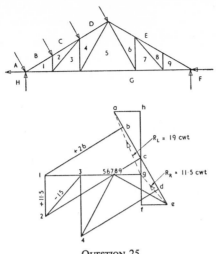

QUESTION 25

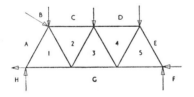

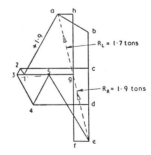

QUESTION 26

EXERCISE 8

See answers to Exercise 7

EXERCISE 9

1. 9 tons/sq in. **2.** 7·13 tons. **3.** 0·37 in., say $\frac{3}{8}$ in. **4.** 7·65 tons/sq in. **5.** 16·8 tons. **6.** $\frac{3}{4}$ in. **7.** 7·3 tons/sq in. **8.** 1·1 in., say $1\frac{1}{8}$ in. **9.** 7·4 tons. **10.** $2\frac{3}{16}$ in.; 9·85 tons. **11.** 0·368 in., say $\frac{3}{8}$ in. **12.** 25·3 tons. **13.** $1\frac{1}{2}$ ft square. **14.** 3·75; 3·71. **15.** 4·9. **16.** 18 in. square. **17.** (*a*) 4·25 tons/sq in. (*b*) 21 in. square. (*c*) 8·2 ft square. **18.** 3·95, say 4. **19.** (*a*) 17·95 tons/sq in. (*b*) 29 tons/sq in. (*c*) 13,000 tons/sq in. **20.** 0·06 in. **21.** (*a*) 5·7 tons/sq in. (*b*) 0·000416; (*c*) 13,700 tons/sq in. **22.** (*a*) 6·8 tons/sq in. (*b*) 0·042 in. **23.** 7·3 tons/sq in. 0·07 in. **24.** 1,200,000 lb/sq in. 0·064 in. **25.** 33,120 lb; 0·062 in. **26.** Copper, 0·01 in.; brass, 0·0112 in. **27.** 2,100 lb/sq in.; 0·001; 2,100,000 lb/sq in. **28.** 800 lb/sq in.; 12,000 lb/sq in. 0·048 in. **29.** 44,800 lb; 0·08 in. **30.** 0·22 in. **31.** 800 lb/sq in.; 16,000 lb/sq in.; 0·064 in. **32.** Brass, 3·75 tons; 2·5 tons/sq in.; steel, 3·25 tons; 6·5 tons/sq in. **33.** 64·3 tons; 64·5 tons.

EXERCISE 10

1. $R_L = 8·2$ tons; $R_R = 5·8$ tons; 16·82 tons-ft at 5·8 ft from R_R. **2.** $R_L = 13·6$ tons; $R_R = 12·4$ tons; 38·4 tons-ft at the point load. **3.** $R_L = 11\frac{1}{3}$ tons; $R_R = 8\frac{2}{3}$ tons; 32·1 tons-ft at $5\frac{2}{3}$ ft from R_L. **4.** $R_L = 3·73$ tons; $R_R = 4·27$ tons; 21·84 tons-ft at 7·73 ft from R_L. **5.** $R_L = 4·2$ tons; $R_R = 9·8$ tons; maximum positive B.M. $= 8·82$ tons-ft at 4·2 ft from R_L; maximum negative B.M. $= 8$ tons-ft at R_R. **6.** $R_L = 9·35$ tons; $R_R = 7·65$ tons; 29·2 tons-ft at 7·65 ft from R_R. **7.** $R_L = 11·125$ tons; $R_R = 10·875$ tons; maximum positive B.M. $= 6·7$ tons-ft at 6·125 ft from R_L; maximum negative B.M. $= 12$ tons-ft at R_L. **8.** $R_L = 6$ tons; $R_R = 6$ tons; 32 tons-ft at mid-span. **9.** $R_L = 11·2$ tons; $R_R = 2·8$ tons; maximum positive B.M. $= -2·24$ tons-ft. at 2·6 ft from R_L, i.e. there is no positive bending moment at any point; maximum negative bending moment $= 9$ tons-ft at R_L. **10.** $R_L = 11·4$ tons; $R_R = 14·6$ tons; maximum positive B.M. $= 22·8$ tons-ft at 12 tons point load; maximum negative B.M. $= 20$ tons-ft at R_R. **11.** $R_L = 13·79$ tons; $R_R = 17·21$ tons; maximum positive B.M. $= -22·4$ tons-ft, i.e. negative B.M.; maximum negative B.M. $= 36$ tons-ft at R_R. **12.** $R_L = 8·58$ tons. $R_R = 13·42$ tons; maximum positive B.M. $= 1·16$ tons-ft at 5 tons point load; maximum negative B.M. $= 21$ tons-ft at R_R. **13.** $R_L = 17·17$ tons; $R_R = 19·83$ tons; 86 tons-ft approx. at 10·79 ft from R_L. **14.** $R_L = 18·5$ tons; $R_R = 13·5$ tons; 97·1 tons-ft at 10 tons point load. **15.** Beam supported at left end and 10 ft from left end; U.D.L. of 1 ton/ft on 10 ft and point load of 4 tons at right end of beam; $R_L = 3·4$ tons, $R_R = 10·6$ tons; maximum positive B.M. $= 5·78$ tons-ft at 3·4 ft from R_L; maximum negative B.M. $= 16$ tons-ft at R_R. **16.** 14 tons-ft. **17.** 8 ft. **18.** $R_L = 15$ tons; $R_R = 14·5$ tons; maximum positive B.M. $= 31·75$ tons-ft at 7 ft to left of R_R; maximum negative bending moment $= 14$ tons-ft at R_L. **19.** $R_L = 14·13$ tons; $R_R = 14·87$ tons; approx. 54 tons-ft at 7·13 ft from R_L. **20.** 6 tons-ft. **21.** $R_L = 9\frac{1}{3}$ tons; $R_R = 14\frac{2}{3}$ tons = maximum S.F.; maximum B.M. $= 36\frac{4}{9}$ tons-ft at $5\frac{1}{3}$ ft from R_R. **22.** $R_L = 21·55$ tons; $R_R = 23·55$ tons; maximum B.M. $= 141·65$ tons-ft at the 4·7 ton load. **23.** (*a*) 3 tons-ft; (*b*) 61 tons-ft. (*c*) 91 tons-ft. **24.** (*a*) 16 tons-ft (*b*) 36·25 tons-ft. (*c*) 70 tons-ft. **25.** (*a*) 20 tons-ft. (*b*) 64 tons-ft. **26.** 80 tons-ft. **27.** (*a*) $R_L = 2$ tons. $R_R =$

4 tons. (*b*) 15·4 tons-ft at 11·54 ft from R_L. (*c*) 13·44 tons-ft. **28.** (*a*) +6 tons-ft. (*b*) −3 tons-ft. (*c*) +1·5 tons-ft. **29.** 10 tons. **30.** 16 ft. **31.** 6 tons. **32.** (*a*) 36·76 tons-ft. (*b*) 51·17 tons-ft. (*c*) 53·7 tons-ft. **33.** (*a*) $WL/2$. (*b*) $3WL/8$.

EXERCISE 11

1. 1,084 in.⁴; 51·57 in.⁴ **2.** 652 in.⁴; 332 in.⁴ **3.** 497 in.⁴; 77 in.⁴ **4.** $a = 1·183$ in.; $I_{xs} = 11·129$ in.⁴; $I_{yy} = 26·53$ in.⁴ **5.** $a = 2·166$ in.; 30·74 in.⁴; 5·75 in.⁴ **6.** $I_{xx} = I_{yy} = 33$ in.⁴ **7.** $a = 1·985$ in.; $b = 0·988$ in.; 17·4 in.⁴; 6·28 in.⁴ **8.** 1,773 in.⁴; 186·53 in.⁴ **9.** Distance of c.g. from top = 3·55 in., 405·8 in.⁴, 92·1 in.⁴ **10.** 5·08 in. **11.** 1,236·18 in.⁴; 1,197 in.⁴ **12.** $x = 5$ in.; $y = 4·29$ in., 496 in.⁴, 116·56 in.⁴ **13.** 3·2 in; 282 in.⁴ **14.** 1·99 in.; 17·4 in.⁴ **15.** 4,167 in.⁴ (or, allowing for two holes from each flange, $I = 3,988$ in.⁴). **16.** 868·6 in.⁴; 43·05 in.⁴ **17.** 35·44 in.⁴; 18·42 in.⁴ **18.** 1,698 in.⁴ **19.** 21$\frac{1}{3}$ in.⁴ **20.** 6 in. **21.** $\frac{3}{4}$ in. **22.** 12 in. **23.** 1 in. **24.** 1·95 in.; 231·3 in.⁴; 176·15 in.⁴ **25.** 320 in.⁴; 52·4 in.⁴ **26.** $I_{xx} = 5,066$ in.⁴; $I_{yy} = 5,166$ in.⁴ **27.** $I_{xx} = 5,066$ in.⁴; $I_{yy} = 1,523$ in.⁴ **28.** 38·67 in.⁴ **29.** $x = 1·36$ in.; $I_{xx} = 9·43$ in.⁴

EXERCISE 12

1. 6,667 lb (2·98 tons). **2.** 12 in. **3.** 37·6 tons. **4.** 29·16 tons. **5.** 5·45 tons/sq. in. **6.** 7·96 tons. **7.** Distance of c.g. from top = 3·93 in.; least $Z_{xx} = 32·1$ in.³; $W = 1,430$ lb approx. **8.** Distance of c.g. from top = 1·86 in.; least $Z = 8·6$ in.³; $W = 7·16$ tons. **9.** 256 lb/sq ft. **10.** (*a*) 100 lb/sq ft; (*b*) 10 in.³ **11.** (*a*) 4·69 in. (*b*) 519 in.⁴; 111 in.³; 66·5 in.³ (*c*) 9·2 tons (based on tension stress). **12.** 19·3 in. **13.** (*a*) $Z = 25·8$ in.³; 10 in. × 5 in. × 30 lb B.S.B. (*b*) $Z = 19·2$ in.³; 10 in. × 4$\frac{1}{2}$ in. × 25 lb B.S.B. (*c*) $Z = 19·2$ in.³; 10 in. × 4$\frac{1}{2}$ in. × 25 lb B.S.B. (*d*) $Z = 160$ in.³; 20 in. × 7$\frac{1}{2}$ in. × 89 lb B.S.B. (*e*) $Z = 118·8$ in.³; 20 in. × 6$\frac{1}{2}$ in. × 65 lb B.S.B. (*f*) $Z = 28·8$ in.³; 10 in. × 5 in. × 30 lb B.S.B. **14.** (*a*) 5·11 tons/sq in. (*b*) 1·74 tons/sq in. **15.** $Z = 8·35$ in.³; 7 in. × 4 in. × 16 lb B.S.B. **16.** 6 in. × 3 in. joists on 8 ft span. 6 in. × 2 in. joists on 6 ft span; Z required for $B = 1·74$ in.³; use 4 in. × 1$\frac{3}{4}$ in. × 5 lb B.S.B.; Z required for $A = 13·85$ in.³; use 8 in. × 4 in. × 18 lb B.S.B. **17.** Total Z required = 120 in.³; use four 12 in. × 5 in. × 32 lb B.S.B.s. **18.** 24 ft; $Z = 36$ in.³; use 12 in. × 5 in. × 32 lb B.S.B. **19.** 70·5 ft. **20.** $Z = 87$ in.³; use 18 in. × 6 in. × 55 lb B.S.B. **21.** Maximum B.M. = 16 tons-ft (negative); $Z = 21·3$ in.³; use 10 in. × 4$\frac{1}{2}$ in. × 25 lb B.S.B. **22.** (*a*) 12·7 tons; (*b*) 4·165 in., say 4$\frac{1}{4}$ in. allowing for two holes $\frac{13}{16}$ in. wide. **23.** 2,880 lb.

EXERCISE 13

1. (*a*) 20,000 lb/sq in. (*b*) 1,167 lb/sq in. **2.** 785,000 lb-in. **3.** 22,000 lb. **4.** 707,200 lb-in. **5.** (*a*) 10,000 lb; (*b*) $\frac{3}{4}$ in. **6.** 22·4 in. **7.** Effective depth $d = 8·15$ in.; $A_t = 0·525$ sq. in.; use three $\frac{1}{2}$ in. bars; overall depth = 9$\frac{1}{2}$ in. **8.** $d = 27·6$ in.; $A_t = 2·24$ sq in. **9.** (*a*) 31·1 in. (*b*) 27 in. (*c*) 24·2 in. (*d*) 19·1 in. **10.** $d = 20·2$ in., overall depth, say 22 in.; $A_t = 1·64$ sq in.; four $\frac{3}{4}$-in. bars. **11.** $d = 19·5$ in., say 21 in. overall; $A_t = 2·22$ sq in.; four $\frac{7}{8}$-in. bars; 3,930 lb. **12.** $d = 16·3$ in., say 16·5 in. with overall depth of 18 in.; $A_t = 1·3$ sq in.; three $\frac{3}{4}$-in. bars. **13.** $d = 10·2$ in., say 10·5 in. with 12 in. overall depth; $A_t = 1·12$ sq in.; two $\frac{7}{8}$-in. bars. **14.** Suitable dimensions are: Beam B, $b = 6$ in., $d = 7·5$ in., say 9 in. overall; $A_t = 0·362$ sq in.; two $\frac{1}{2}$-in. bars. Beam A, $b = 10$ in., $d = 17·9$ in., say 19$\frac{1}{2}$ in. overall; $A_t = 1·45$ sq in.; two 1-in. bars. **15.** $d = 19·2$ in., say 19·5 in. with 21 in. overall. $A_t = 2·87$ sq in.; four 1-in. bars.

EXERCISE 14

1. 0·57 in. **2.** 0·465 in. **3.** 0·79 in. **4.** 16·7 tons. **5.** 0·35 in. **6.** 0·108 in. **7.** 0·25. in. **8.** 0·18 in. **9.** 0·284 in. **10.** 0·515 in. **11.** (a) 1,440 lb. (b) 970 lb. **12.** (a) 9 in. (b) 10·2 in. **13.** 0·228 in. **14.** 0·19 in. **15.** 1,200 lb; 845 lb. **16.** See Table 14.2. **17.** $L = 8d$. **18.** (a) $L = 9·6d$. (b) $L = 6d$. (c) $L = 9d$. (d) $L = 5·62d$. **19.** $L = 24d$. **20.** 0·36 in. **21.** 0·27 in.

EXERCISE 15

1. Beam A, nearly 10 tons/sq in.; beam B, 8·2 tons/sq in. **2.** Beam A, 957 lb/sq in.; beam B, 635 lb/sq in. **3.** $W_A/W_B = 3/1$ approx.; $W = 94$ tons (nearly). **4.** $W_B/W_A = 1·58/1$; $W = 1,550$ lb (nearly). **5.** I required $= 32·5$ in.⁴; 7 in. × 4 in. × 16 lb B.S.B. **6.** I required $= 216$ in.⁴; $d = 9·52$ in. **7.** 8,000 lb; $W_A/W_B = 9·8$; 57,700 lb; 685 lb/sq in. **8.** 8·8 tons/sq in.; 6·95 tons/sq in. **9.** 12·3 tons/sq in.; 4·02 tons/sq in. **10.** $I_A/I_B = 2$; I required $= 221·28$; 12 in. × 5 in. × 32 lb B.S.B.; 4·8 tons/sq in. **11.** 1,230 lb/sq in.; 550 lb/sq in. **12.** $W_A/W_B = 8/1$; 1,350 lb. **13.** 14·64 in., say 15 in.; 294 lb/sq in. **14.** 27·8 tons. **15.** 3·56 tons. **16.** 20 tons; 18 tons-ft; 32 tons-ft. **17.** 3 tons; 10 tons-ft (negative). **18.** (a) 9·4 tons/sq in. (b) Extra load $= 26·1$ tons (total load $= 34·1$ tons). **19.** $R_A = R_B = 5$ tons; reaction at middle support $= 22$ tons; maximum positive B.M. $= 50$ tons-ft; maximum negative B.M. $= 60$ tons-ft. **20.** $R_A = \frac{5}{16}W$; R at middle support $= \frac{11}{8}W$; positive B.M. $= \frac{5}{32}WL$; negative B.M. $= \frac{3}{16}WL$.

EXERCISE 16

1. (a) 4,830 lb. (b) 8,587 lb. (c) 22,320 lb. **2.** (a) 0. (b) 3,000 lb. (c) 8,067 lb. (d) 4,500 lb. **3.** 8 in. × 8 in. **4.** 101,000 lb. **5.** 10 in. diameter. **6.** 14,688 lb; 31,040 lb. **7.** 60·2 tons; 50·8 tons; 41·5 tons; 33·5 tons; 27·1 tons. **8.** 99·8 tons; 90·8 tons; 81·8 tons; 67 tons; 54·3 tons. **9.** 150 tons; 138 tons; 127 tons; 115 tons; 104 tons. **10.** 104 tons; 93·1 tons; 75 tons; 60·6 tons; 49·7 tons. **11.** 10·05 ft, say 10 ft; 5 tons. **12.** 10 in. × 8 in. × 55 lb. **13.** (a) total load $= 35·8$ tons. (b) 60·2 tons. **14.** 31·3 tons; 126 tons; 288 tons; 509 tons; 789 tons. **15.** 210 tons; 7 in. diameter (safe load $= 227$ tons). **16.** 72 tons; 5 in. diameter (safe load $= 77·8$ tons). **17.** 15 tons; 12·3 tons; 9·5 tons; 7 tons. **18.** 5·8 tons. **19.** Suitable angle is 3 in. × 3 in. × $\frac{3}{8}$ in.; $A = 2·11$ sq in.; least $r = 0·58$ in.; safe load $= 8·3$ tons. **20.** $W = 5·2$ tons. **21.** 279,000 lb. **22.** 295,500 lb. **23.** 16·6 in., say 17 in. square; 11 sq in. steel. **24.** 18·7 in., say 19 in. diameter; 11 sq in. steel. **25.** (a) 14·5 in. square; 16·88 sq in. steel. (b) 27·5 in. square; 6·1 sq in. steel. **26.** Timber 133,000 lb; R.C. 217,500 lb. **27.** 10 in. × 20 in.; 8 sq in. steel. **28.** 17·8 in., say 18 in. square; 12·72 sq in. steel. **29.** 195,300 lb. **30.** 11·7 sq in.

EXERCISE 17

1. 2. **2.** Strut 2·5, say 3; tie, 2·08, say 3. **3.** 15·15 tons based on strength of plate. S.S.V. $= 15·9$ tons. **4.** 13·48 tons. **5.** 18 tons. **6.** 19·6 tons. **7.** (a) 10·6 tons. (b) 15·15 tons. **8.** 0·344 in., say $\frac{3}{8}$ in.; 3·32, say 4 bolts, in plate and 3·22, say 4 bolts, in stanchion. **9.** 3·77, say 4; strength in tension $= 17·1$ tons. **10.** 2·88, say 3 in.; 5·1, say 6. **11.** Shear 33·7 tons; bearing 38·6 tons; section

A–A, 24·6 tons; B–B, 27·54 tons; C–C, 26 tons; $W = 24·6$ tons. **12.** $W = 20·8$ tons; $t = 1·05$ in.; 6·7, say 7 rivets. **13.** 2·22 in., say $2\frac{1}{4}$ in.; 2 bolts in each plate. **14.** Width of flat bar $= 2·21$ in., say $2\frac{1}{4}$ in. Rivets in $X = 2·12$, say 3. Rivets in $Y = 1·5$, say 2. **15.** D.S.V. $= 33·7$ tons; B.V. $= 38·5$ tons; tension strength of middle plate $= 27$ tons; tension strength of cover plates $= 29$ tons; safe load, $W = 27$ tons. **16.** 5·95, say 6 rivets; use 6 in. $\times$ 4 in. $\times$ $\frac{1}{2}$ in. angle with packing plate and cover plate.

EXERCISE 18

1. (*a*) 875 lb/sq in. (*b*) 125 lb/sq in. **2.** $f_{bc} = 800$ lb/sq in.; $f_{ad} = 0$. **3.** $f_{bc} = 1,000$ lb/sq in.; $f_{ad} = 200$ lb/sq in. tension. **4.** 800 lb/sq in. **5.** 3·845 tons/sq in.; 2·595 tons/sq in. **6.** $f_A = 0·296$ tons/sq in. tension. $f_B = 0·884$ tons/sq in. tension. $f_C = 5·736$ tons/sq in. compression. $f_D = 6·324$ tons/sq in compression. **7.** 16 tons. **8.** (*a*) Upper face $= 208·3$ lb/sq in., lower face 1,458·3 lb/sq in. (*b*) 2 in. **9.** 4·23 tons/sq in. **10.** $f_A = 1,186$ lb/sq ft. $f_B = 592$ lb/sq ft. **11.** (*a*) 657·5 lb/sq in. (*b*) 357·5 lb/sq in. **12.** 8·75 tons/sq in. **13.** 4·47 tons/sq in. **14.** $f_A = 5·214$ tons/sq in. $f_B = 5·106$ tons/sq in. $f_C = 10·686$ tons/sq in. $f_D = 10·794$ tons/sq in. **15.** 15 tons. **16.** $f_A = 960$ lb/sq ft; $f_B = 0$. **17.** 5·63 tons/sq in. at corner C. **18.** 5·87 tons/sq in. at corner C. **19.** 6 tons/sq in.

EXERCISE 19

1. (*a*) 2,000 lb. (*b*) 3,125 lb. (*c*) 4,500 lb. (*d*) 8,000 lb. (*e*) 50,000 lb. **2.** (*a*) 960 lb. (*b*) 1,500 lb. (*c*) 2,160 lb. (*d*) 3,840 lb. (*e*) 24,000 lb. **3.** 3,000 lb/sq. ft at A; 333 lb/sq ft at B. **4.** 5,000 lb/sq ft compression; 1,000 lb/sq ft tension. **5.** 5,450 lb/sq ft compression; 1,450 lb/sq ft tension. **6.** 2,037 lb/sq ft; 185 lb/sq ft. **7.** 2,444 lb/sq ft; 222 lb/sq ft. **8.** 2,196 lb/sq ft. **9.** 1,632 lb/sq ft. **10.** 15 ft. **11.** 954 and 306 lb/sq ft. **12.** 27 lb/sq ft. **13.** 1,987 lb/sq ft at A; -487 lb/sq ft at B. **14.** (*a*) 2,189 lb/sq ft at A; -281 lb/sq ft at B. (*b*) 2,240 lb/sq ft at A. **15.** 593 lb/sq ft; 458 lb/sq ft **16.** 4·5 ft. **17.** 1·5 ft. **18.** 624 lb/sq ft; 136 lb/sq ft.

Index